1931 I AM
RAT PATROL.
UP A 4:00 AM
WALK AROUND TILL
TRYING TO LOCATE
R NVA IN THE VILLA
IT IS TAIKA WORK.
ARE YOU SENDING SOME
GARLIC AND ONION POWDERS.
I AM LOOKING FORWARD
TO THEM. MY CHILI POWDER

USO A Home Away from Home

P1

Dear Ma & Dad, Today 17th

Here I am Quin yon. (sp).
It is growing dark. You ca
Feel the heat from the Sand.
The wind is Blowing out. To
There are a few Palm trees
The Blow so Beatifully. Mak
think of Florida.
I am in a Bunker.
The Breeze Blows
round it.
matter how

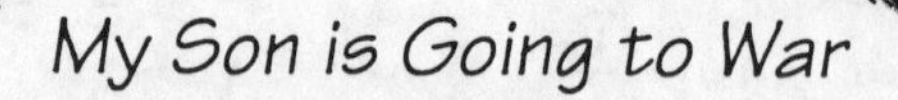

My Son is Going to War

I believed him a child who thought as
a child, because he did the least he could
to graduate from high school.
He is
moody
and keeps
to himself. He
has long hair, black
pointed shoes, tight pants
and a black leather jacket. He
built a doghouse for Jinx the other day.
Then yesterday—in a quiet room with me he
was a man and thought as a man. He said we
are a warring people and nothing can be achieved
until we really want peace. That there is nothing left
for him until people can live and work together in an
atmosphere of honest give-and-take. So . . . my
son is going to war. May God bless and
protect all the sons that are
going to war.

Belva O. Brown
—November 1967

VIETNAM WAR DIARY

Books by Fred Leo Brown

- NON-FICTION -

CALL ME NO NAME

WALL OF BLOOD

VIETNAM WAR DIARY

VIETNAM WAR DIARY

THE DIARY OF A VIETNAM WAR SOLDIER

FRED LEO BROWN

COMBAT READY PUBLISHING

 This edition first published in 1973 under the title of "Call Me No Name" as hard cover.

SECOND EDITION 1998
is published by:

Printed and manufactured in the United States of America.

Brown, Fred Leo
Vietnam War Diary
Includes preface, appendices, glossary, illustrations, photographs.

ISBN 0-942551-15-X

Library of Congress Catalog Card Number
LC 98-94785

1. Vietnam history. 2. Vietnam personal.
3. Vietnam poetry. 4. Vietnam literature.
5. Vietnam illustration and photography.

DEDICATION

Vietnam War Diary is dedicated to three very unique people. Without their concerted efforts, this book would never have been written or have survived thirty-years inside dusty storage boxes.

My mother, Belva Orlena Brown: who experienced the Vietnam War alongside me and is still young at age 83. My wise-woman who came down the mountain and who continues to inspire. The one who is always there with a cup of hot tea and words of encouragement.

My sister, Roxanna Maude (Brown) Nerngtongdee who in 1968 came to visit me on R&R in Sydney, Australia. After I went back to Vietnam, she hitch hiked across Australia to Singapore where she worked at the R&R center. Then on to Saigon with the intentions of saving the life of her fool-hardy brother. "Roxanna by the time you got there, I was already wounded and in Japan," I told her years later. "I didn't know. But I had this plan of breaking your arm or something so they would have to let you go home." Roxanna stayed in Vietnam and for the next seven war torn years worked as a freelance combat journalist. It is through her vision that I can clearly look back to that place in time.

My squad leader, Benji Yamane who on 16 March 1968 died in my arms. As his blood mingled with mine on Hill 45, I subconsciously invoked the Code of Silence and began to gloss over the truth. My sister and mother knew something was wrong and persisted in asking what had happened. One dark night while on guard I raised my eyes to the heavens and asked God if I could speak with Yamane. Yamane told me to "Write the truth about what you feel and see." I have never stopped and to this day write as if it were my last word.

After our worldly toils are done our thanks will be that the children will learn from our Lessons of War.

Contents

Cover photo: Author Fred Leo Brown in Que Son Valley 1968
Poem: *My Son is Going to War* illustrated by John Tylk
Inside back cover: Photograph by Molly McCollam

INTRODUCTION

Fred Leo Brown's **Vietnam War Diary** is a series of letters, mostly to his parents about that distant time and place that happened to America and her children over a quarter of a century ago.

It seems that no sooner has Brown arrived in Vietnam than the North Vietnamese Army started their costly and ill-fated 1968 Tet Offensive. It was a remarkable year "in-country" and in the nation. Martin Luther King and Bobby Kennedy are assassinated. The mood of non-participant young people erupts at the Democratic National Convention.

The most remarkable thing about these letters is the mixture of the mundane and the moral. He wants a knife, he badgers for money, then losses it during a battle and asks them to cancel the checks. He thinks about coming back home incessantly. He mixes with his buddies, they get patches from the family franchise chicken business, but later he notes that after six months, he is the oldest and most alone. He keeps calling for Kool-Aid, as if that child never grew out of him, but after giving children balloons and playing with them, he finds that it is too painful to kill their fathers and brothers and play balloons with them.

We see him casually grow into manhood. It is not a pleasant initiation to watch; letters are marked with little homilies, notes about his officers, familial events, responses to letters from his parents. But it changes. It ceases to be interesting, and grows serious. We watch the speed of change; things that take years to experience happen virtually overnight here. And the vacillation between moral points of view of what he is doing and what is happening at home seems to sweep like a great pendulum trying to find its moral resting place. At one minute he is sympathetic to the Vietnamese, and a day later, he feels the powerful urge of his Army training and the blood lust it instills.

America has made a compromise about this war. What our movies, our mythos, has suggested to us, is that we should not have fought the war because our politicians let down our fighting men and women, never clearly defining a mission. The nation had no right to ask such sacrifice from our personnel. Thus the men and women come off in our popular culture as victims of corrupted policymakers. The Vietnamese War's greatest effect might have been to poison our political system, so that in invading Iraq, President Bush has to say that we cleansed our nation of its Vietnam excursion, that we somehow brought our honor back.

But like all mythos, the truth is difficult to reconcile with it. Fred Leo Brown's book has the ring of morality and compromise, the seeking of working class people who fought the war. We see little of it, and as scholars are beginning to try to understand the war, this kind of book, filled with mundane existence and moral questioning is going to be a most valuable resource.

Of course, the act of autobiography itself is difficult to interpret. Here we have letters to his parents, and it is clear that he is censoring every line, wondering how much he can tell about his life and his feelings, about his actions. In a letter to his sister, we are brought up short by how much self-censorship there was, but we watch him give more extended glimpses of life at war as he writes through the nights on guard duty. The war changes him, as it changed the Vietnamese landscape. One can sense the deep scars our young men felt, why they turned to drugs and alcohol, the glimmers of the morals they grew up with challenged by the facts of their existence. How much should one tell? There is a story behind this one, messier, more painful. It is the story that soldiers are beginning to tell now, and Fred Leo Brown in publishing these letters has brought to light some of the challenges that the myth has left out.

If ever a nation needs to get over something, our nation needs to get over Vietnam. But we cannot get over it as long as we keep it wrapped in mythic paper. Fred Leo Brown's letters strip some of the wrapping from the myth, and we are allowed glimpses into what happened in the lives of the men who went out on patrols, defended perimeters, and found no solace in their Rest and Rehabilitation. It is often a painful story, filtered through the eyes of a boy who came in relative innocence, but was delighted to escape with his life. But is also captures something of the nobility of people in a job that we had no right to ask them to undertake, and how they survived that moral chaos.

—Gerald E. Forshey, Ph.D.
Professor Humanities and Philosophy

PREFACE

This book contains letters written by Fred Leo Brown during his service in the U.S. Army from June 1967 thru October 1968.

Fred Leo Brown was born January 22, 1949. He was the youngest child of Belva and John. Wesley was five years older, Roxanna three years older, Lorraine one year older. His Great Aunt Lillian, born in 1876 had lived at the Brown's house for ten-years. His favorite Uncle Raymond, a Second World War veteran, also lived at the house off-and-on.

Fred was raised on a five acre chicken farm in Orland Park, Illinois. In 1950 his mother and father set-up a trailer at the end of their driveway to sell their original *Brown's Fried Chicken*. The menu consisted of fried chicken, french fries, sliced bread and cole slaw. The idea was revolutionary and caught on quickly. When Brown was five, his family sold the chicken farm to pursue their dream of being successful restauranteurs.

Fred's strongest card was his ability to learn by example and with hands-on approach. He also did well when there was a clear application of the subject matter, or if his teacher was interesting. Outside of that, school was a constant irritation.

On the first day of first grade, Brown lay across two chairs and fell fast asleep. This was a prelude to his upcoming troubles in school. In the first week of school, he could only count to six though others could count to a hundred. In second grade he stuttered so badly he was sent to speech therapy. Early on Fred learned how to cheat by leaning over someone's shoulder. This was a necessary evil since it wasn't until the latter part of second grade that he fathomed the concept of subtracting numbers.

Fred's behavioral problems escalated. He didn't complete his homework or pass tests and failed the first semester of third grade. His family went to Florida for the spring semester where Fred, finding the surroundings inspiring, did homework and passed all tests.

Fourth grade found him out-of-control. His desk was pushed to the front corner of the room for the entire year. He found this convenient for afternoon naps. Fifth grade found him back in Florida where he again excelled in school.

Seventh grade found him involved with a local gang of trouble-makers. Eighth grade found him at Morgan Park Academy boarding school where he graduated as *Most Improved Student of the Year*.

On his return to the public school system, he again fell in with a bad crowd. At the same time his overall health deteriorated. Sophomore year found him so sickly he needed to sleep or rest nearly eighteen-hours a day. Regaining some health, Brown was sent to a work-camp summer school in Maine.

Senior year at Argo Community Public High School found him again failing and the class-joke.

Today's school systems would have categorized Fred as learning disabled. But in those days, he was simply called "lazy," "stupid idiot," "a trouble maker," "punk," "loafer" or simply "dumb ass".

In March of 1967, he joined the U. S. Army for two very good reasons. First: To leverage his teachers into giving him a passing grade and thereby receiving a high school diploma. Second: His atheist father became mentally abusive.

The family restaurant was probably one of Brown's saving graces. Though he worked hard and sometimes twelve hour days, it gave him the unique opportunity to work alongside people in various walks of life. These people gave him different ideas about life and he could watch them decide how best to work.

His proudest day was in 1959 when he worked alongside his parents as they sold 2,200 chickens.

Work had made him independent and very responsible. He learned the valuable lessons of self motivation and self sufficiency. Through his teen years he bought his own bicycles and often times his own clothes. If he wanted to go anywhere, he either rode a bike or walked.

Throughout his youth Fred had suffered from one sickness or illness after the other. In fact, as a teenager he wasn't exactly sure what it might feel like not to be sick. At age fourteen he was 4'8" and weighed 79 lbs. He received his driver's license when he was 5'1"and weighed 102 lbs. On the day of his induction into the U.S. Army he was 5'8" and 132 lbs.

To fully understand Fred it must be noted that he felt betrayed by everyone, including family and friends. His father would often berate hin in front of his fellow workers. Brown found himself at the brink of suicide, strongly believing that he was as worthless and weak as his father would so often tell him. The military offered him an honorable way of killing himself. It also offered a chance, although slim, that he might actually live through the experience. It was a glimmer of light—the only hope this young eighteen-year-old boy had.

Fred had always idolized war heroes and cowboys. At a young age he was given a B-B gun and became a very good shot. So much so, he had no need to aim. Wanting to emulate his idols, he joined the U.S. Army and volunteered for the most dangerous position of the Vietnam War. The position was called pointman. At the moment of contact, the pointman had a life expectancy of 1/10 of a second. The second deadliest position was combat radio telephone operator, RTO, which at the moment of contact carried a life expectancy of 2/10 of a second. For eleven solid months Fred Leo Brown would shuffle between these deadly positions with a sincere desire to either die or becoming a man.

Hatred became a major catalyst in Brown's psyche. So much so that he could actually draw strength from it. So as the death around him mounted, so did the pace of this hatred. But the hatred wasn't focused on the enemy. It was focused on authority figures that didn't seem to care about him and his fellow combatants.

Living long enough to have an opportunity to settle the score with those of authority became Brown's war cry.

Fred Leo Brown
—January 1999

Basic Training
June - July 1967

Department of the Army
U.S. Army Training Center and Fort Leonard Wood
Office of the Commanding General
Fort Leonard Wood, Missouri

Dear Parent, Spouse or other Relative:

Your soldier has arrived safely at Fort Leonard Wood, Missouri.

His first few days of military service will be spent in processing at the Reception Station prior to his assignment to a basic training unit. The majority of new members received at Fort Leonard Wood are assigned for training to a unit at this location; however a possibility does exist that his first assignment may be to another state of our union.

The initial phase of a new soldier's service career is designed to introduce him to another facet of good citizenship. In the course of his basic training we try to help him gain a more realistic appreciation of the responsibilities which Americans inherit along with the many privileges of our way of life. It is hoped that his adjustment to military life is not too difficult and that he learns to appreciate and take pride in the traditions and responsibilities of the service.

The training and development of our young men is very vital to the strength of our nation. We here at Fort Leonard Wood feel that even though they may not choose to make the Army a career, the training they receive will benefit them immeasurably.

We are proud that he has become a new member of the U.S. Army. I am sure that you, too, will enjoy a like feeling of pride in him and will encourage him in his endeavors.

Sincerely,
T. H. Lipscomb
Major General, USA
Commanding

(Printed post card. Written words in italics)

Dear *Ma and Dad* *18 June 1967*

I am now at Fort Leonard Wood Reception Station. I arrived at *1500* hours on *Saturday* 19*67*. I will be here for approximately 5 days for processing and will then be transferred to a Training Brigade. Please do not write me until I send you my permanent mailing address. In the event of an emergency you can contact me through the American Red Cross.

Fred Leo Brown

Co A, 4th Bn, 2cd Bde 1st Platoon, Ft. Leonard Wood, Missouri

Dear Ma and Dad *20 June 1967*

I just got an address. I don't have time to do anything but march around to testing areas.

I am well and feeling good. It is not easy. I expected this. It is getting harder all the time. I feel I will be okay.

Say *Hi* to Aunt Lillian and Roxanna.

Fred Leo

Dear Ma and Dad

Well, this is the first time I have had paper and a mailing address since I left home.

I didn't leave Chicago Saturday until 11:20 P.M. They put me in charge of a group of new recruits going to Fort Leonard Wood. So, I was given checks to fill out for eating and money for train fare.

When I got to Fort Leonard Wood, we went to the *Reception Area.* I did nothing but fill out papers and get shots for six days.

Now I am at the Basic Training Center. We have done no physical exercises yet. The exercising will start Monday.

I am in good health and in excellent spirits. It seems ironic that someone would pay me for getting physically fit along with room and board.

I just don't seem to be able to write. I just seem to exist. I guess this will soon go away when I get into the actual business. Good-by for now. Maybe I will see you in eight weeks.

P.S. Please send me a bottle (plastic) of Liquid Johnson's Black Shoe Wax.

Your son, Fred Leo

Letter From Father

Dear Fred *1 July 1967*

I'm not good at writing letters, but at least I can let you know that I miss you.. And another thing I'm missing is a two pound coffee can of drill bits and those things you make inside threads with after you drill a hole. I thought you might know where it has gone.

I hope you are getting along fine and that you will find answers to some of those troublesome things, the answers to which will usher you into the adult world a bit sooner than if you had remained at home. I have always been concerned about the strange contradictions of the good mind you have and your past inabilities to use it along the scholastic route. Your perceptiveness and your insight as far as getting at the seat of the problems and evaluating the feeling of those about you are a remarkable asset to you, and perhaps will more than compensate for those things which it seems to me could most easily be learned from books. But sometimes ones talents and capacities aren't to be measured by those standards which by trial and error have come to be accepted as the best measurement of the potentials of the greatest number of people.

One of the reasons I find it rather difficult to write is that I can't think of much to say. For news, I sold your camper for one hundred dollars, which is way under what you had expected to get. However now is the time to sell that type of thing, and as no better offers had materialized I figured that much in the hand was worth three times that much if we didn't get it. In addition to the fact it would have deteriorated just sitting there. I had hoped you and I could have gone down to the Cains before you left. Linda left for Tennessee this Saturday morning. Jody, Bruce's sister, would like very much for you to write to her. Now I'm no match maker so I'm not advising you to write to her. But as you go along in life you will find that there are too few people who show any concern for you. If you felt it was a good idea to write to her you could address the letter in our care.

The weather has been hot, business has been good, and your truck is in Martha's garage. I'm going to put the Oldsmobile Starfire and ranch wagon in the old garage. And the Mama's car goes in the new garage. So everything is going to be out of the weather.

We patched and sealed our parking lot and going to dress up the front outside of our store next week. Twenty six hundred dollars. I guess Lorraine and Ray will be here next week.

Your father, who is both proud of you as a person and concerned about your welfare along the difficult path you've taken.

Dad

Dear Dad *2 July 1967*

When I get back home on leave maybe we could go down to Tennessee and see the Cain's. The reason I didn't go before joining the Army was because I felt that when I get out in three years *that* summer versus *this* one would be of more importance to me.

It relieves me to hear that the truck camper is sold. It didn't really matter what the price was.

I am learning a great deal. I have had a First Aid session and I learned a great deal of useful ideas. I am cleaning all the time but I feel it is very good discipline. I must be extremely neat all the time. I am not getting much sleep, but I am a working almost continually.

I very much appreciated your letter. I have never received a letter with as much potential knowledge. I have always agreed with your philosophy. You need not worry about me getting along. It will be very hard at first but within a year I will have made a complete adjustment.

I often find myself thinking about our Brown's Fried Chicken Store. It is in my blood and I am glad of it. I have a dream of having a store in another state. I want to help expand the operation. I feel it will be many years before I will have the knowledge to help run the corporation. I might never be able to, but I am going to run a store.

I have read your letter many times already. It had a great effect on me. It gave me strength and determination. There is much pressure here and I need what you gave me.

You know that I am going to be an Airborne Paratrooper. It is the roughest branch of the service. I might not pass the physical but I feel confident. I also volunteered for Viet Nam. They guaranteed me Viet Nam. I felt hollow when I uttered the name when I enlisted but I must be strong. I try to learn everything so that some day it will save my life.

I am very tired now and lights are going out in a few minutes. I must say fare well till the next time.

Your son, Fred Leo

Dear Ma and Dad *(post card)*

I feel great. Basic should be getting easier from here on in. The conversion was hard to make. By the time you get this card, I will be half way through Basic Training.

I sent you a long letter with a hand grenade pin in it. But I lost it before I sent it on its way. Write me and tell me if you get it or not. I am going to try and call home next Sunday morning.

Fred Leo

Dear Ma and Dad *July 1967*

Guess where I am! I'm in the hospital. I got sick and came to the hospital Monday. I had a 101 temperature in the morning and now it is 99.5. I slept all day. I think my temperature is at normal now. I feel great! Is this hospital nice. I have been watching T.V. all day. Each room has a T.V. and a latrine.

I have a radio also. I have all the reading literature I want. I will probably be back on active duty by Wednesday. I will not miss anything as far as training.

I weigh 145 lbs. I have gained an inch around the waist.

Would you please, right now! START THE TRUCK!

I just rebuilt the motor and it will rust if it is not started. The oil has to be run through the engine.

Man, I feel at ease with myself.

Say, Hi to Aunt Lillian. Tell her I am doing fine.

Well, I must watch T.V.

So bye for now, Fred Leo

Dear Ma

Thank you for the Johnson's Shoe Wax. It made my boots shine like glass. Is my wooden bridge over the ditch still in good shape? How is that little Field Plow Memorial Roxanna and I built before I left?

I'm becoming a real soldier now. I wear my helmet and backpack everywhere I go. I was also issued an M-14 rifle. It is a very beautiful and respectful looking weapon. In Viet Nam the M-16 is used.

My legs hurt bad because of all the marching and running with my pack and rifle. I am feeling good so it doesn't bother me. I realize now that I am weak in the legs but my arms do not hurt.

My whole company has been messing up for the past week. Sixteen men were absent without leave (AWOL). We were next to the worst cleaned dormitory. Basic is actually a very simple program. It may build you up but it only teaches the *mere* basics. I will go to Airborne Parachute School. I will learn how to survive under adverse conditions.

I don't think I will get a leave but I may. It will be about three more months before I get home if I don't get leave after Basic Training.

The hardest thing in Basic is mental harassment.

It is very important for the troopers to get mail. They become very self pitying people. Well, all is well on this end, although the Army is very much like school. But then life is 90% filled with things you dislike. The other 10% is filled with pleasure. I expect it and that is all.

Fred Leo

Dear Ma *August 1967*

I received your letter. It made me feel real good. It gave me a lift I needed.

The men in the Army are a bunch of misfits. They cannot get across what they want to say except by yelling. They are playing a game with people. I am one of them. This is life. I am finally starting to get used to their continued mental harassment. I have found no one gives a *hang* about you. I have no close friends. The instructors like the Army because they like to yell and hurt people mentally. It brings out the basic illness of man, which is *evil.*

I had KP (kitchen police) and worked for nineteen hours straight. Peeled a lot of potatoes and helped with the deliveries. In the two days following KP and preceding KP I had nine hours sleep. Or rather I had only 4-1/2 hours sleep in two days.

The Army is obsessed by cleanliness. I swept and moped our room four times in a single day. At 18 years old, I am very young compared to the people surrounding me. I have eight room mates. Their ages are 19, 25, and 26. And I know a 19 year old married man.

I get mentally down at times, but I just talk to myself. I am not allowed to think. I just stand in lines and march. We have very short hair cuts. I am next to scalped, but it is very humid and hot here. It reads 90 or 95 degrees most every day.

The National Guardsmen with me have to go directly into eight more weeks of training. But guys like me get a thirty-day pass at the end of Basic Training. So I'll see you in a few weeks.

Well, say Hi to Dad. Have Roxanna write me.

Fred Leo

P.S. Doing fine. Food is fabulous, I weigh 5 lbs. more.

Advanced Infantry Training
September - October 1967

Co D, 8th trn Bn, 3rd trn Bde, Weapons Plt., Ft. Fort Gordon, GA

Dear Ma and Dad *September 1967 (postcard)*

Everything okay. I will be home the first of November if I don't get messed up. Which means if I don't get sick.

Hard. I hope I can make it. A lot of action. Fast moving. Well, as things come up I will tell you about it. So, they say the first two weeks are the hardest. I am already through one week. I will write again next week.

Fred Leo

Ma and Dad *September 1967 (post card)*

I am doing what I am because I want happiness. Happiness is having peace of mind. This here is my definition of Happiness. Happiness is not in our circumstances but in ourselves. It is not something we see, as a rainbow after a thunder storm. Happiness is not the station we arrive at but the manner in which we arrive. It is the ability to be tough with ourselves but tender with others.

Fred Leo

Dear Ma and Dad *October 1967*

Well, I am okay. It is not easy but it isn't anything I cannot handle. I am trying to break loose with my strength. I mean I am trying to reach a point where I do not get physically exhausted. I hope I can reach this point.

I have fired the .45 cal. pistol. The .45 is the only Army issue side arm. I qualified as Marksman. In Basic I qualified as Sharpshooter with the M-14 so that's pretty good.

Next Saturday I will take the Airborne P.T. (physical training) test. Well, everything is as good as could be possible.

Fred Leo

Dear Ma

Well, I went to the show today. I don't do much on weekends except catch up on sleep and little things like polish my boots or straighten my foot locker. I took the *Mortar Gunners* test. Out of two-hundred points, I got *198!* Passed that test *hu!* That makes me an Expert Gunner.

Well, I weigh in my clothes, 155 lbs. My legs are stronger but my arms are not able to keep up with my weight. I do less and less push ups. But they are stronger.

I had been going to church. I went three times in a row. I figured it couldn't hurt me and it might help. But I found out, again to my dismay, preachers just don't reach me, or I don't reach them. Well, anyway I am trying. I already read the Reader's Digest. I picked up an Alfred Hitchcock book also. I might be able to start reading again.

The training is good. Physical movement is bearable. So, no sweat. A lot of men have gone AWOL. Five altogether. Well, many things are happening. I haven't got a cold or sickness yet. *Unusual*. So I will write again very soon.

Your son, Fred

Dear Ma

Well, I just finished with a rough week. We had IG (Inspector General) Inspection. We had to work all night one day. I got about two hours sleep.

I am learning combat formations. How to set up security at night and how to travel in a combat zone. I had guard duty this week. I was a guard over a prisoner. One recruit had live rounds on him and the MPs (military police) caught him. Well, in case you never know.

This is my sixth week.

Well, next week will be full. I have night-time training for three nights.

By the way, they fire live rounds in our *assault* course. Well, I will probably *call* next week. Okay. There are a few things that aren't going right. Or rather the way I would like.

Well bye for now, Fred Leo

Dear Ma and Dad

Well, last week I had another physical training test. This was the second time I took this test. The first time was at the beginning of Basic Training. You must get three-hundred to pass this test. Five-hundred is the maximum. The first time I took the test I got *363*. This time I got 393. I have improved a lot. I ran the mile in six minutes fifty-five seconds in my fatigues. I was forty seconds faster than the last time I took it.

I went through the Infiltration Course with the live machine gun fire going just over my head. I crawled 250 yards through the course and with mud up to my ears. It sounds scary but it didn't even give me a reaction.

Well, the good news. I am graduating this Thursday the seventeenth of October and have a thirty-day pass. I will be home by at least Monday. I am coming by bus because I want to relax. So long for now. When I talk to you next, it will be face to face.

Bye, Fred Leo

November 1967

Travis Air Force Base, Oakland, Calf. 25 November 1967

A warm, salty Pacific Ocean breeze licks sweat off the short sleeve khaki clad soldiers as they obediently clamor up the corrugated steel steps into a military chartered commercial PanAm Boeing 707. Army Private Fred Leo Brown and the other soldiers have a one-way ten-thousand mile ticket—destination the Republic of South Vietnam.

Everything seems perfectly normal on this morning as the soldiers give their undivided attention to the standard pre-flight speech from both pilot and flight attendants. Brown and the others make sure seats are in an upright positions, seat belts are fastened and all cigarettes are extinguished.

Hours later the pilot's voice comes over the intercom. "If you look out the right side of the airplane you might be lucky enough to get a glimpse of the Hawaiian Islands. The lights appear like sparkling stars on the dark ocean below."

Hawaii, Brown thinks, That's cool. I've never been there. As Brown raises his seat in preparation for a landing, a steady stream of realization begins to seep into his consciousness. Before him lay the last view, last moments and last fateful steps on American soil.

In the main terminal, Brown notices a rack of comic books. Walking over he reads, ARMY AT WAR featuring SGT. ROCK. Pictured on the front cover is Sgt. Rock in a wide stance firing single-handed a Thompson Machine Gun while cradling a mortally wounded soldier. The soldier's clothes are battle ripped and a bloody bandage is wrapped around a head wound. On the end of his rifle bayonet is tied an American flag so thoroughly riddled with bullets and shrapnel that it reminds Brown of a Civil War battle flag.

The cover reads: THE FLAG WAS DEAD...COULD SGT. ROCK MAKE IT LIVE AGAIN? DON'T MISS...BATTLE FLAG FOR A G.I.!"

Brown lifts the twelve-cent DC comic book from the rack and opens it to the first page. There again is a drawing of Sgt. Rock and the mortally wounded soldier. The soldier says, "SARGE! THE FLAG . . . LOOK AT IT! IT'S LIKE . . . IT'S ALIVE!" Then Sgt. Rock waves his hand and yells to his fellow soldiers, "C'MON EASY COMPANY! YOU'VE GOT A FLAG TO FIGHT FOR NOW!"

Along the far wall a mass of soldiers from his flight impatiently await their turn at a long row of telephone booths. Maybe he should try to call a loved one too. Then Brown remembers his mother's last request, "Write me?!"

At the register, he buys a package of Juicy Fruit gum and a postcard entitled:

Moon Over Diamond Head...
Waikki Beach in the moonlight...
Just a sample of romantic Hawaii

"I love Juicy Fruit gum." He opens the package, slides a stick into his mouth and chews with deep satisfaction. Finding a chair, he sits and writes:

Dear Ma and Dad *25 November 1967*

Hawaii. I am passing by the volcano of Hawaii. The airport was beautiful. As soon as I got off the PanAm plane I ran to the terminal. The wind was strong and there was an occasional rain drop. I am on a ten hour flight to the Philippines now. We will re-fuel there and then on to Nam.

Doing fine, Fred Leo

Mailing the card, he walks over to an open air window and leans over the sill. In the floodlight bathed courtyard palm trees sway in a cool breeze, with rain droplets gleaming and sparkling on their leaves. Brown's thoughts stray to film clips about 7 December 1941 surprise Japanese bombing of Pearl Harbor. "A date which will live in infamy," he could hear the words of then President Franklin Delano Roosevelt as he declares war on Japan.

Yeah, Brown thinks. This place was a combat zone, not hardly . . . he adds up the years . . . twenty-six years ago almost to the day. You'd never know it by the looking around.

Chewing out the last fruity flavors, he removes the gum and smashes it under the window sill. I'll be back through here in a year, he thinks, and God willing, touch this gum. But I'll have gone through the war. Then in a movie star John Wayne voice, he adds, "Will I be the same old lovable me?"

Brown walks outside to let the refreshing mist bath his face and bare arms. The wet concrete glistens, mirrorlike, reflecting the surrounding lights. The farther from the terminal he gets, the more blustery the wind. Then a sudden gust sends his overseas cap flying.

"*Ahhh.*"

Like the Ginger Bread Man, the cap flees away defying his efforts to snatch it off the ground. As a last resort, he jumps and plants a foot firmly on top. Slapping off the dirty water, he tucks it under his belt.

A fine rain falls as he savors the fresh, invigorating ocean air and wonders what he'd be doing if he were here on vacation? Maybe he'd rent a motorcycle and go riding along the white sandy beaches? Or maybe he'd grab a big lunch bag and go hiking in search of the island's tropical delights?

"Tropical delights? Yeah, the girls." He nods approvingly and laughs out loud. "Lots of itsi-bitsi-tini-winnie-yellow-polka-dot bikinis around here."

A flash from the aircraft's strobe light catches Brown's attention. His plane looks so vulnerable against the volcanic-black sky that boils around it. A lightning bolt breaks across the sky, illuminating the World logo painted on the plane's towering tail.

Standing isolated and alone, Brown muses about how the guys in his senior high school class had reservations about leaving home for college. "What a joke." Here he is on the final leg, or is it the first leg, of an incredible journey that could easily end in his death. The trepidation of the unknown sends a shiver running down his spine.

"Don't think that way," he tells himself. "You're right," he agrees. "I shouldn't."

Fellow soldiers begin re-boarding, their black figures and stilted movements making them appear like chain-gang prisoners. Rejoining the group, he grabs the cold handrail and–two steps at a time–reaches the platform. Stopping short of the hatch, he turns to take a last look at America, fills his lungs and enters.

At cruising altitude, some soldiers begin to jabber a lot while others sit almost comatose. To amuse himself, Brown begins to study the plane load of soldiers. He tastes the irony that the majority of these cropped-hair soldiers are under twenty-one years of age and not even old enough to vote, let alone legally buy a beer. Yet they are deemed old enough to fight and die for their country.

Khaki shirts proudly display an array of insignias and badges. These details of a soldier's dress reveal a great deal about their service accomplishments. But only a few of the passengers, like Private Brown, wear the infantry's cross-rifles lapel pins and the distinctive blue braid ropes looped around their right shoulder.

The ones with the Vietnam Theater pins—the distinctive sign of previous war service—were easy to locate. They have that square shoulder, chin up, self assured appearance that translates into, "Done that. Been there." Is the aura artificial? A sculpted facade or is it experience and confidence put there by knowing the ropes of survival in a combat zone? In any event, they were held in high regard on this overseas flight.

"Hey there, buddy," Brown's seatmate leans over. "You see that sergeant in the third row down on the other side?"

"Yeah." Brown shifts to get a glimpse of the soldier in question. "Light haired guy on the aisle, right?"

"Yeah, that's him," the seatmate confirms. "Back in Oakland he told us how he wasted some Charlie Cong in a *firefight.*"

"Holy . . . really." Brown pushes-up to take another look. A *Sergeant Rock* right here.

"Name's Skeeter." He offers a hand.

Brown shakes the clammy hand of a dishwater blond hair, big eared, long faced man. The skinny GI with a broad smile of large crooked, yellow teeth projects a *good old boy* mannerism.

"Name's Brown," he says with a reciprocating smile.

"You ever wonder about Vietnam?"

"You mean the country?"

"Yeah."

"Well, ummm. . . .." Brown lets the words trail off because, well no, he'd never given it much thought.

"I've heard tell it's punier than California. Can you believe that?" Skeeter elaborately scratches his nose. "I've seen lots of pictures in the newspapers. Watched it on the tube, too. All's I can tell is it's a mess of mountains, jungle and swamps, rice paddies and the likes. And real close to the equator."

"Yeah, so it's gonna be hot."

"Damn right." Skeeter leans over. "We'll be sweatin' buckets soon enough."

"That's kinda the way I visualized it, too," Brown rejoins, trying to sound informed. Though in fact, he'd never thought of Vietnam as something real. Like a *real* country. He envisioned it simply as **WAR**, and war never seems as if it's anywhere—just *somewhere.* Like in those comic books, at the movies or on television.

"You ever watch *Combat!*?" Brown asks his seat-mate.

"Sure. Great show." Skeeter rolls around his face is within inches of Brown. "Real life stuff. That's what I like about it. And that's why I always watch *The Rifleman,* too."

"How about the *Andy Griffith Show*."

"Yeah, let's go fishin' Barney."

"Ever see that *Combat!?* episode where Vic Morrow is out by himself and happens upon this German soldier?"

"No. Can't recall," Skeeter says, scrubbing his face. "A good un, huh?"

"Oh, yeah. One of the best," Brown assures him diving into the story line. "See, Sarge is way out front by himself on reconnaissance making sure the area is clear. But time is short. You know, like it always is. So right in the middle of the path is this blown-up farmhouse and inside is this wounded Jerry.

"The German slides his rifle through an opening and . . . Blam! Blam! Just misses Sarge who hits the dirt. The Jerry bears down on him but keeps missing. Sarge rolls and crawls away making it to cover. He peeks out from behind a log." Brown simulates the log with his hand and stretches his neck over the top. "And spots the German. They fire back and forth, then Morrow comes up with a brain storm. He takes off his helmet and rigs it up on a moving tree limb."

Brown narrows his eyes. "So while the Nazi is taking pot shots at the jiggling helmet, Morrow scoots around the back, swings the rifle through the bombed-out wall and gets a drop on the Kraut. The guy senses him. Then hears dust trickling off the bricks. He slow-ly turns and seein' . . . he ain't got a chance in hell. Ever so slowly he sets down the rifle. Relaxing back, he stares into Sarge's cool calculating eyes."

The story telling excites Brown. "Then," Brown raises his hands to simulate, "Sarge's trigger finger tightens—but at the last second stops."

"Why? Drill 'im man. While you got the chance. The Jerry would do the same thing."

"But he doesn't. See, that's the whole point, man. So Sarge lays down his rifle too. Then gives the Jerry a drink from his own canteen and redresses the German's bloody leg."

Brown smiles at the twist in the story. "And like all good soldiers, they share smokes.

"There's this kind of communication between the two soldiers. One minute they're enemies trying to kill each other, and the next, they're trying to save each other's life."

"What do you mean?"

"Well, let me finish." Brown takes a moment because he wants to finish it right. With both hands poised he continues. "So Sarge let's the Jerry take up the rifle and they both leave the farm house. The German begins hobbling away, his back to Sarge, the expression on his face nasty. Then suddenly he swings around." Brown jumps in his seat a little to add drama. "Comes to attention his heels clicking and raises his hand in a crisp salute. Sarge comes around and he too comes to attention. They salute *soldier to soldier*."

"Wow," Skeeter says, relaxing back in the seat. "I thought sure Old Sarge was gonna have to drill 'im."

"You know," Brown says, understanding that combat is the business of death—close and intimate, "If one of 'em were killed, the war wouldn't end any sooner. The world wouldn't be any safer. A soldier is *not* a murderer and a murderer is *not* a soldier. Anyway, that episode makes me think about Nam."

"Would you like something to drink," the soft female voice startles both soldiers.

"Well, now that you ask. How's about a Coke."

"Sounds good to me," Brown agrees.

A soldier seated in front and across the aisle asks, "So how much longer we got, Hon?"

"Approximately eight to the Philippines, then another six from there, sir." Serving the drinks, the stewardess pleasantly nods and moves on.

"Smoke?" Skeeter asks opening an airline's four-pack of Winstons.

The unwritten rule is 'never refuse a cigarette offered by a soldier.' Nodding his thanks, Brown takes one and lights up. After a smooth draw, he exhales to watch the smoke swirl upwards, scattering at the air vent to meld with the rest of the white haze hovering throughout the cabin.

Skeeter settles back. "Ya know what really sticks in my craw?" Skeeter's eyes load with malice. "Those blue-blooded featherbedders. The ones who say how great this war is. How it's good for the economy. And it really fries my eggs when those same flag-wavers buy their little darlings out of it at the same."

"Buy 'em out?"

"That's what I'm sayin'." Skeeter pitches his head back. "Them politicians and those rich folks put five-hundred smackers in the right hand and get their kiddies a 4-F permanent-deferral. But most of 'em get the student-deferral by going to college, marrying their high school sweetheart and get a hardship-deferral, or just taking a free ride in the National Guard." He huffs.

"Awww, what the heck." Skeeter defuses his anger. "I ain't college material anyway. So why not see the world. But I'll tell ya what, if I'da gone to college, I'd become a teacher."

"Teacher? How so?"

"Because teachers gets a permanent-deferral."

"Permanent?"

"Teachers don't gotta serve and no one knows how long this war is gonna last. Do we?"

"Well, I'm no head either," Brown admits feeling a comradery. Fact is, he had joined the U.S. Army then told his teachers what he'd done. They all gave him passing grades, a high school diploma and a pat on the back. "I couldn't pass a course in college if my life depended on it." Brown surprises himself by the open admission. "Even in high school, I spent most of my time scratching my head, looking at the pictures and turning pages."

"Tell ya what. They'd get ya one way or the other in the end, buddy," Skeeter said. "Believe me, I know what I'm sayin'. As for me the judge said prison time or marchin' time."

"Wow. What did you do?"

Skeeter shrugs off the question. "At least I'm in the motor pool. Rather be a grease monkey than out trampin' around through some jungles fightin' and shit. What about you?"

Exhaling smoke like a tough-guy, Brown proudly announces, "I'm combat infantry."

Skeeter yanks the cigarette from his purplish lips and takes in Brown's insignias for the first time. "Oh man, some hard luck." He looks sympathetically at Brown. "I'm sorry. Really, man."

"Sorry?" Brown is stunned by his seatmate's reaction. "I volunteered."

Shocked, Skeeter's eyes widen with disbelief. "You joined? Don't tell me you're an RA."

"Well, yeah." Brown stares baffled. "I mean I joined the Army for three years signed up for combat in Vietnam."

"Damn man." Skeeter rolls his eyes. "That's like volunteering for death row."

Slumping into his seat, his mental state in peril, Brown turns to stare absently out the window.

"I mean, hell. I ain't no coward," Skeeter continues. "If it comes right down to it, gimme a rifle and I'll go shot 'em up. I'll even kill a commies with my bare hands, but I'm much better at covering my own ass."

Feeling drained, Brown holds desperately onto his fragile self-esteem that has just been decimated. His mind flashes back through painful memories.

As a child, he had been sickly, had stuttered and the most embarrassing of all, was a bed wetter. During his whole life, he had been the brunt of many a joke because he was small and skinny. Only recently had he made 5' 8" and 142 pounds.

His parents had owned a small farm in Orland Park, Illinois, where they raised chickens, hogs, and a few other farm animals. Some of his best childhood memories were of life on the farm. Take those lazy days of summer when he'd grab his BB Gun and take the dogs out to the woods to chase after rabbits, squirrels and raccoons. And those winter times when he'd sled down the hill or tie the toboggan to the International Harvester tractor.

Despite the farming and on-the-side well drilling business, the Brown family fell onto hard times. Scrambling to make ends meet, in 1950 they opened a carry-out fast-food restaurant under the name,

"Brown's Fried Chicken." The entire Brown family, including the four children—Fred being the youngest, became the first employees and an All-American family dream was born.

Through his formative years both parents worked full time, so he and the other children learned quickly to become self-sufficient. By his teenage years, when the business was becoming successful, the people in Brown's middle-class suburb of Bridgeview thought he had a storybook life. All the riches a kid could want. But while other children were watching TV, doing homework or playing sports, nearly all of Brown's off-time was spent sorting chicken giblets, peeling potatoes, shelling shrimp, slicing potatoes and cabbage, emptying fifty-five gallon steel garbage cans, breading chicken, straining deep-fat fryers, packaging orders, moping the floor, and the list went on and on and on and on.

Even though he worked alongside everyone else, Brown's fellow employees became envious. They marked him because he was a "Brown" of Brown's Fried Chicken. By his senior year in high school, the store manager had relegated Brown to cleaning dishes, floors, coolers, grease traps, bathrooms and walls. Vicious rumors of his incompetency circulated and even his parents became prey to the lies. Believing everything he heard, Brown's father fired him.

Fred just couldn't believe . . . couldn't believe his father . . . his own flesh and blood would listen to a bunch of liars.

And what was his father doing right now? Mr. Good Time Charlie, always telling those earthy jokes. Always quick with a smile, fast with the hands, especially on a woman's butt. With him, women could sleep their way to the top.

It was hard to admit that for years his father had mentally abused him with incessant yelling and criticizing. Fred felt as if he could never do anything right. But based on how he excelled in the military, Brown was beginning to unravel all the deception.

Yeah, Brown remembered how many times his father never came home at night. Out all night on business? Brown had often been called stupid but he wasn't dumb. At least not that dumb. And what kind of plans did his greedy old man have this night?

Looking out the window Brown thinks, I'd rather die in a combat zone than have to listen to my old man's crap. But that is the saddest truth of all because outside of joining the Army in trade for a high school diploma, Brown did want to die. His father had pushed him to the edge. Like a deranged wolf after a helpless lamb, he came at

Fred relentlessly while spreading gossip and rumor like an old lady. His father had stripped him of self-worth and integrity till he found himself saying, "I wish I was dead."

He sniffles as he stares into the black of night over the cold jetliner's wing. The "secret" enlistment had taken place at the Armed Forces Recruiters Center of Oak Lawn, Illinois, three months before graduation from Argo Community High School. As he signed the dotted line, the only thing that went through Fred's head was, "I'm tired of being pushed around. I ain't no wimp and if I gotta die to prove it. Well, that's just what I'll do."

It is much more complex than it sounds. Though never baptized or a church goer, he is a strongly religious boy. So religious in fact that he had decided to put his life in God's hands. Someone will have to die on a distant battlefield and it might as well be him.

It wasn't until the sixteenth of June 1967, the day of induction, that Brown told his mother and father about his commitment. His father didn't find the news particularly interesting, but his mother took the day-off to drive him to Chicago's downtown Induction Center. Just before Brown stepped from the car, he looked into his mother's face. Tears came to both their eyes. His heart reached out to her. They hugged. While embracing, he began to understand that his mother didn't hate him. At that moment, he felt he had reconnected with her.

"Ma," Brown had said, "If I live through this, I'll come back a man."

They landed briefly for re-fueling in the Philippines.

Six hours later the pilot's voice burst over the intercom, "This is your captain speaking . . . ," begins the imminent, dreaded announcement.

Brown tries to control his anxiety, but his blood pressure climbs till a dizziness sweeps over him. He and the others obediently raise their seats, fasten their belts, and extinguish their cigarettes. Brown's heart skips a beat as the landing wheels rumble into a lock position.

"We are presently over the South China Sea and are approaching the coast of South Vietnam," the captains laconic announcement continues. "We will be landing very shortly at Cam Ranh Bay Military Air Base."

"Civilian planes like night flights, so they don't get hit," a soldier across the aisle explains. "The airfield takes rockets and mortars all the time."

"I ain't up to no runnin' through no mortar barrage," a shaken soldier confesses.

"I'll consider myself lucky if my legs even straighten out."

"I'd feel a lot better if they'd given us something to defend ourselves with," another soldier remarks.

"Yeah, like some M-16s."

"A few grenades."

"For some reason I feel like a duck in a shootin' gallery."

"I'm gonna keep my eyes peeled for mortar tube flashes and anti-aircraft tracer fire," another soldier says as he gazes out the porthole.

Brown could hear others working out escape plans in case of a firefight or crash landing. He listens intently while trying to formulate his own plan of escape.

The GI across the aisle speaks, "They refuel in the Philippines so they don't have to hang around here any longer than necessary. You watch . . . this plane 'll be back in the air as soon as they get rid of us."

A few morbid jokes about riding in a ready-made steel coffin make the rounds, followed by hard-edge laughter. However, the jokes go flat on one particular GI who sits directly in front of Brown. While gazing, the soldier wraps his arms around himself and begins rocking. Suddenly, he jerks his head from the window as though he just saw something. Something like a thousand howling, starving wolves with saliva dripping from their long fangs, all fighting to get into position for the anticipated grand feast. Wolves ready to rip, shred, tear him limb from limb. The horror of the imagined blood bath pours into his veins causing his breath to border on hyperventilation. He slaps down the window shade.

The plane dives through a washboard of air with Brown grabbing onto the armrests. Hitting clear sky, the plane bottoms out, tossing Brown's stomach as if he is on a giant roller coaster.

Brown looks at the panic-stricken GI with beads of sweat running down his checks. Then the GI calmly lowers his head and looks at his crotch.

Say they survives the landing what then? Would he have to run for his life? And in which direction are the bunkers? If he can just make it to the bunker. Then he'd have time to find the weapons and ammo to fight off the attack?

I hopes they don't think I can save their life just because I'm an infantryman, he laments.

Will he actually die in this combat zone? Or will he become a prisoner of war? Fingernails pulled out one by one. Arms yanked out of their sockets. Face beaten bloody. Feet and hands bound then shoved into a dark hole where rats would . . . *ugh*.

Take three deep breaths, he calms himself. But the unknown world of this combat zone keeps crowding him. Keeps trying to break him.

In the thick silence, he thinks perhaps the stewardesses should take time out to say a few words of compassion. Maybe even lead them in a chorus of Ninety-nine Bottles of Beer on the Wall. He smiles amused with himself. I know, Brown thinks, Why not play *God Bless America* over the PA system and we can all join in. Yeah. Then, after the song, the crew could say something like . . . Three cheers for these nice brave soldiers, the defenders of freedom, liberty, and justice for all!

Sarcastically, Brown thinks maybe he has it backwards. It is the soldiers who should give a grateful round of applause for being flown to their death in the comforts of a civilian jetliner.

The cabin noise increases as hydraulic pumps work the wing flaps. The plane rolls from side to side. Brown spots the attendants strapping themselves in as they prepare for the eerie night landing. Within a bubble of anticipation, Brown thinks about what they had said back home. "There's a light at the end of the tunnel. Chances are the war'll be over before you even get there."

A quiet, desperate chaos replaces the restrained jokes. Why doesn't someone yell "Geronimo!" to add some bravado. Maybe it would lighten things up little. Or maybe yell in unison like in Basic Training, "Let's kill some Commies!"

The cabin seems to stretch like a cartoon drawing as the plane swoops in for the landing.

While his knuckles turn white, Brown breaths rhythmically to stay in control. **"Aaaa**

aa

aa

aa."

The tires peal rubber as they meet the tarmac. Immediately the jet engines are thrown into reverse thrust, sending the plane into a dizzy, frenzied vibration. Brown and the other soldiers bounce around, fighting to stay upright in their seats. Reverse thrusters wind down, the plane taxies till the brakes grind it to a halt.

The intercom crackles and the stewardess comes on telling them to secure personal belongings . . . . "Now gentlemen, I want you to be good soldiers. I don't want you to do anything I wouldn't do. I'll come back around in three hundred and sixty-five days, pick you up, and take you back home. Take care—keep your heads up. See ya soon."

Ventilation is switched off and instantly cabin odors become overpowering. "The smell could gag a maggot." The cabin temperature begins to escalate, and Brown finds himself struggling for breathable air. Calming himself, he takes out the last piece of Juicy Fruit gum and starts to count the seconds, seconds that stretch into long minutes until the front and rear hatches thud open. The anxious soldiers literally drenched in sweat, slowly, stiffly, tensely begin to depart.

Nearing the exit, Brown is greeted by a blast of humid, strangely pungent air. He passes through the yawning doorway and gets his solid breath of air and his first view of Vietnam.

"Move it," soldiers dressed in combat fatigues shout from the bottom of the ramp. "Come on. Step on it. Let's go. Move it! Move it! Move it!"

The GIs clamber down the steel steps, their carry-on bags banging against the hand railing. One GI slips and skids a few steps, causing a brief jam-up.

"Hey, soldier! You're in a combat zone. We might have incoming mortars at anytime. You wanna get everyone killed?" a directing soldiers shouts.

"Sorry, sir. I . . . ." The GI regains his footing.

"Hurry it up!"

The GIs get funneled into a rope enclosure.

"Alright, now listen up! Listen up. Everyone close it up." While speaking the staff sergeant uses exaggerated hand signals. "Come on, close it up!" He herds the GIs into the enclosure.

Nearby, under a galvanized roof shelter, stands another group of soldiers dressed, for the most part, in jungle fatigues. Unfettered, they casually study the new arrivals. It is soon apparent these soldiers are to board Brown's plane.

"Hey, NFG! Welcome to sunny Viet Nam," one soldier taunts from the galvanized shelter.

"Vacation capital of the world. The land of fun and sun!"

"You ain't lived till ya done d'Nam, man," another one yells.

"Hey you bunch of cherries," the cat calling continues, "if some gung-ho Hershey Bar tells ya to take the hill, tell him to kiss your ever lovin' . . . . If'n you don't, you're sure in hell gonna buy-the-farm."

"Wind up dead," another rejoins, then spells, "as in D-E-A-D."

The jubilant outgoing soldiers start for the aircraft ramps acting like guys on the way to a big Hollywood party.

One last distinctive shout reaches Brown's ears. "When I see your girl, I'll tell her you said `Hi.'"

"Thanks," the soldier next to Brown utter.

A baggage cart rolls over to a dimly lit area and everyone scrambles to retrieve their overstuffed duffle bags.

"Okay, troops. Let's hurry it up with the gear," a lieutenant shouts dressed in starched combat fatigues donning a soft cap. A few minutes later he continues, "Follow me!"

He leads them along an oiled gravel road, the crunch of stone under their feet amplified by the stillness of the warm night air.

Strange, Brown thinks, the officer did not call them into formation, nor has them running for cover.

The roar of jet engines signal the departure of the PanAm Boeing 707. Brown glances over his shoulder to see the black fuselage rush, liftoff and get swallowed by darkness.

They turn left from the main gravel road onto a dirt trail that leads them to a row of fairly new plywood and canvas barracks.

"Wake up zero-five-hundred hours," the Lieutenant says at the entrance to a sleeping quarter. "Breakfast at zero-six-hundred hours, and formation at zero-seven-hundred hours. Fall out in the morning with soft cap, full combat uniforms, pistol belt with first aid pouch, and full canteen of water attached.

"Troops, relax." The officer softens his voice. "This place is relatively safe. There hasn't been any enemy activity against this installation for quite some time." An audible sigh of relief passes through the ranks. "So find yourself an empty bunk and get some rest." He takes a step back and shouts, "Dismissed."

The loner that he is, Brown ventures away from everyone and to the farthest tent. He crosses the wood plank bridge over a drainage ditch, pulls open the screen door and quietly enters.

Just past the threshold, he stops to give his eyes time to adjust. He hears the sound of heavy breathing. Near the back of the barracks, he stops at the foot of a bunk, leans over and feels the canvas to make sure it's empty. Satisfied, he drops the duffel bag.

Unsnapping the bag, he fishes around and locates the poncho and liner. About to lay down, it dawns on him that he's far too anxious to sleep. His muscles scream for a stretch after such an incredibly long flight which has taken him through eleven time zones and to the opposite side of the globe.

Gingerly, he walks the length of the barracks and back outdoors. No one is around as he pauses on the other side of the plank bridge. Overhead, in the crystalline sky, the moon hangs like a lantern, giving off an ethereal, almost fluorescent glow. Black wisps of clouds sail stormily across its face, looking like old three masted sailing ships rolling through a molten sea. Soaking in the breadth of the heavens, his dwindling reserve of innocence seeks out the brightest star.

"Star light, star bright
First star I see tonight
I wish I may, I wish I might
have the wish
I wish tonight. . . ."

27 November 1967

"Shake it up, troop! It's zero-five-hundred hours." A voice bugles through the row of barracks. A mystical eminence hangs in the electrified air, at this, their first predawn wake-up in South Vietnam. The energy-sapped troops, jolt awake with eyes shooting wide with dawning realization.

"Let's move it!" the NCO commands as if playing a bit-part in some movie that's been played on late night TV a thousand times.

At this reveille the traumatized troops fall true to form. There are the usual grumbles and use of profanity, the tossing back of the warm cozy blankets, and then the rushing around like dazed cattle. But there's more.

Even though the troops try to make this seem like the *usual*, there is the unmistakable awe that tingles their sense of touch, smell, sight and sound. There is a radiant glow coming from behind their eyes because they are now in an honest-to-God combat zone. Yes, you really can die here.

With a moderate temperature, soldiers find they need only to dress in underwear. So with toiletries in hand, fatigues draping over shoulder and with unlaced boots on, they hurry over to the plywood-and-screen shower rooms.

After a fast shower and shave, Brown hurries back to the bunk where he quickly dresses. That's when he notes the tag attached to the combat boots. It reads: 'Boot, Combat, Tropical, Spike Resistant.' He breaths deeply while taking in his surroundings. "Welcome to Vietnam." After adjusting the pistol belt to his waist, he attaches the canteen and first-aid pouch.

With time to spare before breakfast, he goes over to the Water Buffalo next to the showers. After drinking his fill of robust water, he fills his canteen.

Sniffing the air, he detects the smells of fresh brewed coffee, powdered eggs, hash-browns and bacon. Following the wafting smells, he passes through the cadre area, and comes to the noisy generators used to supply electricity to the canvas tent mess hall. The whirring motors are enclosed by six-foot-high rows of sandbags.

"It's all so real," Brown laments. He stops some five-feet from the war-absorbing sandbags and stares. "I'm actually here."

Like some cheap corner prostitute, the sandbags beckon him, taunt him, wanting him to touch them. Want him to place both hands on them with fingers moving into every crevice. To hold them in loves embrace until he surrenders unconditionally to their forbidden fruit. The burlap begs him to stretch and rub his spine passionately against them like a grizzly bear. They implore him to climb on top, roll around lustfully—needfully. They plead with him to let their cold penetrating fingers of temptation soothe his fretting brow while he stares intimately into the heavens and hums a sweet lullaby.

He dare not touch the seemingly harmless brown burlap, but did permit his mind to peel away one more thin layer of denial. To permit the "what have we done" reality to creep a little closer.

After several helpings of breakfast, Brown hurries to the

formation. From there, he is escorted with some seventy others to a large canvas tent with side flaps rolled up. Stepping inside, he feels a breeze streaming through like a cool compress gliding across a feverish brow.

Walking briskly over a carpet of trampled vegetation in the process of dying, turning brown and bio-degrading back into soil, the soldiers slide into twelve rows of metal folding chairs.

Taking a chair four rows back, Brown has a commanding view of a large blackboard and an eight-foot table covered with pamphlets.

The five-foot-eight, ruddy-complexion instructor in his mid-forties, uses peripheral vision to scrutinize every move. The jungle fatigues with camouflage insignias and patches, belt and buckle, boots and utility cap are all "ready for inspection, sir!" In addition to canteen and first-aid pouch, he carries an army issue Colt .45 and a leather handle Ka-bar survival knife. The knife with weathered leather scabbard has the 'old soldier' look.

As the GIs continue to file in, the hard-tanned, crusty instructor begins to pace impatiently. In his grasp is a wooden swagger stick with shiny brass .50 caliber bullet on the butt and a .30 caliber serving as tip, which he brandishes through the air and smacks on his palm.

"Alright grab a chair. Let's go. We ain't got all day," he booms. The room immediately quiets.

"My name is Instructor Sergeant Manning," his voice bellows, as the final creaking noise of troops settling on metal chairs subsides.

"And I will be your instructor for this block of instruction. First," Sergeant Manning announces, "I'd like to take this opportunity to welcome you to the Republic of South Vietnam. Secondly, this is a war zone," he says pointedly. "And thirdly, if you don't listen up," he leans into the audience, "you are all gonna die." He pauses to let the words settle.

"Play time is over," he fires, his square jaw jutting so forcefully that it looks like it could chew through a bullet. "Now who has an infantry MOS. Don't be shy, raise your hands." Sergeant Manning appraises the twenty-five infantrymen, including Brown with meekly raised hands.

"You infantrymen listen close." Manning strode across the room surveying all the youthful faces. "As for the rest, I can assure you, your Uncle Sam did not ship you across the big pond so you could lie on a sandy beach under the warm Vietnam sun."

"Everyone, look at the soldier to the left of you. To the right of you. To the front and behind you. Look into their faces . . . their eyes." Sergeant Manning challenges them to follow his instructions. Muted laughter begins to pierce the silence.

"What's so funny!" Sergeant Manning explodes in a voice so critical that it feels like a whip to the face. "There's nothin' funny about it. Fact is . . . in just a few short days from now one of the soldiers you just looked at might very well be dead. KIA. Killed in action. That's right, troop," he cranes his head, "like I said, this is a war zone. Not some sissy training center where you get weekend passes.

"Now" he growls, "folks back home consider this a little conflict—an intervention. Let me put it this way," he continues in a machine gun style. "If my life is on the line, it's plain. It's simple. It's **War!** Do you understand me?!"

"Yes, sergeant," the room shouts in unison like AIT trainees.

Sergeant Manning starts to outline what he calls fundamental survival techniques. As the lecture continues the sergeant becomes larger and larger, taller and taller to Brown, till he takes on the aura of a demigod from Greek mythology. Zeus smiles down from the clouds pleased with his son, *War God*.

"The secret of survival," Sergeant Manning professes, "is knowing the right things. If a soldier is forewarned, he should be forearmed."

The audience obediently nods their understanding.

"Vietnam ain't a place where you pitch a pup tent with your girlfriend. Throw another log on the fire and sing campfire songs. No, Nam is mean. It's mother nature at its very best with more diseases than we have names for."

He persists in his "charge the hill" manner. "Besides the fact that it gets so hot you could fry eggs on your steel pot, there's the monsoon rains that drench, drown and chill you to the bone. There are blood suckin' leeches, killer bees, ants, scorpions, roaches, spiders big as your face, and mosquitoes in swarms the size of helicopters with appetites the size of a shark." He stops abruptly to take a breath. "Did I miss anything? Oh yes. The black rats. Which are big enough kill poor Rover let alone chew your dick off if you don't pay attention.

"There are cobras, kraits, and bamboo vipers," Sergeant Manning continues. "In fact, of the one-hundred-thirty-three species of snakes, one-hundred and thirty-one would love to kill you.

"Pay attention. Stay alert. Stay alive!" Manning shouts. "Because Charlie Cong is out there waiting. He's in a hole, under every rock, behind every bush, hanging from every limb. He'll wait as long as it takes. Why?" Lashing the swagger stick, the .30 caliber bullet ends-up pressed into the forehead of an unsuspecting soldier. "Because he loves to kill GIs." He went on lecturing about the importance of staying calm when in contact with the enemy.

Brown wonders if combat automatically makes you tough and strong like this sergeant. Just think, he fantasizes, when I go home I'll be squared away, standing straight and tall just like him. They'll respect me just like they do those Second World War veterans.

"**Sol-jerrrrrr!**" Sergeant Manning's voice erupts so suddenly that Brown and the others jump, their steel chairs groaning. "What's wrong with you. You brain dead?" he yells hanging over a soldier, the swagger stick pushing into the soldier's chest. "This is Vietnam and while you were busy yappin' your jaw, Charlie Cong got through the wire. He just slit your throat." The Ka-bar knife, which shows up magically in his hand, helps the visualization. "You understand me troop?"

"Yes, sergeant," comes a shaky noise.

"Goddamn right you do." Pointing with swagger stick he says, "This trooper here isn't infantry. So he probably think what I'm saying is not that important."

Manning curled the edges of his lips as he again addresses the room. "Well, this may come as a shock but Victor Charlie doesn't care about your color, who your daddy is, your MOS. On this guard, no mamma's boy is gonna make it out alive! Is this clear?"

"Yes sergeant," the room shouts in unison.

Handbook for U.S. Forces in Vietnam is distributed.

"Our mission is to free the people of the Republic of South Vietnam from communism," Sergeant Manning explains. "This can be . . ." he scrunches his lips, "excuse me. I meant, this *will* be accomplished by eliminating the Vietcong, better known to most as VC or Victor Charlie. The VC employ guerrilla tactics and therefore are an elusive foe," he begins to lecture. "And since Charlie Cong has very little military equipment available they have become experts in the art of camouflage, deception, booby trapping, and ambushing."

Sergeant Manning moves to the blackboard and chalks in a horizontal line intersected by a below-grade "U-pit." He chalks slashes protruding upward from the bottom of the pit. "This is a VC *pungi* pit."

"Pungi pits are camouflaged with sticks and debris." Manning draws a cover over the pungi pit. "Your weight will break through the cover and the force will run the sticks through your boot and foot. They are very hard to extract because the bamboo has a fish hook tip. And watch for poison ones.

"Now, VC cannot operate in an area unless civilians cooperate," Sergeant Manning explains. "The VC preach propaganda in the villages, and depict the US," he says leaning into the audience, "yes that means you, as bullies out to push 'em around." He punctuates with the swagger stick. "So, treat civilians with respect. Get them on our side. Okay? Win their hearts and minds." With both hands he smooths the air.

"Victor Charlie is a ruthless fighter," Sergeant Manning explains, his mood hardening. "They will give little orphans—ice babies I call them—harmless looking baskets with a block of ice containing a hand grenade. Ice melts. *Cablamm!* Stay on your guard.

"When it comes to ingenuity Victor Charlie is pretty good. He can take a discarded piece of trash, a bullet, C-ration can, or just about anything and turn it into a booby trap," he explains.

"VC keep to very simple, but very effective rules.

> When the enemy advances, withdraw
> When he defends, harass
> When he's tired, attack
> When he withdraws, pursue.

"Point being, Charlie doesn't rest. So if you wanna live, neither should you."

On the black board he prints in big capital letters, *NVA*. Then says, "NVA. North Vietnamese Army which is backed by both China and Russia. They have uniforms, modern weaponry and are expertly trained. Their usual tactic is to ambush and fight to the death. You'll encounter the NVA up north near the demilitarized zone—the DMZ. They will also be encountered along the Ho Chi Minh Trail. If you didn't know, the Ho Chi Minh Trail is the main supply route which passes along the bordering countries of Cambodia and Laos." Manning places the chalk in the blackboard gutter.

"Alright." He claps dust off his hands. "This is a war of attrition. That means we do to them what General Custer did to the Redskins during the American Indian Wars. We've determined the number of Victor Charlies in Vietnam. When we have successfully eliminated them—mission accomplished and we go home."

"Question?" he points.

"Private Murphy, signal corps," the young soldier states. "Sergeant, how do we know the difference between the VC and civilian?"

"Fair question," Sergeant Manning says with an understanding nod. "Now an innocent civilian won't run. For the rest of 'em we have Rules of Engagement. For example, you see a dink in civilian clothes walking some fifty meters away and it appears that he's unarmed." Manning scans the room to make sure he has everyone's undivided attention. "First holler, *Dung lai,* which means, stop. If that doesn't get his attention you fire a round over his head. If the dink is still hard of hearin', you yell, *Lai dai,* which means, Come here dink and pronto. Then fire a second round over his head. If he still ignores you, yell, *Dung lai, lai dai,* which means, Ya better stop or I'm gonna give ya a new asshole."

Laughter rings through the tent, relieving some of the strain of the in-country orientation. Sergeant Manning gives a wide grin.

"Now, it's time to switch your rifle to Rock 'n' Roll. Fire for effect. Kill a commie for Christ."

Catcalls reverberate off the tent's canvas ceiling, and even Manning bursts into laughter at his own flamboyance.

"Remember every weapon captured saves the lives of an innocent woman and child. Every enemy eliminated saves the lives of twenty innocent civilians." He takes a deep breath. "In a few minutes you can smoke'm if you got 'em. So I'll make it quick."

With raised arms, he quiets the room. "We have designated freefire zones. That's where you kill 'em all and let God sort it out. Deer huntin' season. Oh*hh* baby you know what I like."

Returning to a dead serious poise, Sergeant Manning draws his Marine Ka-bar. "I reckon you think it might come down to this." He raises the knife so everyone gets a good view. "Something we combat veterans refer to as the 'spirit of the bayonet.'"

Lust sweeps across War God's face as he slices the air with the survival knife's nine-inch keen edge, light glistening off the blood tempered steel. "Let's talk about hand-to-hand combat, shall we?"

He lovingly runs his finger over the razor edge of the Ka-bar as though stroking a woman's shiny long hair.

"Ninety percent of the combat tactics you learned back in the states was pure hogwash," he claims. "It's different when you're in it for keeps."

Sergeant Manning's eyes narrow, his neck muscles tighten like banjo strings. "Let's just say you wind up doin' the tango with a gook. You won't be able to protect your back." He stabs with the knife, then swings to clutch and stab. The ducking, bobbing, weaving, dodging and slashing turns into a kind of kinky dance.

Out of the corner of his eye, Sergeant Manning spots a snickering NFG. "I'm not boring you am I?" Without waiting for an answer, Sergeant Manning yanks the soldier off the chair.

"No-oooo, sergeant," the GI's bubbles from fright.

"Well, I'm glad you volunteered troop," Sergeant Manning snarls as he begins to stalk the GI like a panther.

Manning lunges, thrusting the Ka-bar knife into the solar plexus of the soldier. The GI shrieks and buckles in agony.

Everyone gasps.

"Move! Jump! Dive! Hit! Kill! *Kill, kill, kill!*" Sergeant Manning snarls while continuing to twist the knife farther into the terrified soldier.

Sergeant Manning steps back, his eyes licking the blade as if full of blood. Only then did Brown realize that with the speed of a magician the Ka-bar had been turned around so that the leather handle had punched the stunned soldier.

"Charlie Cong will flop to the ground like a Raggedy Ann doll." He shoves the pale soldier back into the folding chair.

"Fast and deadly," Sergeant Manning coaches. "No time for chitchat. Don't think about it." He leans over the troop, "just *do* it.

"And remember, stay away from the rib cage," Sergeant Manning adds like he is teaching from an instruction manual entitled *Combat Fever*. "It's the soft spot in between," he explains. "And don't forget the upward twist." He gestures with the knife. "That's what rips through their guts and spells instant death."

"Take a ten minute break," Sergeant Manning barks.

Brown, like the others, stands stiffly, pulls clothes from his skin and stretches to release anxiety from the blistering lecture. A sultry breeze ripples through the tent causing the canvas flaps to wave hypnotically. Somewhat mesmerized and still unhinged by the grand performance, he takes a deep cleansing breath, turns and stiffly walks outside.

Squinting from the harsh sunlight, he takes in the military installation with its swaying palm trees and army tents scattered across the flat plain.

The soldiers hover around the water tank drinking their fill, pouring water over their heads and topping off their canteens.

In Basic Training his platoon was forced to run in heat like this. One member of the platoon collapsed from heat exhaustion and died on the spot from heart failure.

Everyone begins filing back into the tent. On their chairs they find the NINE RULES card of the Military Assistance Command, Vietnam (MACV).

The cover reads:
THE VIETNAMESE HAVE PAID A HEAVY PRICE IN SUFFERING FOR THEIR LONG FIGHT AGAINST THE COMMUNISTS. WE MILITARY MEN ARE IN VIETNAM BECAUSE THEIR GOVERNMENT HAS ASKED US TO HELP ITS SOLDIERS AND PEOPLE IN WINNING THEIR STRUGGLE. THE VIETCONG WILL ATTEMPT TO TURN THE VIETNAMESE PEOPLE AGAINST YOU. YOU CAN DEFEAT THEM AT EVERY TURN BY THE STRENGTH, UNDERSTANDING, AND GENEROSITY YOU DISPLAY WITH THE PEOPLE. HERE ARE NINE SIMPLE RULES:

*DISTRIBUTION — ONE TO EACH MEMBER OF THE UNITED STATES ARMED FORCES IN VIETNAM.

When the soldiers are seated, Sergeant Manning picks up his own copy of the card. "Let's go through these Nine Rules of Conduct," he announces. "Read along with me.

NUMBER ONE: Remember we are guests here: We make no demands and seek no special treatment.
NUMBER TWO: Join with the people! Understand their life, use phrases from their language and honor their customs and laws.
NUMBER THREE: Treat women with politeness and respect.
NUMBER FOUR: Make friends among the soldiers and common people.
NUMBER FIVE: Always give the Vietnamese the right of way.
NUMBER SIX: Be alert to security and ready to react with your military skill.

NUMBER SEVEN: Don't attract attention by loud, rude or unusual behavior.
NUMBER EIGHT: Avoid separating yourselves from the people by a display of wealth or privilege."

Manning reads the last one as though addressing a Boy Scout Troop:

"And NUMBER NINE: Above all else you are members of the U.S. Military Forces on a difficult mission, responsible for all your official and personal actions. Reflect honor upon yourselves and the United States of America."

He drops the card on the table. "Let's make it simple, just remember this little maxim: For every action there is a reaction.

"Case in point, let's say a couple of GIs ram their jeep into an old gook. Both gook and the pig-in-a-poke get killed. Now, the next time the Commie recruiter comes waltzing to town handin' out booby traps and rifles what do you think that dead gook's son is gonna do?" Manning's eyes rifle back and forth across the room.

With that said, Manning bulldozes through the middle row of the room, dumping seated GIs right and left as he makes a beeline for the exit. Without looking back, he bellows, "Let's *win* their Hearts and Minds, and go home! Dismissed."

With lunch an hour away, Brown decides on some exercise. Wanting to jog but since the boots aren't broken in, he opts for a brisk hip rotating, arm swinging walk.

Meandering to the main gravel road he remembers hearing, "Yeah, soap outside of this installation will be hard to come by." Finding no PX (Post Exchange) sign, he begins a search.

A rawboned soldier in faded jungle fatigues steps onto the path. The mustached soldier with dark aviator sunglasses has sleeves rolled above the elbows. His pant legs are also rolled over the boot tops. The GI's overall alien appearance mystifies Brown. How could he get away with such a messy appearance?

The shoulder-warped GI bends at an angle reminiscent of someone carrying a heavy backpack. And he slogs along kicking up dust as if there is a ball-and-chain attached to each battered jungle boot. No signs of military spit and polish here.

He'll know where the PX is, Brown decides. Approaching, Brown makes note of the soldier's wide arms swing that seems programmed to miss pistol belt ammo pouches. Plus, his right hand seems to have a built-in curl for carrying a rifle.

"Hi there!" Brown ventures in a bright voice. No response. Determined, Brown double-times to sidle-up from behind.

"Jeez, it's a hot one today," Brown continues in a cheery manner, "I'm sweatin' bullets already and I ain't even doing nothin'. Guess you get used to it though, after you've been in-country for a while, huh?"

The six-foot lean, dark-haired soldier glances passively. A cigarette dangles from his lips and after a long draw, he exhales with the cigarette still in his mouth. "Talking to me?" he askes in a flat voice.

"I'm an NFG," Brown blurts thinking the NFG name might humor him. "Just dropped in last night."

"Well, NFG you can call me No Name."

"No Name? Well, No Name it looks like you've been around some," Brown says, now unconcerned about finding the PX and soap.

"Yeah. Yeah. I'm cool," No Name answers with pride, the cigarette bobbing in his mouth. "Deros'in outta here. I'm a short-timer. Dig it. Yeah, I'm so short I gotta stand on a box to tie my boots. I'm so short, I'm next. No, I ain't next, I'm gone."

Without an effort at eye contact, No Name continues to ramble, "Freedom bird in a wake-up, man. You dig it? I've done my time in the d'Nam, man."

Though unaware of the soldier's meaning, Brown wants to keep the conversation alive. "Yeah, you're right there." Taking note of the colorful tiger tattoo on the soldier's forearm, he says, "Nice tattoo you got there."

"Bangkok,"

"Bangkok?" Brown repeats but gets no more reply. He notices No Name's hat. A faded, ragged-edged full brim camouflage hat that has loops in its headband. Loops that secure a brass cartridge, a grenade pin and a P-38 C-ration can opener. Then he spots a loop with a tooth secured with trip wire. What kind of animal did that come from? Or was it a human's molar?

"Nice hat you got there. I'd rather wear one of those then a steel pot. Those helmets weigh a ton and no matter what, they give me a headache."

"Mean the boonie hat?" No Name says, finally slowing his gait.

Brown nods eagerly.

"Yeah, well, it just depends, ya know." He looks with penetrating hawkish eyes. "In some places they make ya wear the pot all the time—even to the shitter." The combatant chuckles a little. "Some commanders are cool though. Just depends, ya know." No Name's icy stare locks onto him. Brown blinks.

"Just depends. Like everything around this green suck. Just depends, man."

No Name takes a guarded look over his shoulder. "Firefight. Incoming. Wasted. KIA. WIA. Bean's and Dicks. Ham and Mothers." Then he changes to a child's voice saying, "No Name want numba-one shoe shine?" He continues in a raspy baritone, "Rolling Thunder. Bird. Huey. Gunship. Foxtrot-Six. Dustoff. Medivac. Echo Mike." He levels off. "Like everything around this suck hole, just depends. You know what I'm sayin'?"

He doesn't have a clue, but at least Brown is now certain he's talking to a bonafide combat soldier.

Continuing along the gravel road, a military crisp officer begins walking toward them. Since stateside soldiers salute officers, Brown prepares for a brisk salute. However, the combatant keeps deadly aim at the blank space ahead, deliberately ignoring the fast approaching officer. Taking a chance, Brown decides to follow the combatant's lead. The officer passes without incident.

"You don't salute yahoos in a war zone. It gives away the senior personnel to the enemy," No Name says sarcastically. "Which ain't a bad idea, one less Hershey Bar—now I think about it."

"That makes sense." Apparently No Name has a deep seated disrespect for authority figures. Well, thinks Brown, so what. He's probably a good fighter and that's what war's all about.

"Say, how is it out there . . ." Brown motions beyond the perimeter. "The jungle? Rice fields?"

"No sweat, GI." There is a finality in the words, as if Brown has just been given the definitive answer.

"No sweat," Brown repeats. Now *sweat* is a word Brown understands. You sweat after running five miles. You sweat while working in a sweltering restaurant's kitchen. You sweat at that pivotal moment when it's time to kiss the girl. Yeah-hhh. And it's an altogether different kind of sweat when you hear, "Heah you there!" Or when the teacher says, "Put your books away. Now remember this is a very important test." Uh-oh*hhh,* The test had slipped your mind because you'd spent the night making-out with your girlfriend.

You sweat when chased by the police, by a gang of kids, or by a car. Oh, and how about a night in jail and facing the judge next morning? There are all kinds of sweats and reasons they occur, and Brown is learning new ways all the time.

Brown understands *sweat* because he had always lived in a world of sweat. And it is all too obvious the heat is going up.

"You're serious huh? You wanna know what it's like?" No Name takes a draw on his cigarette and looks over casually. "Wow, man," he says in a warm voice. "Never thought about it, you know. Uum*mmm*."

He rubs the nape of his neck. "It ain't bad all the time. Meet a lot of groovy guys. Ya party a lot. Lot of number-one boom-boom. Then sometimes . . . ."

The lean combatant's demeanor switches frighteningly fast to dead serious. "Sometimes . . . there's shitty choices." He looks through Brown. "A thatched hut with a cooking fire. Mama san, papa san, baby san, sitting around, shootin' the breeze. Except one of the guys just bought-the-farm and there ain't nothing there. Then it's hell, real hell." No Name pleads for understanding. "Like no other kind of hell."

"Yeah, I know what ya mean," Brown says off-handedly.

"NFG, you couldn't imagine what I mean," No Name says viciously.

Taken back but not giving up, Brown ventures, "Say, how can you tell the difference from incoming and friendly fire?"

"You a boonie rat?"

Brown stares in confusion.

Behind the dark glasses are watchful, ever measuring eyes. "Eleven bush? Grunt?" No Name asks. "Infantry?"

"Infantry. Yeah, infantry right."

"Practice hittin' the ground. Practice all the time 'till it gets to when you hear anything . . . anything at all, you'll drop like a rock. *Incoming!"* he gives an ear splitting holler. "Hit the dirt with no question." No Name pauses then adds caustically, "'Cause there's theirs, then there's ours, but ain't none of it friendly."

The combatant pulls off his hat to wipe sweat from his brow. The sunlight shows on the harsh face, revealing deep lines that have been etched across the forehead and around the mouth. They are a legacy of cruel times, dog-eat-dog days spent under a merciless sun, drenching rains while marching through jungle. Lips meant for laughter have become cracked and grimly thin. The dark aviator sunglasses make his eyes appear like tar pits.

"Want some incountry advice?" He flings off his aviator sunglasses and locks haunted pain-sharpened eyes on Brown.

Brown nods.

"Trust only your M-16 and a full magazine," No Name explains. "Because in this green suck it's kill or be killed."

28 November 1967

At the morning formation, the assignments are again announced through a bullhorn by an officer standing on a four-foot high platform. And like before, the soldiers called, obediently step to the front and pick up their freshly cut orders. Since this is Brown's second day and fourth formation, he doesn't feel so apprehensive.

What he observes is a unit designated "signal," "engineer," "mechanized," "artillery," and "motor pool" elicits no blunt response from the formation. However, when cavalry, airborne, or infantry is attached to a units name, a shiver runs through the entire formation. After thinking 'poor guy' there is an audible sigh of relief from the remaining soldiers.

On this particular day, the cavalry, airborne and 196th Light Infantry Brigade are called *painfully* often.

Brown questions his neighbor. "Why do some units get called so much?"

"I'm thinkin'," his neighbor replies, "that if they're taking a lot of casualties they need a lot of replacements. "Say like, airborne. There's a big battle on Hill 875 near Dak To," the soldier explains. "You ain't airborne, are ya?"

He shook his head.

"We're both lucky then," the soldier claims. "But still, they have TDY, 'temporary duty,' which means they'll send you anywhere they need ya—regardless of your MOS. They'll turn an engineer into an infantryman right here on the spot." The soldier gives Brown a knowing nod. "You don't want go to the 196th either, they're in deep shit up there in I Corp."

"Don't say."

"Private Brown, Fred Leo, 198th Light Infantry Brigade!" came the orders over the bullhorn.

Brown, thinking they said the 196th Infantry, stiffens. His blood feels like it might curdle. He forces, "Here, sir!" with what seems like the last air in his lungs. Moving one foot in front of the other, he propels himself forward.

With orders in hand, he realizes he'd been mistaken. He will join the 198th Light Infantry. Whatever that meant.

Next morning at the airfield, Brown hands his orders to the dispatch sergeant. The sergeant checks the flight schedule. "Lemme see now, the 198th Light Infantry." His finger runs down a list. "That's up north in I Corps. Ah yes, that's part of that new Americal Division they just formed up in Chu Lai."

"Chu Lai?"

His finger stops on a line. "Uh*uu*." He glances over the airfield, "You see that C-130 over there? The one with the M-37 and jeep being loaded?"

Brown follows the dispatcher's finger to a distant aircraft painted in brown and green shades of camouflage. "Just go on over and show them your orders."

Brown hoists the duffle bag over his shoulder and ventures into a fray of war machinery with its expended fuels, dust and high torque, high revved engines. He walks slowly taking time to look over the panorama that unfolds before his eyes.

One plane after another trundles away, turns onto the main runway, the engines pushing full throttle. In other parts of the airfield, helicopters set-off a whirlwind of debris as they labor to lift off vertically. His eyes take in the rolling dust, spinning propellers, forklifts, bustling vehicles laden with war equipment and supplies, and thick black smoke spewing from exhaust pipes.

At the rear hatch of the C-130, he yells to an airman dressed in OD aviation clothes, "You headed to Chu Lai?"

December 1967

LZ Gator, base camp of 198th Light Inf. Battalion, Southwest of Chu Lai along Highway One, I-Corp South Vietnam

Ma *1 December 1967*

Well so far I have a unit. I do not have a permanent address yet. By the end of the today, Friday, I will have an address and I will send it to you. Everything is alright. I still am in good shape.

So long for now, Fred Leo

3 December 1967

Like shabby corn stalks in a desolate black crow caw field in autumn, the two NFGs stand silhouetted against a tempestuous eastern sky. They watch forlorn as the guard jeep drive across the barren terrain, its tires spitting rocks as it grinds up the hillside. It vanishes over the knoll but the groan of its little four cylinder can still be heard. Then an eery, black silence envelopes the area.

Down the grade some hundred yards sets a desolate sandbag bunker built on a peninsula protruding westerly. Beyond the bunker the ground dives under a flooded rice field. A half mile from shore a vegetated mound of dirt juts like a miniature extinct volcano.

With the feeling they are so far from help their bodies would be reduced to skeletons before reenforcements could arrive, Brown and Okie stand stoically facing the *dead* zone. Their hearts sinking with the fading sunlight.

Slowly and at the ready, they crouch, moving guardedly toward the bunker. At just a few yards away, Brown feels the bunker's thick, chilly atmosphere pouring from the entrance. With backs against the sandbags, Okie signals that he's going in. Brown holds his rifle at the ready, as Okie spins through the entrance.

Moments later, "Clear!"

Entering, his boots release more fumigant odor as they press into the bunker's spongy earth floor. It is an old bunker. Rebuilt. But still a very old bunker—in war terms. It reeks with the stench of mildew and gunpowder to the extent of almost choking off his nostrils.

The dirt floor sucks in brass cartridges, cigarette butts, C-ration cans. The pulpy wet support timbers are bayonet scarred. Hiding in the cracks and crevices are crawling insects that peer questioningly, their antenna's registering both excitement and confusion.

A gnawing chill enters his pores. Brown's soul writhes at the thought of the endless death a bunker like this bespeaks. Till dawn they are trapped in this cage of shoveled earth. Locked into the fight. The inferred question is, will they make it through the night?

Otherwise, the bunker seems harmless enough, almost peaceful. The quiet tranquility of the area only adds to the disorientation.

He fingers the bayonet on his pistol belt and wonders if he should fix the bayonet. No. Remembering Sergeant Manning's demonstration at the incountry orientation, Brown decides it would be best to keep it ready for hand-to-hand combat. He sucks a shallow chesty breath, steps to the front rifle slit and stares bug-eyed over the surrealistic terrain.

"Check it out, Dorothy," Okie says, standing at his side. "We ain't in Kansas no more."

"This would be a perfect beginning to a war movie," Brown whispers, voice suppressed by the damp air.

"Yeah, like they'll all come running out of the water and from behind and . . . ."

"We run around screaming, 'We're gonna die. We're gonna

die.'" Brown tries for humor.

"End of movie."

"Whatdoya say we check around."

"You mean search for an escape route?"

"Exactly."

"Say, I need a smoke," Okie says as they leave the sandbag fortification. He pulls out a C-ration four-pack. "Camel?" he offers. Within cupped hands they light and begin smoking.

Cool outside air bolsters their courage as they walk smoking to the flooded rice field.

"There's no good place to run." Okie looks around at the flat faceless terrain. "Or hide. If anything happens we'll have to stick it out at the bunker."

"Yeah, we'll go down like Davy Crockett at the Alamo."

"I think you should know something," Okie says looking around a little spooked.

"Yeah?"

"Well, you know how they take a sword and draw a line in the sand expecting everyone who's not a wimp-ass coward to cross?"

Brown knows.

"Well, I'm a firm believer in the philosophy of 'Knowing when to cut and run is the better part of valor.'"

"Fight another day." They silently consider their chances of escape. "I just had an idea," Brown announces. "It's a slim one, but it just might work. You hold 'em off while I run back to base camp and . . . ."

"Well, well, well. Will ya listen to this. Blood and guts Brownie is turning out to be a wimp." Okie jests. "But I do like the idea except one small change."

"That is?"

"I drag your skinny ass along as a shield." They chuckle at the visualization. "Or better yet. If you hold 'em off, I'll put you in for the Congressional Medal of Honor. How's about that?"

"Posthumously?"

"You'll be a national hero," Okie rejoins. "I'll make sure you're buried at Arlington National Cemetery."

"Thanks."

"Only the best for my buddy."

Brown picks up a few large stones. Bobbing them in his hand, he throws them one at a time into the flood water. His fingers slide around a smooth, flat stone. Poised, he sends it skidding across the water's surface.

"Skipping stones on the pond," Okie remarks in a country drawl. "Hell, why not." He reaches for a handful and joins in flinging rocks across the water's surface.

"Whoo-wee. Would ya lookie there. Four jumps," Brown claims. "No, it was five. Five, man."

"I only saw four?"

"Can you do any better?"

"Shit, Brownie. You think I just fell off the turnip truck?" Taking the challenge, he searches for a winning flatty. But on the next two tries Okie's stone sinks on the second and third skip. "Once I made it skip nine times. Clear across the pond, up the other side and knocked a squirrel right out of a tree."

"I'm sure you did." Brown squats at water's edge.

"See that. Brown? That was . . . a good six times."

Tossing the cigarette butt into the water, Brown slides his hands into the cool liquid and swishes his fingers. Standing, he shakes water off his hand, the movement startling Okie.

"What?" Okie jerks the M-16 into firing position.

"See somethin'?"

"No. Thought you did." Scared, they step backward while scanning the area to the bleak horizon.

"Whatdoya say we get back to the bunker?" With shadows stretching with the approach of twilight, they bolt for the bunker.

"Last one there's a rotten egg." The scamper around the back and inside.

"You should have seen your face," Okie says laughing at Brown as they sprawl out on the benches.

"Me? How about you."

"I'm all tuckered out" Okie sighs.

"Funny how this bunker's beginning to feel like home."

"What's for dinner?"

Hearts pattering like a rabbit, they place their rifles on the wooden sill and search their field-of-fire.

"Should have brought along some hand grenades or a claymore mine."

Brown stares with angst because—no matter how preposterous is might seem—he'd never been trained on the M-16 rifle. At Fort Gordon, Georgia during Advanced Infantry Training, AIT, he had been trained as an infantry mortar gunner. Because of that, the instructors had forgotten to qualify him and the other mortarmen on the assault rifle.

To cover the oversight, their DI hurried them over to the firing range where they went through the rudiments of the M-16. The magazine, trigger, selector switch and charging handle. After ten minutes of instruction they had said, "Okay, as you can see, there ain't much difference between this here M-16 and the M-14 rifle on which you're already qualified."

There were two M-16 rifles, so two at a time Brown's platoon stepped to the firing line. They were instructed to first fire off a few rounds on semi-automatic, then switch to automatic and finish the magazine.

In the waning light, Brown inspects the rifle realizing he isn't exactly sure how it fires. But he had studied the pamphlets and had watched the other soldiers as they worked on their weapons. And he sure isn't gonna let anyone know his secret. Ever.

Okie takes the first one-hour guard while Brown stretched out on the two-by-twelve by eight-foot wooden bench.

"Brownie," Okie whispers an hour later, gently touching his shoulder. "You're guard."

Brown swings his legs onto the ground.

"I might be seeing things but I think something moved on the left side of that volcano hill."

"Really?"

"There was some splashing noise."

"Animal?"

"Probably."

"I'll keep a watch on it." Brown slides to the front bench and props his weapon on the front sill. For safety sake, he bumps the magazine to be sure it's secure. Then he checks to see if the selector switch is pointed to semi-automatic. A round in the chamber? Ooooooh! He swallows hard. Hurrying outside and over to the side wall, he rocks back the charging handle and slams a round into the chamber. The noise of the bolt engaging sounds extremely loud.

"What are ya doin' Brownie?"

"Nothing," Brown assures him. "Just wanted to make sure everything was working. That's all."

Staring through the front rifle slit, Brown's heavy eyes labor from one imagined or otherwise movement to another. His ears strain to detect silent danger. As a precaution, occasionally he goes outside and peers around. Finally, the minute hand reaches midnight and it's Okie's guard.

Distant booming and firecrackerlike sounds wake Brown from his shallow, fitful rest. He grabs the rifle and jumps to the front rifle slit. "What's up?"

"Someone's getting hit."

Brown heard the distant sounds but can't tell in what direction. Peering from the back of the bunker, he sees flares dangling in the southeast sky near Highway One. Flashes from periodic explosions can be seen—the sounds delayed by seconds.

"It ain't that far from us," Okie said a little nervous.

"Maybe, I should keep watch out back? They might try attacking us, too."

"Attack or not, Brownie, this old boy's gotta get some shut-eye. How about it?"

"Go ahead, I can handle it," Brown says bravely. "It's my guard anyway."

Long anxious minutes pass as Brown listens to the sporadic explosions and contemplates their flickering light. How many people have just died? he wonders. The battle finally subsides.

Back at the front rifle slit, he takes off the steel pot to let the night breeze cool his forehead. His eyes feel so tired. His lids so heavy.

What would it hurt if I close my eyes for say . . . a second? he thinks. No longer. Just a second or so, that's all. He tries to convince himself. That's all, just to rest them. Just a few . . . . His lids close.

His eyes shoot open in panic. "Oh, shit," he swears, grabs the steel pot and shoves it back on. He quickly scans the terrain through the front rifle slit, then runs out back to check.

"Shoooo," he sighs, relieved that everything seems okay. No harm done, but he knows better than to have let this happen again.

Sergeant Yamane, Brown's squad leader, doing the rounds drives up in the guard jeep. "Binh Son Bridge has been overrun," he reports. "It was held by the South Vietnamese, but we had a couple of battalion advisors over there." He looks in the direction of the bridge where the light and noise have subsided.

"Been quiet for some time now."

"The radio got knocked out only minutes into the firefight so we have no way of finding out what happened, but it doesn't look good." Yamane is an agile Japanese American that reminds Brown of Bruce Lee, the martial arts movie star.

Though shrouded by darkness and in a dangerous bunker, he nevertheless feels bathed by Yamane's strong aura. It's as if his very presence could save Brown's life.

"This isn't a twenty-four-hour bunker," Sergeant Yamane explains as they walk back to the jeep. "So in the morning you guys can just walk on back to the chow hall."

"Walk?" Brown questions. "Alone. By ourselves? It's a long ways isn't it?"

"There a problem?" Sergeant Yamane seems startled by the response. Then realizes how uneasy it must feel for Brown, this his first time out. "Don't worry, it'll be okay."

Sergeant Yamane gazes across the rice fields. He pats Brown on the shoulder. "The VC probably had a good reason for hitting the bridge tonight. But there's no good reason for them to hit us," Yamane explains. "It'll be dawn before you even know it."

4 December 1967

Next evening Brown has bunker guard with Bedford. Their line bunker covers the northern perimeter. Through the front rifle slit, Brown stares over the mine field, past the razor edged concertina wire to the lush vegetation of the distant valley.

"This is the bunker they've been snipering at," Bedford remarks casually, propping his M-79 grenade launcher on the front ledge.

"You mean we're gonna get shot at?"

"Roger that, but believe me, Charlie couldn't hit the broadside of a barn."

"I hope you're right."

"Well, let's put it this way, Charlie doesn't get much ammo so he can't be wastin' it on target practice," Bedford explains.

"So how ya like that M-79?" Brown wonders—the constant inquiring mind.

"You mean, my pet rabbit Thumper?" Bedford says, patting the weapon that looks like an oversize sawed-off shotgun. "I call it

Thumper cause it packs a wallop. A man's best friend in the bush." Bedford's M-79 vest has rows of pouches filled with fat looking, oversized bullets. He sheds the vest, his biceps bulging from the weight and places it gingerly on the bench.

"That vest must weigh a ton."

"Pretty much, but it's wrapped around your body, not like a field radio. So it ain't all that bad."

Sliding a round from the vest he holds it up. "This here's an HE round. High Explosive," he explains. Gripping the stock of the weapon he thumbs a lever and the breech opens. He slides in the HE round. Then with a flick of the wrist, snaps the chamber closed.

"They're almost as powerful as a grenade, but they only explode on contact. That way you can pinpoint a target some two-hundred yards away or knock a dink out of a tree."

Pointing it toward the valley he pulls the trigger. "Pho-o-o-sh!" It sounds like a rocket. Then in the distance, "Ca-blam-m-m!"

"Thought I saw something," Bedford chuckles. "A lot of places to hide in that jungle."

With smoke still spilling from the weapon, he opens the chamber and drops out the expended cartridge. Reloading, he hands the weapon to Brown. "Try it. Just point and fire away. You'll be surprised how easy it is."

Brown takes the weapon, one he's never seen before, and aims.

"Hold on!" He puts a hand on Brown's shoulder. "Just hold the butt down like I did. There's no need to aim it like a rifle. And don't touch the barrel, it'll burn the skin right off your hand."

Following instructions, Brown points it like a garden hose, and pulls the trigger. He's amazed to find he can actually follow the slow moving projectile that explodes near the intended target. "Wow man, this is great!"

"Thumper's real useful in a lot of different ways," Bedford maintains. He points to four other different types of rounds in his vest. Stating that one is a fleshette which is used like a shotgun round. Then there is the Willy Peters or white phosphorous rounds, "That could barbecue a dink or turn a hut into a bonfire in minutes." He also carries a CS gas canister and an illumination round.

"How did you learn all this stuff about the weapon?"

"Had some hands-on in the states," Bedford said loading another round. "But when I got to Nam, they just said who wants Thumper. What the hell?" Bedford straightens his back, and the rakish way he holds his head shows strength of character, self assurance, and an abundance of courage. "It's easy," he explains. "Just can't be afraid. Wanna try another one?"

"No, that's okay." Brown takes up his M-16. "Say, think I could fire off a few rounds?"

"Sure. Why not. Maybe we'll scare 'em off and they won't come around tonight."

Pulling back the charging handle, he slams a round into the chamber, switches to semi-automatic. Then without using the sight, he pulls the trigger. It jumps in his hands and Brown releases the trigger. "Trying to get the hang of it," he explains feeling sheepish. "Just a few more rounds." Relieved that it fires properly, he ejects the empty magazine and loads a fresh one.

"No tracer rounds?" Bedford notes.

"Supply doesn't have any," Brown maintains, though it never occurred to him.

"Go back down there and tell 'em I sent ya. Make every fourth round a tracer and two to finish off. You see two tracers, your outta ammo. Time to reload. Plus they'll help ya figure out where you're shootin'," Bedford explains.

"Say, you got some nice tattoos there, man." Brown points to Bedford's arms.

Rotating his arm, he displays a multi-colored eagle. "Yeah, I like 'em. Get a load of this one." He pulls up the sleeve and turns to show off the tattoo of a red rose with "Mom and Dad" on his shoulder.

Brown marvels at Bedford's vitality. During the day Bedford hide his piercing blue eyes and thick bushy lashes behind dark aviator sunglasses. He always wore the steel pot set back, walking with shoulders square and chin held in. His entire six-foot 180-pound frame emanates an aura of strength and as with Sergeant Yamane, Brown feels perfectly safe with him near.

The soldiers sit inside the bunker, peering northwest at cloud-covered mountain peaks. The blazing yellow sun lowering itself into a cocoon of clouds, sends glorious orange and red strobe lights showering over the Southeast Asian jungle, and streaming onto the open plains. For an instant, the sun seems to suspend its departure. It's as if the sun, on the verge of leaving, has discovered some unfinished business which now makes its farewell a reluctant one.

To the northeast sets Chu Lai with its lights sparkling. Beyond, appearing like a black hole, lies the South China Sea. Breathing, he detects sea air mingling with the aroma of lush vegetation. Twilight softens the gray lines of the mountains while dusk eats them away. The balmy breeze turns chilly and the two soldiers pull on their field jackets.

"Monsoon's on the way," Bedford announces, his voice hushed like the dusk. "The nights get cooler and cooler, then the rain'll start."

Artillery fire can be heard in the distance. Both soldiers stare through the front rifle slit to the distant light flashes which are subsequently followed by a thunderlike sound.

"That's a battery of 105 howitzers."

"Someone in contact?"

"No. Probably some H&I."

"H&I?"

"Harassment and Interdiction. Which means they're either firing for practice, like we just did, or they're firing on suspected VC positions," Bedford explains.

"Has an eerie sound, doesn't it? I mean the real thing. So how many people are gonna get hit tonight?"

"Good question." Bedford relaxes on the bench and absently begins to rub the nape of his neck, a brass bracelet jingling with the rhythm of his wrist.

"Get the bracelet in Nuoc Mau?"

"Yeah, it's a Montagnard Friendship bracelet," Bedford says. "You oughta get yourself one."

"I will. I know just the place where I wanna get it too."

Bedford also wears a gold neck chain and pendant that sets against the taped dog tags. To Brown's knowledge only hippie-types and fags would wear that much jewelry. But Bedford is definitely neither a flower-child nor a fag. He looks more like the kind of shaggy, hell bent, leather-jacket hooligan you'd expect to see blasting through town on a ear-shattering Harley-Davidson Chopper motorcycle decked out in full regalia. Or, in another place-in-time, Bedford would have been a cowboy, complete with red bandanna, ten gallon hat and Colt six-shooter. He'd be galloping on a horse across the wide-open plains of America's Wild West whooping it up, rope in hand on a cattle drive.

"It's gonna be a bitch out there in the bush," Bedford sighs. "Miserable as hell."

"Thank God, we only have day patrols."

"Ain't gonna last."

"We goin' out soon?"

"Yeah, soon enough. We'll rotate off bunker guard and go into the field. Then we'll be out for maybe a week or so."

"So how we gonna do guard?"

"Two hours on—two off. Okay?"

"Want me to take first guard?"

While fumbling through his pockets in an effort to stay awake during guard, Brown happens upon a pen and some paper. Yesterday he'd slid them into his pants side pocket thinking he might, at some time, write home, but had forgotten all about it till just now. He flattens out the paper where the moon's light will gather on its clean white surface. The empty page seemed to invite his imagination to take a journey of release. His hand begins to glide magically over the smooth surface, the tip of the pen leaving behind a legacy of a time and place.

Dear Ma and Dad *5 December 1967*

I am definitely in Viet Nam There is no doubt. I got off the plane at Cam Ranh Bay. I then went to Chu Lai. I am now in the 198th Light Infantry. It will be a while before I can become a mortarman so I am just straight infantry.

The men in my Brigade are killing themselves. They drop hand grenades and shoot each other by accident.

The first night I was here, we were hit hard by the VC. A place a mile or two away was over run and *flattened.* One man was killed in my Brigade and two men wounded.

I am a *bunker* guard. If you are not in the field you pull bunker guard every night.

I have seen all those rice fields. The distant mountains are beautiful. They are usually covered by clouds. Luckily, I have been able to keep cool. I haven't gotten real hot.

Cameras, radios, tape recorders, TV sets are all half price or less. This guy just bought a Canon 35mm camera similar to yours, Ma, for $100.

I got $140.00 clear last month. Not counting the U.S. Saving Bond.

I am now a *Private First Class*

Your son, Fred Leo

Dear Ma and Dad *6 December 1967*

This is URGENT!

You must send me two metal file blades.

Send in envelope and tape off ends and cut then in half if necessary.

Send immediately. Please.

I am about to go out in the field for a week or two. I will not be able to write.

When I return I will write.

Unless. Maybe you could send a piece of paper and envelope with your letters for a few times.

Fred Leo

Dear Uncle Ken, Maude and Karen *7 December 1967*

It is actually cool in Nam. I couldn't believe it. I had to wear my field jacket last night. So far I am drawing equipment and what I can't get, I steal. I am trying to find out how to do things the best way.

I walked to *Nuoc Mau,* a friendly Vietnamese village and got a hair cut from a barber using those old hand clippers. The children run around with shoe polish and shine your shoes for a dime. I am able to communicate fairly well with them.

I haven't seen much action yet, except fighting goes on all

around me and a few bullets came my way. So, right now I have it pleasant. I am just in a changing stage where I become used to the idea of being in a combat zone. Well, I must go now.

Fred Leo

8 December 1967

Brown had noticed mortar tubes surrounded by large circles of sandbags three feet high several plateaus below the mess tent. Having some free time, Brown decides to go for a look. From a distance, he sees mortarmen hauling and stacking ammunition crates, cleaning the tubes, policing the area, and in general staying busy.

"Hi, there," Brown greets. "I'm a mortarman, too. Guess I'll be transferring down here with you guys pretty soon, huh?"

All the mortarmen stop working and turn with astonishment and surprise plastered all over their faces. The plaster breaks and they fall into blatant, wild laughter.

"Lemme guess," one mortarman blurts. "You're an NFG, right?"

Brown nods.

"What are ya, goofy?" another declares. "We don't need no one. Especially no NFG."

Puzzled by their reaction, Brown feels blood rushing to his face, his ears reddening.

"Listen, buddy," one of them says regaining some composure. "Half the mortar platoon is already TDY. They're humpin' the boonies with the straight-legs. We call it PDY—Pretty Damn Permanent Duty, cause we ain't seen hide nor hair of any of 'em since."

"Oh, yeah right. I know," Brown stutters as he tries to retain his composure.

Another mortarman starts mimicking a sergeant. "'And you'll be going in the bush next, unless you ladies get your gear squared away. And quit your bitchin'!'"

Again, they double over in hysterics. One mortarman begins

choking on beer and a buddy starts pounds his back. Another begins readjusting his jaw, the laughter having cramped a jaw muscle.

"You hard of hearing!" one of them hollers and again it is followed by a round of laughter.

Brown stands agape. What did they mean? He is never going to be transferred to the mortar platoon? But he was trained as an infantry mortarman. And there's a world of difference between *that* and straight leg infantry. Reflecting on AIT at Fort Gordon, Georgia, he was amazed, even then, that anyone could survive the brutal "straight leg" infantry training, let alone the *real* thing. The meaning of all this is unthinkable and far beyond just simply terrifying. Nearly crying, Brown turns and stumbles away.

The combat helmet comes in two parts. One is the helmet liner which includes the head-webbing and head band. Second is the steel pot which gets an optional camouflage cloth cover. They slide together to make a combat helmet. During training Brown had always gotten a headache after a day of wearing the full combat helmet. So, Brown had taken the camouflage cover and simply put it over the liner. But like falling asleep on guard, this can't go on. That is, not if he wanted to live.

Opening the foot locker, he pulls out the steel pot and assembles it properly. The letter about the files was to cut holes in the helmet, now he realizes he shouldn't have sent that letter. Oh well. Can't do anything about that.

Next, he buckles the pistol belt around his waist, laden with the newly obtained ammunition magazines. Donning the heavy steel helmet, he drapes a towel around his shoulders. Then he snatches the assault rifle and heads to supper which will be immediately followed by guard duty.

He has decided that if he is going to be an infantryman, he is going to do it right.

Dear Ma and Dad *10 December 1967*

By the way I need a sheath knife. The kind of knife that doesn't fold up. Could you buy me an eighteen inch long knife like that? I need it for carving, chopping and cutting. Try and get it with a wooden handle so it is camouflaged a little. Be sure it has a strong leather case so I can use it for a long time. Remember that I have a three inch wide pistol belt and I must put it on the belt.

I am going to use it to replace my bayonet. The bayonet is clumsy and useless as a knife. So the sooner I get the knife the better.

Also upstairs in my dresser there is a plastic box with six plastic drawers. In one drawer is an *oil stone* to sharpen the knife. Please send it with the knife. Surprisingly enough they don't sell knives around here. I thought they would.

Well, I was issued a lot of gear. I also *picked up* a lot. I picked up a *Claymore mine* with an electric detonating cord. I also have a trip flare. So now when I go out in the field I can set them out and they will help to protect me.

Remember I said, "I will not wear the steel pot?" Well, I took it off and camouflaged my light weight helmet liner instead. I made it look like the Steel Helmet. But then I decided against it, so I'm wearing the whole helmet.

By the way, I have to have something to combat my *headaches* I started getting them again. Please send something good. I can't be worried about headaches.

Well, I am going to get a camera soon but I don't know exactly when. I want to buy a real good one like yours. Do you think I could learn how to run it good. Because if I could then, I can send home beautiful color pictures instead of drab, black and whites. By the way the only way to get them developed is to send them home. So then you could tell me what I do wrong.

Tell me what you think I should do. Maybe I should get a movie camera. But I think still pictures are better myself.

By the way I am in a rifle platoon. I am not a mortarman right now. I might become a *tunnel rat.* They haven't got anyone yet. I'm small so I may become one.

Right now, I am guard on top of a hundred foot high tower. The tower is also on a hill. I can see the *South China Sea*, Chu Lai and about ten miles in every direction. The mountains have clouds covering their peaks. It is beautiful. Some rice patties are green and others are full of mud or water. They are all surrounded by a foot wide dike to walk on.

I got enough nerve to go to the village on Highway One yesterday. I got a hair cut down there. The villages are usually compared to a Border Town. The little kids run around and insist they shine your shoes. You cannot tell the age of these people. I might be able to when I know them better.

They can speak basic English. When something is good, they say it is *"Number One,"* when something is bad they say *"Number Ten"*.

Well, I was issued the M-16 not the M-14. It is dirty because while on guard last night it rained bad and I couldn't keep it clean, let alone my dirty self.

I found where I can get a hot shower. Only four other guys know about it. It is a secret. Everyone else has to carry water to a bucket tied on a pole then open a valve and pour it on themselves.

I love the fragment proof vest, but they laugh at you if you use it because they don't see much sense in it. I have two of them. I found one. I am going to save one and bring it back to the States brand new. Well, I must go. So long.

Your son, Fred Leo

11 December 1967

Their boots crunch loudly on the gravel road leading down the winding hill from LZ Gator. Only occasionally do the soldiers glance to watch the morning's half-red-ball sun working its way over the horizon. With such a clear blue sky, it will not be long before they are drenched with midday heat.

When the eight soldiers of second squad arrive at Highway One, they turn north and begin to file through the awakening village of Nuoc Mau. Through the crisp air the usual morning sounds filter through the air of roosters crowing, dogs barking, and fowl squawking in the back lots.

The smell of charcoal and wood in family fire pits waft through the air along with the smells of oriental spices and food being reheated or cooked for breakfast.

Throughout the village chickens dart from one potential feeding spot to another while being harassed or chased by other chickens, ducks or dogs. The usual morning wind comes up and begins to spawn little dust devils that scoot across the flat dusty road surface making everyone nearby shield their faces from flying debris.

Brown spots Lan, the girl he always bought his Coke from. Last visit he'd brought her a single blue wildflower and she had reciprocated by slipping a Montagnard bracelet over his right wrist. "Numba one." She had smiled so sweetly. "It bring GI good luck."

Wildflower

A dainty blue
wildflower
within a patch
of weeds tries
desperately to grow, but the mean thorny bushes,
question, "What's in it,
for us?" A passing soldier
spots the choked flower.
He kneels and gently plucks it.
Then gifts it to the lady of his eye.
At twilight the soldier lays down his
rifle and presses his palms together in
prayer. "Dear Lord, I thank you for this
day and for the wildflower.
It gave of itself, yet
asked for
nothing in return."

Lan stands outside her stall, the front flaps already propped up. Although the wind occasionally blusters, Lan continues to smooth out, neatly folding and stacking clothes and other wares across the table top in preparation for the day's business.

After a yawn demurely covered by a hand, she stretches her back and moves her head side to side. Then absently, she combs fingers through her long silky black hair, sweeping it away from her face letting it cascade over her shoulders.

Sneaking a curious glance at the procession of soldiers some fifteen feet away, her eyes pause on Brown. Thinking she might actually recognize him, Brown smiles shyly, then begins to exaggerate the effort of humping the squad's heavy PRC-25 radio.

She responds with a gentle smile. Brown raises his arm to show her the brass bracelet and she nods.

At the open-air market near the northern end of the village, bicycles and small mufflerless motorcycles laden with carrying baskets are propped against scraggly trees or wooden posts. The Vietnamese merchants are already busy selling fruits, vegetables, and some unfamiliar looking perishables. They are also selling fish heads and tails, fins and whole fish, crabs, live pigs and chickens with their feet tied with string.

Lean, dusty Vietnamese bargain noisily at the market. While off to the side a child wearing only shorts and a yellow T-shirt stands hugging a chicken, its head tucked under his chin. Other children scurry about with switches chasing dogs, pigs and fowl that scavenge about the back yards.

Gliding toward them is a barefoot, flat faced woman with a shoulder pole heavily weighted with opposing baskets of wares. She passes with a little girl clinging to a pant leg, thumb in her mouth. Watching the woman, Brown tries to understand the mechanics of her stationary upper body and the lower body's smooth, swivel-like motion.

In place of America's farm-to-market trucks are tettering stick bed two-wheel carts drawn by a single water buffalo or a man. Some carts use the old fashioned wooden wheels, while others have the updated version with military salvage truck axles, wheels and rims.

To the west flooded rice paddies glisten glasslike as they stretch to the distant grey, mist covered foothills. A warm sultry breeze ripples over green carpets of rice sprouts.

Even at this early hour the fields are attended by a multitude of peasants wearing the traditional conical *Nong la* straw hats and black pants rolled past the knees. They toil from dawn till dusk bent over planting young rice sprouts in cool ankle deep water. Others turn the thick heavy soil with wooden plows hitched to the lumbering bulk of a water buffalo, Vietnam's version of a John Deere tractor. Not far from the road, a water buffalo drinks paddy water while a little girl lounges on its back.

After hours of moving at a ground eating pace, second squad veers left from the road onto a trail. The wide trail snakes its way northwest across the countryside and soon degenerates into a narrow path. The footpath alternately drops below, then rises above the water line with field grass lapping to obscure compete sections.

A half hour later, the trail starts widening again but with a limited view it appears to be leading them into a blind canyon.

Pushing past a clump of twelve foot tall elephant grass, a rural farming community nestled in the side of the hill looms into view. Small huts with straw mat walls and scallop eaves dot the landscape. A perfect ecology of trees, foliage and humans exist against the vegetation covered hillside making it appear like a South Seas Island paradise.

Shepard and Green are ordered to set up a blocking force at the head of the trail leading toward the foothills, while the rest of the squad begins a routine search-and-destroy.

The village proper proves to be a maze of footpaths, prickly hedge rows, run-off ditches and flourishing vegetable gardens. Partially covered by dense clumps of bamboo and shrubbery is a maze of plaited walls and fences. The afternoon sunshine makes it appear absolutely picturesque.

Serving as RTO, Brown shadows Sergeant Denning. With him in tow, Sergeant Denning makes his way to the middle of the hamlet. They come upon a raised courtyard of stamped, hard earth, as solid and level as poured concrete, in front of an ancient looking pagoda. Carved into the roof trusses that line the edge of the structure's terra cotta shingles are fish heads painted in bright colors.

Sergeant Denning and Brown climb three concrete steps to the courtyard wanting to inspect the stately pagoda. As they cross, children begin to pour through the building's center doorway. A female instructor casually walks through. She stops just beyond the door and takes a wide stance, crosses her arms and plants a disapproving expression on her face.

Sergeant Denning nods a curt acknowledgment and sweeps past.

Inside they find there is only one big room with a single wall mounted blackboard. Placed on the dirt floor are sitting boards and a few well worn books. Finding nothing of military value, they leave the pagoda through the back door and step down the narrow flight of steps.

"Shooo-o," Sergeant Denning hollers, his arms flailing to keep balance having tripped on a chicken nesting on a step.

They step into a muddy alleyway littered with duck and chicken droppings that leads to a steep hill covered with sparse young trees and scant underbrush. Various types of wild and domestic fowl poke through the vegetation, perch on low hanging tree limbs and transportation crates, or peck for insects in and around the mud puddles.

Finding nothing after a cursory search of a few huts, they join the rest of the platoon at the far edge of the farming village.

"What's the odor?" Green asks. "I smelled it before but not this bad."

"Maybe the outhouses is nearby?" Brown looks around.

"Naw that ain't it," Green decides, "because I already checked and there ain't none around."

"You talking about that pungent smell? Right?" Second Squad Leader Sergeant Yamane questions.

"Yeah, that's it," Green confirms wiggling his nose. "What is it?"

"*Nuoc mam.*"

"That's cool. So what's *nuoc mam*? Some kinda incense?"

"It's fermented fish sauce. Every house I went through had a crock full of it."

"Smells to high heaven around here and that's all I know," Okie injects.

"Are you sure it's only *nuoc mam*?" Brown wonders.

"I know what you're thinkin'," Yamane says. "But have you noticed how every house has a small garden?"

They all listen.

"The garden is the outhouse. They dig a little hole, squat and crap. No smell. No mess."

"No toilets. That's so . . . ."

"To squat for a shit is anatomically correct as well as more sanitary than sitting on the pot," Yamane informs them.

"Really?"

"They call it night soil," Yamane continues to explain "It's fertilizer to them. And to them, it's a mystery why we burn ours at LZ Gator."

"That's what my pappy always said," Okie laughs, "why burn up good fertilizer."

"So about that *nuoc mam*, they actually put that smelly stuff on the food?" Shepard asks.

"And eat it?"

"Tastes pretty good once you get past the smell," Yamane says. "And from what I've heard, *nuoc mam* with rice can give you all the nutrients your body needs."

"Well, lookie here," Green interrupts. "The little beggars."

Four smiling Coke-kids from Nuoc Mau come hustling over. "GI buy Coke. Numba-one Coke. You look very, very hot. Fifty cents, please."

"Damn right I'm hot," Shepard said, pulling out some MPC.

"Where do they get the Coke?" Brown asks.

"There's a bottling plant near Chu Lai," Yamane explains. "You ever notice how guarded they are about the bottles?"

"Yeah, matter of fact, I know exactly what you mean." Brown remembers how Lan scolded him when he had once walked away with a sixteen ounce bottle.

"The bottle is more important to them than the Coke itself because they can only get as much pop as they have empties." Everyone buys a drink.

After a fifteen-minute break, second squad starts to hump up the side of a steep hill on a path that snakes through chest-high thorny brush. Exhaustion sets-in and Browns' knees begin to ache so badly he falls behind. Finally resorting to crawling up the steep incline, he loses sight of the squad.

Rifle shots shatter the silence. Soldiers already at the top of the hill, begin shouting.

"There! Over there!"

"Where?"

More rifle fire rings out.

"THERE!"

"Damnit, they're gettin' away!"

Noticing the direction of the noise, Brown veers off the path and with a gargantuan effort tries to head straight toward the commotion. But after a few steps, he finds himself entangled in a maze of thick vines which trip him at every step.

"Dung lai!"

"Don't yell at 'em! Shoot 'em!" Sergeant Denning screams. The air again fills with the roar of M-16s and the explosions of Bedford's M-79 grenades.

"Incoming! Get down!" Sergeant Denning shouts. "Everyone hold tight, I'll get some artillery in here." There is a pause. "Brown! Brown! Where's the RTO? Brown! Brown! Damn it," he swears. "We've lost Brown." His voice thick with disbelief.

Hearing his name, Brown vaults the thorny foliage which tears at his pants cutting his legs. Progress is painfully slow. Figuring he has to do something, he takes the radio handset and starts calling their platoon leader.

"Two-six, this is two-five kilo, over." After a second try, the lieutenant's RTO acknowledges him. Breathlessly, Brown says, "We've got enemy contact. Over."

"Roger, do you need support? Do you need a dust-off? Do you need artillery. Over."

"I don't know. I'm trying to catch up with 'em. Over," Brown pants into the handset. Finally clearing the bushes, he spots Sergeant Denning crouched, rifle aimed at the saddle between two knolls. Hustling over, he collapses sweat soaked and exhausted.

"Where the hell ya been, private!" Sergeant Denning's eyes rage red. "On the scenic route? We're in a goddamn *firefight*." He yanks the handset from Brown. "Trying to get everyone killed?"

Brown shrinks, more frightened of his platoon sergeant than of the ensuing firefight.

"No movement, Sarge," Yamane calls from shrubs some twenty feet to the front. "But I think there's one hiding over there." Yamane motions. "The other one tossed a rifle. I think he and the rest got away. Down a hole or something."

After a short communication on the PRC-25 radio to put artillery on alert, Sergeant Denning passes the handset to Brown. Acknowledging Sarge's hand signals, the soldiers rise and begin to comb the area trying to flush out the enemy.

"There!"

"Where?"

"There. Over there!"

Again rifle fire explodes. A VC jumps, snakes, bobs and weaves through the scant cover. Then amid the pounding noise, the VC lunges like a football player going for a pass and collides with the ground.

"Brown! Drop the goddamn rifle barrel," Sergeant Denning shouts as Brown prepares to fire over Okie's head. "Killin' your own men don't count!"

Sergeant Denning snatches the handset from Brown. "Two-six this is two-five. Over." He receives an acknowledgment. "Roger. No casualties. One enemy KIA. Wilco. Two-five. Out." Sergeant Denning tosses the handset. "Where do they find these new recruits? Huh?" Signaling for everyone to move, he rises and follows them down the knoll.

Keeping the rear abreast of the situation, Brown signs off. "Roger dodger, over and out." At the moment, he feels he's quickly becoming the veteran.

"Roger dodger!" Sergeant Denning screams over his shoulder. "Is that what I heard. Roger dodger! Where do you come up with this shit?" His eyes bulge. "You stupid idiot. You drop your lolly-pop on the way over here?" He snatches the handset.

"Wilco. Out," he demonstrates and shoves the handset into Brown's chest. "And that's all you say when you sign off. You understand?" The he spells, "O-U-T. Out!"

Following a short conference, Platoon Sergeant Denning and Squad Leader Sergeant Yamane amble back to the squad, both in contemplative moods. They inform the soldiers that they will set up for a night ambush. The plan is to use the dead VC as bait, and thereby lure his comrades into a trap.

"Echo two-five, this is Minuteman on your push. Over." Hearing the helicopter's transmission on the handset Brown quickly hands the receiver to Yamane.

"Minuteman, this is echo two-two. Papa wilco." Yamane looks up in the sky till he locates the helicopter. "Roger, your position is ten o'clock our lima. Over."

"Ahhh roger, copy that," came the pilot's vibrating voice over the receiver, "pop smoke for identification. Over."

Yamane nods to Brown who pulls the pin and tosses a yellow smoke grenade into the designated landing zone.

The Huey identifies the color of smoke, and turns toward the saddle. It hovers at twenty feet while determining the most level spot, then descends for a landing.

Shepard, Green and Yamane hustle, bending at the waist, to the chopper with one hand steadying their steel pots. Soldiers on the helicopter begin handing out C-rations, a rifle scope, extra grenades, and four claymore mines.

"Say," Shepard says after the Huey's departure and lunch, "it's our first VC, right? So why not take a picture?"

"Yeah, how about it?"

Okie raises his camera. "Did someone say picture?"

Brown is smitten with a sense of *deja vu*. The soldiers take on an eerie resemblance to gunfighters from the Old West. This is the posse riding out from the saga-brushed streets of Tombstone, Arizona.

Brown's mind hears the Marshall say, "To steal a man's horse or cattle is like taking his life. We will not stop until everyone involved pays in blood. If we don't every cowpoke drifter who rides through these here parts will say we're easy pickings." The gunfighters stand puffed proud, clutching their Winchesters and Colt revolvers.

"Here's to Luke the Gook. The deadliest game on earth!"

"On three. One, two, three. Say cheese."

Yamane and Sergeant Denning synchronize watches while there is still light. Then the soldiers march away hoping to trick the VC into believing they have left permanently. An hour later, Sergeant Denning and two others peel-off. The plan is for them to double-back and watch over the corpse. To make a "good show of it" the rest of the squad will continue snaking through the area.

"Pass the word," Yamane whispers, as everyone slides into a ten-foot deep irrigation ditch, "we're holding up."

They rest, eat and in the waning light, camouflage their face and hands with dual colored camouflage grease.

Before starting back, Yamane personally checks their equipment and camouflage. He bounces rucksacks to check for noise, adjusts a few straps, pulls back a few rifle bolts to check the action and in general makes sure every soldier is prepared.

Yamane returns to his RTO, and bumps the canteen on Brown's pistol belt. "Even water swishing can give you away. Remember that."

Taking the handset he calls, "Echo two-five this is two-two. Break squelch twice if you read me. Over." Yamane waits for the pre-arranged signal. Two fuzzy-airy sounds come over the handset. "Roger that. We are moving out at this time. If you acknowledge break squelch twice. Over." Sergeant Yamane listens. "Roger. Two-two. Out." He hands off the receiver.

"How ya doing with the radio?"

"You mean with the transmissions?"

"No. The weight"

"It's heavy," Brown concedes.

Yamane looks him square in the face.

"I can handle it," Brown says though his body aches and his knees throb mercilessly.

"You sure?" Yamane places a concerned hand on Brown's shoulder.

"No problem," Brown assures him with a forced smile.

Yamane turns to address the soldiers, "Alright, saddle-up we're movin' out. Shepard you got point."

While moving under the cloak of darkness, Brown marvels at how Yamane can lead them in the black pitch through this foreign land with no perceivable markers, avoid open spaces and stay on course. It seems as though Yamane can look at a map and the landscape will rise from the paper. Brown follows in awe. Yamane is definitely the man to watch. The man who he will mimic in every detail. In every way. This man alone, Brown believes, can get him through the war.

At one of the two ambush sites, Brown takes first guard. In the still of the night, Brown presses and massages the ligaments and connecting tissues of his throbbing knees.

Removing the steel pot, he pours water over his head letting it drain over his face. The salt tastes strong on his tongue as he takes the towel from around his neck to wipe off. He rolls his head around, then arches his back with vertebrae cracking.

Exhaustion invades every pore of his body. Second squad had been on the move for eighteen hours with negligible rest. Brown prays that nothing will happen—his mind and muscles can't handle a 'run for it!'

He grabs the enormous unmounted starlight scope. He'd never seen one before but had read an article explaining them in a *Popular Mechanics* magazine. These night vision scopes amplify the light of the moon and stars so you can actually see at night. He peers through the lens and finds the terrain a light greenish hue. He adjusts the focus then begins to sweep the landscape for signs of movement.

Concentrating on one particular shrub, he takes the scope away and with naked eye tries to see the same shrub. Problem . . . . No matter how hard he tries, he cannot synchronize the starlight scope's greenish view with the black terrain of his unaided vision.

Setting the scope aside, Brown remembers how Yamane attached the rifle sling to the M-16. The strap went through the triangle sight, over the shoulder and around the rifle stock. In this way the weight of the rifle would be on the shoulder and it would remain horizontal and at waist height. And the beauty of it was, with the use of one hand, the weapon is always ready to fire. Silently, Brown begins to re-set his rifle sling in the same manner.

Keeping a watchful eye, he remembers from incountry orientation "VC never rest." Well, Brown thinks, I'm pooped out all right, and I can barely stay awake. He takes the wristwatch, turns it ahead fifteen minutes and shakes Okie. "It's your guard."

"God . . . already?" Okie complains as he wipes sleep from his eyes. "I feel like I just laid down."

"I know what ya mean." Using his steel pot as a pillow, Brown plops back, covers himself with the poncho and crosses his ankles. With rifle across his chest, he falls asleep.

Sergeant Yamane wakes Brown for a second turn on guard. "I tell ya, Brown," Sergeant Yamane whispers. "The VC should have been here already. I think the ambush is a bust. But stay alert anyway, okay?"

"Right." Being present at the moment of first-breath or, last-breath is to share a most intimate moment with the universe. In civilian life, relatives and close friends hurry to witness a dying person's last wishes and final breath. But in war, it's only the shooter who will share that most solemn of experiences. In that moment when the enemy perishes, the shooters establish a relationship, a bond with the enemy. A connection so poignant that, if not careful, will choke them in years to come.

From the grave he says, "Today mine. Tomorrow yours."

On second guard, the world seems at peace. No rush to do anything. His mind wanders back to the first time he had seen death as an eight-year old boy.

". . . Think he's old enough?" his mother asks.

"I don't see why not, he's got to learn sometime," Brown's father responds rather gruffly.

"Okay, we'll let him see Nana," his mother agrees.

Following everyone else's lead, Brown walks into the funeral parlor and kneels in front of his grandmother's casket. Her face is flat and lifeless. Even though everyone agrees she looks wonderful, she didn't, because she was dead.

"Nana, I really liked you a lot and I'm gonna miss ya," Brown said to himself. "But before you go—remember that baby cat? The one I put in your lap and it jumped and scratched your arm?" He searches his grandmother's face believing she is listening.

"Dad was so angry, he took the cat out and chopped its head off. I really didn't know the cat was gonna do that. I'm sorry. I love you and I'll always remember you. Have a good trip. Love you. Bye-bye."

The image fades into his second experience with death. He had been a high school sophomore and a greaser-punk who did marginal work at school. He ran with a bunch of rowdy troublemakers, the kind who would demolish a car with baseball bats just for fun. "Can't go out tonight," he told them. "They've got me working till closing and again tomorrow morning."

From what he'd heard, his gang of friends had bumped into another gang. Knives flashed and a member of his gang lay bleeding to death.

Brown had slid into the funeral parlor, trying not to be too noticeable. Near the casket of the slain gang member, teenage girls in their short lacy dresses milled about, weeping and dabbing their chapped faces with tissue.

"Why did this happen? Is there no God? So young. So . . ," a woman chokes.

The boy's mother, dressed in black, keeps from collapsing by holding onto one sobbing mourner after another.

"We all loved him so very dearly." A procession of people told her.

"He was a bad boy sometimes, but he didn't deserve this . . . not this," the mother cries.

Brown knows how he appears in black pointed Beetle boots, blue jeans and black leather Cabretta jacket. Knows these people must detest him and his kind. Brown stands as the epitome of what parents call "bad company." He leans self-consciously against a wall. Next thing he knows, the mother lay passed-out on the floor next to the casket of her lifeless son . . . .

He yawns widely and checks the guard watch. It is five A.M. That means it is time to wake everyone. No wait! He remembers changing the watch. He turns it back fifteen minutes.

The western sky turns a slight tinge of yellow. Brown takes a drink, stretches and relaxes. They have made the night. "Ahh men."

Having only a few minutes left by himself, Brown soaks in the energy of this special time of the morning. A time that gives a weary soldier on guard duty mysterious reflective powers. He looks over at the others knowing they have touched the bottom of their sleep. As for all soldiers, the curve of the REM cycle automatically shifts direction at the light of dawn and begins to lift them toward the recognition that it cannot go on like this much longer.

This is the hour that harkens the dawning of a new day. When the early bird catches the worm. When the animals hunt. When Victor Charlie melts into the countryside and slide back down their holes. When the American soldiers take back the Vietnam countryside.

"Man, a Coke would taste real good right about now."

14 December 1967

Another day . . . another long arduous patrol. Reconnaissance platoon marches south on Highway One under a lemon meringue sunrise. There has been a heavy overnight rainfall which makes the lush vegetation glisten and sparkle as if diamond studded when sunlight shows on their wet surfaces. The air so thick with humidity to breath is to drink.

The expansive flooded rice fields brim with young deliciously green rice sprouts that ripple in the wind appearing like waves on an ocean. Above is a deep blue sky lightly blanketed with mackerel shredded clouds.

A few hours into the march, they veer left off Highway One toward the ocean. They make their way along rice field dikes zig-zaging in a general southeasterly direction. On the far side of the expansive fields they find a foot path that leads to a small tidal bay that flows languidly toward the Son Tra Bong River.

"Echo two-two, this is two-five. Over," comes a transmission on Brown's field radio.

"Yamane, Sarge is on the horn," Brown announces hurrying over to hand off the handset. This is the first time he didn't preface Yamane's name with sergeant and anticipates some type of rebuff.

"Echo two-five this is two-two. Over," Sergeant Yamane replies.

"Charlie tango. Two-five. Out."

Yamane hands off the handset without reprimand. "Pass the word, we're holding up. Chow time," he calls. The news is met with sighs of relief. "Spread out and secure the area."

The soldiers position themselves near the river's edge on a white sand beach under shady palm trees. They shed their rucksacks and steel pots letting a luxuriant South China Sea breeze cool their weary, sweaty bodies.

While ratcheting the P-38 around the edges of the C-ration can, Brown takes in the view. The serenity reminds him of a painting at the Chicago Art Institute, "A Sunday on La Grande Jatte—1884" by George Seurat. The painting depicts a pristine city beach, perfect in every way. People dressed in their Sunday best stroll along with children in hand as they soak in the afternoon sun.

Taking a spoonful of cold Ham and Lima Beans, he remembers the concession stand at *Romeo Beach.* Oh my God, Brown remembers how those hot dogs tasted. How he'd open the steamed bun and smother mustard, relish, ketchup and diced onions all over the hot dog. And for dessert they sold his favorite ice cream bar, orange sherbet push-ups.

"Intelligence S-2 says the VC are gonna try and take the bridge tonight," Sergeant Yamane discloses. "That's why we're headed there."

The water inside the can setting over burning twigs, starts to boil. Yamane opens packets of instant coffee, sugar, and powdered cream and mixes them all together.

"The Binh Son Bridge, huh?" Okie says.

"Yeah," Yamane confirms, "they hit it last when you and Brown were on bunker guard."

"Who spilled the beans?"

"Apparently, on one of our 'search and destroy' missions, we picked up a VC." Yamane takes a sip of instant coffee. "And the interrogators got him talkin'."

It is rare for the leadership to give out specific information about a mission or even a destination. Everything is done on a 'need to know' basis. So everyone is pleased to hear anything, anything at all. Even when the prospects are frightening, it helps to know what you're up against.

Twenty minutes later, Sergeant Denning begins to pace along the sandy river bank. "Alright, let's hurry it up with the chow!" he snarls. The soldiers know that is Sarge's idea of a five minute warning.

Brown looks into his can of ham and lima beans. They don't taste all that bad when heated. He considered tossing the remains but decided any nourishment is better than none. He digs into the concentrated foodstuff for one more bite. Everyone finishes eating, buries the cans and quickly assemble.

"Alright, saddle up!" Sergeant Denning barks. "We're moving out!" He points the way. "Green, you got point." He addresses the rest, "Keep it spread out. Fifteen feet apart. Bunch up and one round will kill ya all. And I don't wanna to see anyone drag assin' behind." He looks pointedly at Brown.

Green strikes out along a narrow mud path that snakes along the edge of Son Tra Bong River. The current of the glistening river stirs a colony of sea anemones and other rich aquatic plant life. Fish jump, bugs buzz and frogs bounce on lily pads searching for the next morsel.

The enchanted surroundings are reminiscent of Florida's swamp lands, swamps with mangroves and their interlacing above ground roots, saw grass, palmetto trees, hanging Spanish moss. Black water swamps filled with alligators, snakes and pecking egrets. He listens to the lush sounds and wonders if that might be the caw of a bird the Seminole Indians call the Rain Crow.

On the opposite mud bank is a thatch structure similar to a Seminole Indian dwelling. In Florida the Seminoles lived along the river with their primary access to the main road being rickety rope foot bridges. Brown's family, who lived in Florida in the mid 1950's, often stopped at the roadside stalls where the Indians sold their handmade wares. They would buy little trinkets and give away extra fish they might have caught that day.

On one occasion, while idly looking through the Indian wares, Brown had found himself suddenly face to face with a stoic Seminole. Two deep set pearl black eyes peered from dark walnut colored skin the texture of rawhide. Scared, he side stepped to where his mother stood talking to an Indian woman.

"When the winds blow off Lake Okeechobee, I hear tell," his mother had said, "it's the ghost of their greatest war chief, Chief Osceola."

Maybe it was in the way she said it, but from that moment on he was fascinated by the mysterious Seminole Indians.

As they continue along the river path, he follows the flight of a pretty butterfly, and the wake of something wiggling through the water . . .a water moccasin? "I hope we don't have to wade across this river."

By noon the rusty steel Binh Son Bridge looms into view as it spans over one hundred feet across the river. The suspension bridge is a blueprint of those pictured in Europe during the Second World War. A few shacks with galvanized roofs are all that is visible of the neighboring village.

On the inclining gravel road leading to the bridge, a platoon of Charlie Company soldiers busy themselves with either filling or stacking sandbags to build up the fortification. Others are busy making repairs on the bridge's permanent guard house.

Reconn begins to climb the steep muddy embankment to the road. They slip, claw and grab onto any vegetation available to get up the slippery, furrowed incline—the heavy rucksacks don't help—and finally achieve the road bed.

They are ordered to take-up positions across the bridge. Grabbing some sandbags, Okie, Bedford and Brown move over the iron bridge's wooden decking headed for the eastern end. Just past the bridge on the right, they drop their rucksacks, detach their entrenching tools and start in earnest to dig a foxhole.

After nearly three continuous hours of chopping, digging and shoveling dirt into sandbags, the sweat drenched soldiers wave over their squad leader.

"Better than humpin' the bush," Yamane says walking over.

"I guess," comes an undecided chorus.

Yamane scrutinizes the position. "A foxhole-trench, huh." He nods in satisfaction. "Looks good to me. You probably have the best fortification on the whole perimeter." He glances over his shoulder at the darkening sky.

"Better wrap it up. It'll be night soon." Yamane steps around their position, down the embankment and disappears underneath the bridge.

Minutes later, Doc Holliday saunters pass, and he too, disappears underneath the bridge. Brown, Okie and Bedford look at each other, drop their shovels and sandbags.

"Done," Bedford proclaims.

"I'm starved." They grab their C-rations and join the others under the bridge.

"Brigade says three hundred VC are on the way," a sergeant claims. "The dinks wanna finish off what they started a few days ago. They wanna blow this thing to kingdom come." Everyone under the bridge follows the sergeant's gaze to the bridge's huge iron superstructure.

"It'd take a lot of dynamite to do that."

"A whole case of it."

"What I don't understand," another sergeant states, "is why the PFs from the town don't protect this thing like they're supposed to?"

"You watch," another sergeant announces, "when the geese get restless, the PFs will *dee dee mau*. Pronto. That's what happened last time. They left. And our guys got slaughtered."

"I wouldn't doubt if the Puffs aren't VC themselves," a skeptical soldier adds. "They take off their issue and shit. Then a few minutes later they come back blastin'."

"Hey," Yamane calls spotting them. "Brown, Okie. Eat up top in your foxhole. Someone's gotta be on guard."

Making their way back Brown questions, "So they're saying the Vietnamese won't fight?"

"I don't know," Okie answers. "You heard it same as me."

"Listen, I'm gonna look around," Brown decides. "Might pick up some information. Won't be long?"

"I'll tell Yamane you went for a crap," Okie says. "But make it quick. It gets a little lonely around here, especially with three hundred VC on the way."

Crouching, Brown heads for the middle of the bridge and stops at a machine gun defensive position.

"Now when it starts, let our mortars do their job." The platoon sergeant briefs his troops. Brown glances to the far end of the bridge and spots three sandbaged mortar tubes emplacements. "If they keep coming, the M-79s can start laying it on. But wait till they're good and close before you open-up with the machine guns and M-16s. We don't want 'em to know what we got up here."

The sergeant lifts his rifle. "Keep your rifles on semi-automatic. Switch to automatic only in an emergency." He points to the selector switch. "Make every round count."

"We'll wait till we see the whites of their eyes," a soldier says and they laugh.

"That would be nice." The platoon sergeant nods. "Better than blastin' away like a bunch of maniacs!" All the soldiers mumble their understanding.

"Okay, from here on out someone stays on guard. And for chrissake whatever happens—hold your position!"

Goose bumps sweep over Brown's arms. He swallows hard. His

heart pounds in his ears. Eyes bulge. Up to this point everyone had acted professional enough, but with an attitude that this is only as serious as a carnival duck-shoot.

Brown turns and jogs, hoping to make his foxhole before the battle.

"Ya miss me?" Brown blurts hoping to sound calmer than he feels.

"Yeah, with every bullet so far," Okie jokes. "So what's the deal Sergeant Rock?" Brown replays every frightening detail, and when finished the day has turned into night.

"So, Yamane," Okie asks as their squad leader makes his rounds, "what's the deal with the geese?"

"Geese?" Yamane stands perplexed but after a moment it dawns on him. "You mean as in guard dog, right?"

"Yeah."

"Here's how it works," Yamane explains. "At night the villagers set cages of geese around the perimeter. Usually near the trails. If geese hear anything . . . something as small as a twig crack. Anything at all, they make all kinds of racket. My advice is if you hear the geese, wake everyone. Pronto."

"Yamane, shouldn't we have a machine gun down here with us," Brown wonders.

"Yeah, right," Okie joins, "how we gonna hold off three hundred VC if they charge us?"

"I'm sure there's a plan of action," Yamane assures them. "From here on out if it moves . . . kill it. No questions asked. Let's draw straws to see the order of guard. Then get some rest. We've got a long night ahead of us."

If the command has planned well the soldiers will see the light of day. But if just *one* soldier did not do his sworn duty, all might perish.

On first guard, Brown raises his collar to keep out the chilly humid night air. With rifle cradled, he rubs his hands together and blows hot air over them. "Believe me, it ain't always hot in Vietnam," he says under his breath.

Nerves jangling, jaw tense, Brown reaches for a Lucky Strike, thinking a smoke might relax his nerves.

Leaning into the foxhole, he cups then lights the cigarette. For each draw, he drops low behind the sandbags. Concentrating on each muscle between toes and temple, Brown tries to release tension.

Analyzing the field of fire, Brown feels the taunting shadows of night. But where did the shadows come from? It's as though they just suddenly appeared. He squints at what appears to be a row of huts, their multiple openings and protrusions casting an assortment of weird shadows and shapes. After a last draw, he drops the cigarette and with clenched teeth, prepares to blast away Audie Murphy style . . . at? At? Nothing. Nothing moves.

In many a school yard brawl, Brown had depended on someone else pulling the first punch. In that way, he'd have time to pump up enough anger for a significant retaliation. But here, in the pitch of night, the only thing that matters is—who fires first. He'd have to pull the trigger *cold* and the last thing he wants is to chicken-out.

No way, man. I can't fail my buddies, he declares building up solid determination.

A splash somewhere under the bridge catches his attention. Senses alert, he pans in that direction. A VC swimmer setting-up the dynamite charge? Should I wake everyone? Should I take it upon myself to sneak under the bridge and check it out? In that way I would become a hero. But if I wait and the bridge explodes, what would I say? Everyone would die because of me.

He decides that if he hears anything at all, he'd sneak under the bridge. Taking off the helmet, he holds his breath in hopes of hearing more. Nothing except the soft murmur of the river flowing languidly along.

It's time to formulate his own defense scenarios and the appropriate counter measures. Judging the distance and time between himself and the huts, Brown figures it would take eight seconds for them to reach him. Swinging the M-16 rifle around, he begins madly dry-squeezing the trigger, pretending to fire at one imaginary VC after another.

Then he dares confront the worst attack scenario. The VC have floated down logs loaded with dynamite. At this very moment they are busy strapping the explosives to the superstructure. Meanwhile, other VC will mass attack to cause a diversion. There is nothing Brown can do about keeping the dynamite charges off the bridge, but if attacked, he will have to hold them off long enough for the other soldiers to get on line.

His hand closes around the steel casing of a hand grenade set on the sandbag shelf. If he throws it too hard, it'll go right over their heads and roll into the river. Best to cook-off a few seconds of the eight-second hand grenade fuse before lofting it. Then with some luck it would explode in the midair. But that's only if he's daring enough to actually let it cook-off.

For practice, he tightens his grasp on the grenade, slides his left index finger into the ring and yanks the pin free. Then, he flings his arm forward still holding tightly to the M-29 fragmentation grenade. Satisfied, he replaces the cotter pin. Pounding out deep depressions in the sandbags, he places four grenades within the dents next to the two claymore mine detonators.

Next, Brown sets an ammunition magazine on a ledge within the foxhole. For the next few minutes, he practices inserting and ejecting the magazines until he feels comfortable with his reflex speed. And finally, he decides on more fire-power. He flips the selector switch of his M-16 to full-automatic.

Brown moves low into the foxhole. "More VC please." He grins. With eyes wide, he waits.

By the second turn on guard, Brown has resorted to eating and chain-smoking to keep himself awake—let alone alert. Rifle fire occasionally echoes in the distance. "Where are you VC?"

Racked by another surge of weariness, he slumps, his head bobs, his eyelids droop to half mast.

Brown shakes himself awake. Frightened by the lapse, he quickly scans the field of fire while shaking uncontrollably. "Wooooo, man," he breaths a sigh of relief.

Taking a drink, he then pours cool water over his head. I gotta learn how to stay alert or I'm gonna get everyone killed including myself. Damn, man.

When concentrating for more than a few seconds on a single spot things become blurred. To alleviate this, he keeps his eyes in constant motion, scanning and re-scanning the area using peripheral vision. No movement . . . none whatsoever. By the end of guard, Brown resorts to slapping his face and pinching his cheeks in an effort to stay one-hundred-percent alert.

He touches Okie's shoulder to wake him for next guard.
As soon as Okie sits up, Brown dives into the land of sleep.

Startled by a touch on the shoulder, Brown wakes to the dark figure of Yamane leaning over him. It couldn't be his guard—not yet? Dazed from exhaustion, he struggles to prop his sagging body, as nausea sweeps over him. His mouth permeated with nicotine, tastes as though he'd eaten a dozen cigarette butts. He looks at the guard-watch, it reads four A.M.

"I got it," Brown says finally with his head clearing. Yamane nods and rolls over inside his sleeping poncho.

Detecting noise, he turns to see a slouching Sergeant Denning against the backdrop of the bridge's black steel webbing.

"They've taken some incoming rounds on the bridge but outside of that . . . not a damn thing," Sergeant Denning swears wearily.

Brown shrugs.

"When the PFs took off a little after midnight, we thought for sure." He clenches his jaw in exasperation. "Aaah, what the hell. It still might come-off. Stay alert. We ain't outta it yet."

Brown stares after Sergeant Denning, marveling at how vigilant he appears. Then it dawns on him that it's raining.

"How long's it been raining?" Brown asks nobody and shivers. He pulls the poncho tight around his shoulders. For added warmth, Brown takes the towel and drapes it over his head and puts the steel pot back on. Though his ears are covered, it doesn't much matter because the rain begins to pummel the ground and river till it reaches a thunderous pitch.

Arriving at his unit, he was under the impression that everyone would gather around the "old camp fire" to reveal their deepest fears, thoughts, hopes and dreams. An *esprit de corps* type of thing that all the movies expound upon. But here—in real life—that is hardly the case. During the times when the soldiers might have talked together, the sergeants would yell "Let's get moving," or "Spread out! One round could kill ya all." At other times, the exhaustive duty left them too drained to converse except superficially. After more than a week with reconnaissance, Brown knew very little about anyone's background. And because the soldiers didn't have names sewn on their uniforms, he wasn't even sure who-was-who in the platoon let alone their inner most thoughts and feelings.

The downpour continues with the foxhole filling with run-off from the bridge. Brown slides out of the flooded trench and sits hunched in the mud with rain streaming off his steel pot. Occasionally, he rearranged his poncho in a futile attempt to keep out the cold.

While pressing on his growling stomach, he thinks about a nice big hamburger with everything on it, ketchup and french fries and a chocolate shake—no make that a strawberry shake. Thinks about a warm shower and a nice warm bed.

His ears perk at the faint sound of the town's rooster crowing. The churning black sky begins to give way to an ever growing gray light and the sheets of rain begin to sway in an early morning breeze. Brown's legs are numb . . . circulation in his feet has been lost a long time before.

"Brown," Platoon Sergeant Denning calls from the bridge. "Tell everyone to grab some chow then saddle up. We'll be movin' out."

Dear Ma and Dad *16 December 1967*

I just got back. Here's what's been going on. First we raided a VC village. We captured over a hundred VC. Then we tore the village apart looking for weapons. It was quite an experience. It had a horrible smell because there is no sewage. I noticed the only people in the village were either young, or old people.

Then we went to the *Bien Son Bridge*. It had been over run last week by VC, but fortunately they didn't destroy the bridge. My job was to protect it against an invasion that intelligence said would come. They told us we were to be attacked by three hundred VC. But nothing happened. There were four men in my *sector*. We had seventeen hand grenades, five claymore mines and about 5,000 rounds of ammunition.

Finally we came back to base camp, LZ Gator. We had lunch and then we were put on *emergency action*. We were moved out by helicopter and were dropped in a Hot LZ (Landing Zone). The machine guns on the choppers were blasting the whole area.

Then we started the sweep through the VC strong hold. We killed *seven* and captured numerous weapons. We didn't have any casualties. I found a knife that I was going to send to you but I lost it. We then walked about fifteen miles home to base.

I was RTO (Radio Telephone Operator) all that day. Man that RTO set was heavy. The steel helmet isn't hurting me. I am surprised. I have only slept in a bunk three times since I was here.

Say *Hi* to Aunt Lillian and send me that hunting knife. Okay. By the way, you can forget those steel blades for cutting metal. I was thinking of cutting holes in the helmet to lighten it up.

There is only one thing I need bad—SOCKS. They don't have

any that I can get a hold of. Send me at least five heavy pairs of socks. Big and heavy. Size ten. Okay. Right now I have one pair clean and I am wearing them.

It is definitely *Monsoon* here. I am soaked half the time. I have gone through rice patties up to my chest.

Well, I must sign off. By the way I am going back in the field for three weeks. I am going to *Chippewa*, wherever that is.

Well, write me. Okay.

So long, Fred Leo

Dear Ma and Dad *17 December 1967*

Surprisingly enough, a few nights ago I could see my breath in the air. It was about 45 to 55 degrees outside. The humidity was at 100%. I would have liked to have been there this Christmas season. The funny thing about Christmas this year is it is just a word. No meaning.

Well, fortunately I went on *sick call*. The day we killed that VC was the day I should have gone. My legs, wow! Going up and down those hills looking for weapons. By the way, I am the official RTO for my squad. The addition of the twenty-five pound RTO set doesn't help much.

My company moved out but not me. I'm on sick call. *Ha, ha.* So far I have been taking it easy for two whole days. I also got a hot shower, and I have elastic bandage wraps for my knees now. I will probably always use them. We walk an average of ten miles a day. Matter of fact, often more.

If I don't turn into a non-thinking un-hurt-able machine, I will not make it. So that is what I am trying to do. It isn't easy. They don't let you rest. Ever. They just keep pushing. In AIT I could look forward to the weekends. No such luck here.

I have been here three weeks. Also I have been in the Army six months. Two-and-a-half years to go.

I don't have time to get drunk. I am always too tired to go down to the beer hall. Don't worry about me becoming an alcoholic. I wish I could. I quit smoking because I got real sick a few days ago and I couldn't eat. Ever since then I quit. My headaches haven't come yet. Just luck that's all. I have aspirin to take if I ever do get headaches.

Right now I am on bunker guard. I am in a bunker that gets snipered at every night. Nothing happens during the day.

I don't know if I told you or not, but in April or May I am going on R&R to *Japan*. I will have about a week off. I will buy a real good camera there and then I will always have a good camera.

Ma, you know that electron watch you have. The gold one that buzzes. Does it have a good flourescent striping on it so you can see it at night? If it does, do you think you could send it to me. My watch still runs, but I can't see it at night. By the way, if you send it, put a new battery in it.

Say *Merry Christmas* to all the people at the store for me. Okay.

344 Days left in Nam. *BLA!*

I think, many, many questions about myself and people and life will be answered here. If luck and God are with me. Don't worry. I do enough for *everyone*.

Fred Leo

19 December 1967

Springing from the Huey, Brown joins second platoon after two days on sick call.

"Hey, man!" Green waves, welcoming him. "The Slow Poke has arrived! You're Longhorn's RTO, dig it?"

Brown nods to Green, then glances over to Sergeant Denning, who's helmet cover bore the inked skull and horns of a Texas Longhorn.

"Guess now we're both Slow Polks," Okie says pointing to his rucksack with PRC-25.

The doctor had stressed that he "take it easy" for a week but with only two days off, here he is. And to carry the radio is definitely pushing it. His knees are still wrapped, swollen and painful to the touch. He doesn't know how he can possibly make an entire day with an added twenty-five pound radio. Brown, resigned to his fate, kneels and re-shapes his rucksack to make room for the radio.

"Saddle-up. We got a *COMBAT ASSAULT!*" Sergeant Denning shouts.

The soldiers stop and turn with slack jaws. Then a buzz goes through the ranks like an electric current.

"Move it!" Sergeant Denning hurries over to confer with their platoon leader, an officer that Brown has never seen outside of base camp.

"Combat assault!" Yamane echoes. "You heard the platoon sergeant. That means we'll be in a freefire zone in twenty minutes!" He hurries through the perimeter shouting, "That means that if it moves, kill it! Check your grenade pins and make sure they're secure. Make sure your rifles are locked 'n' loaded. Hurry it up!" Yamane glances over to Sergeant Denning to verify the urgency. "We got five minutes to move out."

Brown's mind nearly goes blank. So this is it. The battle of his imagination is going to turn real. All those threatening times in the last weeks have in essence prepared him for this. He looks at his dirty rifle. "Oh no!" he mutters. He looks over and spots Okie running a cleaning rod down his rifle barrel.

"Okie, could I use that?"

"No cleaning supplies yet?"

"They're always out."

"We'll steal ya some next time in," Okie says laying the rod on a rock. "It's there when you need it. Might put a little oil on the bolt, too," Okie advises.

Pulling out the magazine and clearing the weapon, Brown mindlessly pours oil onto the bolt. Yamane happens past just as Brown tries to swish the oil around with a cotton patch.

"Brown! What are ya doin'?" Yamane yells, stopping in his tracks. "That's not how you do it."

"In Basic they said the M-14 could be done . . . ."

"This isn't Basic and that's not an M-14. That's an M-16. You can't clean it like that," he says exasperated. He turns and bugles, "Come on men, let's move it!"

Brown takes the rifle cleaning rod and begins frantically plunging it through the barrel. "Okie, is this right?"

"Jesus, Brownie. Were you trained as a typist? The wire brush, followed by the cloth to wipe out the dirt. Then put a little oil on a clean cloth and run it down. Use the same cloth to rub the outside of the barrel to stop it from rusting."

"What?"

"Forget it." Okie snatches the cleaning rod and packs it away.

Brown, wiping off his rifle, moves the selector switch to lock, loads a magazine of ammunition, then pulls the charging handle.

"Saddle up! Chopper's in-bound! Let's move it out!" Yamane yells from across the clearing.

"Damn!" Brown curses while hoisting the heavy pack off the ground, shoving his arms through the rucksack straps.

Yellow smoke markers billow from the landing zone. Brown hurries over to Sergeant Denning while adjusting the shoulder straps and bumping-up the rucksack to make it settle more comfortably against his back.

The blades of the four choppers suck the yellow smoke upward as they come in for a landing. Conversely, when they near the ground, the blade wash sends the smoke scurrying across the rice field. The roar of the Hueys makes Brown wonder how anyone could possibly believe a helicopter could make a surprise attack.

The warrior emerges from Sergeant Denning, who's senses are at full alert, mind at full speed and with full clarity. Arms swinging and pumping, Sergeant Denning hand signals the soldiers onto their respective helicopters. The veins in his neck pulsate and bulge as he shouts over the engines clamor.

The soldiers recognize the dangers and seem prepared to accept the unknown. It is time to close the training manuals, turn off the television set and stop the conversation. It is now time to learn from reality. Just do it.

With everyone else on board, Sergeant Denning with Brown in tow, jog under the blades and flop onto the chopper's platform. The Huey slowly lifts against the enormous weight of six infantrymen in full combat gear. It rocks while searching for equilibrium as it moves into the sky over a tropical Vietnam, and speeds off in pursuit of the other three Hueys.

Because of the sway, at one moment Brown has a panoramic view of the landscape, the next only blue sky. When the chopper banks hard, Brown finds himself leaning over the edge of the platform. His pulse quickens, beating as wildly as a rabbit. He anchors his hands on the metal decking and holds his breath.

The Huey levels out giving him a chance to push against the other soldiers and scoot away from the edge of the platform. Within fifteen minutes they start the descent.

The door-gunners commence blasting away with their machine guns. Hot expended cartridges fling off into space. Red tracers plow into the tree line foliage. The combined rhythmic beating of the helicopter blades and thumbing of the machine guns send adrenalin pumping through Brown's body.

The chopper careens to make a second low-level pass. Sergeant Denning opens fire. Seeing his opportunity, Brown squeezes off two short bursts from his M-16 feeling immensely relieved to find it working smoothly. Soldiers in all four choppers fire to soften the LZ.

The four helicopters drop close to the ground with soldiers preparing to disembark. While their chopper floats fifteen feet above the flooded rice field, Brown feels a hand slap his shoulder. He turns to find the door-gunner frantically waving him to jump. When he hesitates, the gunner tries to strong-arm him off the platform. Brown continues resisting because from that height and with some seventy pounds of equipment, the impact would not only sprain an ankle but surely crush a knee joint or break a leg. Sergeant Denning, alert to the situation swings his rifle and shoves the barrel into the gunner's shoulder.

"Drop the chopper!" Sergeant Denning screams. After a quick communication with the pilot the Huey drops to within six feet.

"Tick! Tick!" comes the impact of incoming enemy rounds. Brown jumps with arms wide. On impact, he sinks past his knees in a slimy goo of mud and rotting vegetation. Pulling his feet free he begins to haul himself forward.

"Move it, Brown!" Sergeant Denning yells, splashing into the thick mess next to him. "Hurry up! We've got incoming. Let's get to cover."

Brown does his best to stay close to Sergeant Denning, raising his feet high to clear the water and slosh through the field, while preparing himself to drop into the goo if fired upon.

Glancing back, Brown sees Bedford preparing to leap from the chopper's platform. However, at the last possible second, he grabs hold of the obnoxious door-gunner and yanks him clear out of the seat. Bedford jumps while dragging the gunner behind. Both soldiers crash head-long into the flooded paddy.

Spinning from Bedford's grasp, the gunner starts protesting then realizes the chopper is leaving him behind. With arms flapping madly, he tries to attract the attention of the Huey's crew, but to no avail.

The noise of the chopper fades. "Okay, let's move it out! And don't fire until we make contact!" Sergeant Denning orders. The soldiers rise cautiously from their meager concealment and begin sloshing toward the tree line.

Noticing Brown's radio antenna, the door-gunner races over. Out of breath, soaked and covered in mud, he pulls off his helmet. "Call the chopper back." He looks anxiously as the Huey continues flying away. "Come on sarge? Get me outta here."

"Gunner," Sergeant Denning says in a harsh, even voice, "don't give me orders."

Dear Ma *20 December 1967*

This place is an old abandoned Marine base camp. I just found out that the same night I left LZ Gator they got mortared. Only two rounds. The rounds hit right next to the tent where I would have been sleeping.

Chu Lai was mortared again last night. We couldn't find where they were coming from. I haven't heard anything about the damage.

This morning first platoon was being held on a hill by some VC or NVA. The VC had an M-79 grenade launcher and automatic weapons. I don't think anyone was hurt.

We are not patrolling the area because we might be CA (Combat Assaulted) out of here. We are waiting for instructions on the subject. But I think we will stay right where we are tonight because it is almost three P.M.

Well the chopper is going to re-supply us soon so I best close and get this on the *Whirly Bird*

Bye for now, Fred Leo

P.S. Be sure and send envelopes. Okay. And paper.

Dear Ma *21 December 1967*

Wow!! Was I glad to get your letter. It was post marked the 12th and it got here the 20th. I was afraid maybe you had the wrong address. Well, I have been in the field for a day now. When I got off sick call they brought me into the field by chopper. Presently a few of our men are in a *skirmish* with some VC. I am *hiding* and going to an ambush site. We are presently real hot on VC. Earlier today we were following the blood trails of some wounded VC that we came in contact with.

I am writing on the butt of my M-16 rifle. I personally have not shot at a VC but I am there right after the shooting and know what has happened. Unfortunately I am nervous. You never know what the next moment will bring. I don't know yet if I have the *natural* or conditioned reflexes to kill a man. I will know in the very near future. The night is settling in and the clouds are darkening. The mountains look majestic in the distance. I will continue tomorrow. "OUT."

Today is the 22st of December. It is 12:40 A.M.

The moon is so bright I can write. On our way to the ambush site we shot and killed a man. He didn't look like a VC because he was carrying beets. He probably had a family.

Right now I am drying my boots and poncho. The sun is bright and very hot. I am waiting for a chopper to set down and give us *C-rations*. The *Bob Hope Show* passed through *Chu Lai* yesterday. Man, I would have given a lot to see that show but I couldn't because we were on operation.

You asked me if I get my money in cash. Yes, I do. I told the Army I wanted $45 a month. The rest is made out to you, Ma, as an allotment. So you will get a $100 or more check a month plus my board.

Tell Dad, I approve of the Oldsmobile Cutlass. It is a nice car.

Ma, you notice I write often. The reason you *know*. A lot is happening. It is harder than I thought. At eighteen, I am the youngest man in my platoon by almost a year.

Please write *often*. About anything, anything at all. Bye now.

Thanks, Fred Leo

P.S. I am glad to receive the paper and envelopes.

22 December 1967

Second squad wakes from the night ambush lying in four inches of icy water. A heavy mist cuts visibility to near zero and the cold temperature turns their breath into white vapor.

"I'm freezin'!"

" I thought Nam was supposed to be *hot!*" Green moans through chattering teeth. They move around, arms rotating trying to get warm while they eat a can-for-breakfast.

"I ain't cold." They turn to find Okie sitting on a log with two branches connected to his rucksack frame draped with a poncho. "It's warm in my one-man hootch."

Everyone has their towels tucked under their steel pots and down their shirt collars. Their shirts are tucked inside pants and pants stuffed into boots.

"If you can't keep warm enough, stuff ration boxes inside your shirts," Yamane advises.

"What're we gonna do today?"

Yamane doesn't respond but continues packing his gear.

"Same old shit, huh?" Shepard gripes spooning fat caked food into his mouth.

"Yeah, here we go round the mulberry bush, so early in the morning," Green sings. "Hell, there ain't no dinks out in this swamp. They're home high and dry roasting peanuts over a campfire. Ain't nothing out here but us dumb fools. Shit."

"Quit the bitchin' and get ready to move out!" Yamane yells. Rain starts falling in earnest. One sweeping curtain of water after another.

"Saddle up, we're movin' out!" Platoon Sergeant Denning's voice trumpets through the downpour.

For days Reconn has moved through boot-deep mud, flooded

fields and an array of spongy terrain all the while getting pelted by a near constant avalanche of water.

The soldiers rise sluggishly with head and shoulders drooping wearily as they make final preparations.

"Alright you men, come on," squad leader Sergeant Yamane calls. "Let's move it out." He turns. "Okie, you got point." Yamane points to a faint trail that leads through thick, rain-drenched foliage mixed with elephant grass.

The forward soldiers quickly disappear as they drop behind a curtain of water.

Twenty minutes later Yamane and RTO Brown work their way to the front. "What's the problem?"

"I can't get through this crap!" Okie complains, tired of pushing through the matted eight foot tall razor edged elephant grass that has fallen across the trail from the weight of the water.

"Yamane, we better get outta here and head for high ground," Bedford says. He hands Okie the long blade machete.

Okie snatching it, slides his fingers along the edge. "This thing couldn't cut warm cow poop. A stick would work just a good."

"Yeah, water is getting deeper all the time." Yamane turns around. "Green get up here. You got point."

Soaking wet and with everyone's wrinkled hands bleeding from elephant grass cuts, Reconn finally breaks through to a main trail. That's when Brown notices small soggy sheets of paper lying about in the foliage and in pools of muddy water. He snatched one off a bush. "What the heck is this?"

"Our propaganda. It's called a Chieu Hoi. They air-drop 'em from those little observation airplanes we've been seeing buzzing the area. They're free passes," Yamane explains, collecting a leaflet from a bush. "All a VC has to do is take this here *Chieu Hoi*," he holds it up, "over to the nearest Americans and surrender."

"But mostly they use them as ass wipes," Bedford says from behind.

"Good idea." Brown smooths out the leaflet so he can see what's on it. "I mean it's good idea if they want to surrender."

"Or when they're surrounded, they'll hold 'em up and say 'I was trying to give-up," Bedford continues sarcastically.

"And that's another good idea." Printed in three languages it reads, *"Safe-Conduct Pass To Be Honored By All Vietnamese Government Agencies And Allied Forces."* On top of the writing are pictured the flags of six different nations along with a larger South Vietnamese flag. On the back side, just below the words *Chieu Hoi* is a picture of two Vietnamese men. One, with a carbine rifle slung over a shoulder, is a South Vietnamese soldier. While grinning widely, he has a friendly arm wrapped around the VC convert who wears black pajamas. A second Chieu Hoi leaflet has pictured a Phantom jet screeching off leaving behind a VC lying bleeding to death in a rice field.

The water rises and second platoon finds itself plodding through calf-deep water, trying to avoid stepping into each other's imprint for fear of slipping. The trail peters out at a flooded rice field plain.

"No way man. Can't cross it," Bedford says staring across the undefined expanse of water.

"Shepard, you got point," Yamane calls.

"No way, man," Shepard pleads. "I'm not goin'."

"Tell me we ain't goin' out there." Green looks over at Yamane. "I'm gonna drown."

"What's the hold up," Sergeant Denning shouts on his arrival. "Let's go. Move it out!"

"God, save me." Shepard shakes his head and slides off the ledge into waist-deep water. "If I drown . . . ."

"Who's got the soap? Shee-it." Green sliding in behind him.

"Better not be no big black snakes out here," Shepard calls over his shoulder. Cautiously, he searches for the field dike. Finding it, he rises to knee deep water.

One at a time the soldiers slip into the water to face an expanse that stretches far beyond their vision. The skyline and grey fog meld seamlessly with a black cloud sailing through them like a three-masted *Jolly Roger* pirate ship rolling on the high seas.

An hour later, land is still nowhere in sight. Moving through chest deep water, a weak dike gives way under Yamane. Splashing with arms treading, he tries to keep balance then slides off the dike sinking past his chin. He gives a throaty cough as his mouth goes under water.

Brown thrusts out the rifle and Yamane clamps his hand around the barrel while fighting to regain a footing. Thrashing with one hand and pulling on the rifle barrel with the other, he finally regains a footing. During the struggle he has spun around and now faces Brown. Breathless and blinking, water drips from his whisker ashen face. Then a spark returns to his pearly black eyes and the corners of his mouth crinkles as determination begins to replace resignation.

"Easy does it, Shorty." Brown smiles. "A guy could drown out here."

"Life's a bitch." Yamane spits water and they chuckle. Taking a deep breath, he cautiously balances himself and turns back around. Then he feels for the break in the dike. Making a concerted leap-swim, he bridges the gap. "Be careful."

They continue at an excruciatingly slow pace with visibility cut so low that Brown can only see three soldiers to his front. The hours stretch on and it frightens him to think they might not get across. They might have to turn back. The compass would take water then malfunction leaving them to trudge until they have no strength left. Then, one by one, they would slide exhausted beneath the surface.

"Land ahoy!" Okie passes the word.

"Thank God."

During the two-hour crossing they had gone from neck deep water down to knee deep water and back up to drowning level. At the moment, they are in shoulder-deep water, holding their rifles overhead. But by the time they reach shore, they're waist deep. Slithering from the flooded field, they let muddy water drain from their rucksacks, clothes and boots making them appear like swamp *things*. Nearing complete exhaustion, the soldiers tramp a hundred yards inland to collapse next to an irrigation canal bordered by a heavy growth of bamboo.

In the middle of the torrential downpour, everyone tries to revitalize their bodies while sitting under ponchos. They eat, pass-out, try to smoke, sing or hum to themselves—whatever it takes to bring their bodies back the from brink.

As for Brown, his body hurt so bad it felt like every organ had been pulled loose, stretched to the outer limits. He sits near comatose with head back to drink water draining from his steel pot. The shakes would only leave for seconds at a time. Using all his might, he tries to regulate his body temperature. And the shakes hurt. His teeth hurt. Everything hurt really bad along with the throbbing knees.

"Yamane, listen, man. My feet are rotting away," Bedford pleads. "Look." Eyes red with exhaustion, Bedford raises a raw, swollen, cracked and bloody foot as proof. "Doc said I gotta go back."

"Yeah, you're right. If we can get a chopper to land in this soup." Sergeant Yamane looks around at the atmosphere. "Matter of fact . . . there's probably a couple more candidates that need to go back."

Yamane begins checking his charge, leaving Brown to fend for himself. An RTO is usually attached to the command post (CP) but in this case there is no CP. So, Brown has no position—no place in particular to set-up. Dragging the rucksack over to lean against a log, he remains standing in six inches of water.

Laughing, he realizes he's actually real thirsty. Guess being submerged all day doesn't stop the thirst. Finding a clear spot of water, he leans over to fill his canteen. While drinking he shivers from the cold. The rain and fog have become so dense, breathing makes his lungs feel water-logged.

In this abysmal predicament, with the ground bone-cold, the only way to conserve warmth is by standing. Rocking, Brown tries to make minute adjustments with his clothes to lock out the chill. But there is only so much he can do because he can't stop the steady stream of rain that flows down his spine, along his legs and into his submerged boots. Brown wrings out the towel and places it back around his neck.

"Brownie, don't just stand there, help with the hootch," Okie calls. Brown has managed to stop shivering, so is reluctant to respond. "Come on, man help out. Go get some tree limbs. We'll pretend we're Boy Scouts."

"Boy Scouts? Yeah, okay." But before he could locate any decent branches, Yamane recruits him to bring cases of C-rations from the chopper pad.

"A chopper made it in?" Apparently. The buffering effect of 100% humidity and poor visibility made Brown unaware of the landing.

Groggily, he lugs two cases from the LZ, passing soldiers with pathetic, rueful looks on their faces. Some of the destitutes shiver alone, while others huddle together beneath leaking ponchos. Brown notices that many sit trance like, mouths sprung, staring with rusting eyes that mirror the fluttering bluish flames of their bread can stoves.

With strength for only one twenty-pound case on the second trip, Brown grinds to a stop, too tired to continue. He drops the case upright on the mushy ground and sits on it. Wringing out his towel, he places it back around his shoulders. Then he tucks and pulls his shirt tighter around his body, crosses his arms and shuts his eyes.

The cold monsoon rains drive his weary mind perilously inside himself. Would this day ever end? He looks at his boots to see mud oozing to his ankles. After a few minutes of heavy breathing, he lifts the case over his shoulder, pulls his boots free of the sucking mud and wobbles on.

"Don't know much about history;
don't know much about biology. . . ."

A single unaccompanied voice singing a song comes streaming from the direction of the hootch Okie and the other soldiers have finished building.

"Don't know much about science books;
don't know much about the French I took . . ."

Brown rounds the corner and saw all the soldiers under the poncho hootch harmonizing with Doc Holliday singing the lead.

"But I do know that I love you,
and I know that if you love me too
what a wonderful world this would be . . ."

Okie and the others have stayed busy and the tent stood completed with huge palm leaves closing off the two entrances.

Losing his grip, the heavy case of rations tumbles to the ground splashing water. The edge of the case catches him in the shin. He tumbles to the ground and rolls in pain while clutching his hurt leg.

Hearing the noise, Okie pokes his head past a leaf. "Well, lookie here," he says staring at Brown lying in water. "Glad you could drop-by. Now come on out of the cold and warm your bones."

Spotting the C-rations, Ziggy gives out a hoot, "Wow, man. Great. Chow time."

"I'm starved."

"We're all starved."

"Five dollars says I got spaghetti."

"I brought 'em this far," Brown says crawling out of the rain, "you can bring 'em in."

With scant room remaining inside the shelter, he drops into a dink squat—wrap arms around legs and lower butt onto calves—his feet flat on the ground. Since being in Nam, they have all learned the value of a "dink squat" and it's usefulness when there is no dry ground or space to sit.

"Wow! What a great swim," a soldier says palming water from his hair. "The water's warmer than you guys think," he claims. "Why don't you come join me?"

Everyone turns to the soldier wearing dripping wet rolled up pants and a wet towel thrown across his shoulders.

"Get lost Lady Godiva. Can't you see we got a party going on in here."

"Yeah well, it's better than sitting around, moping," he defends himself. "Come on! Who'll go in with me?"

"Five card stud poker, discard two," Doc Holliday says as he produces a deck of worn playing cards. McKinley got his nickname for being a card shark. He was the lead singer in a band back in his home town and knew the lyrics to all the top hit songs. While dealing, he begins to hum the Buddy Holly song, *Peggy Sue,* to everyone's delight.

With everyone crowded together, body heat begin to warm the tent. Brown's starts to warm up and his clothes actually dry out a little.

Soldiers seeking companionship begin to arrive and cram into the shelter that is now decked with C-rations crate cardboard. It starts raining harder and Brown finds himself pushed to the edge of the shelter, where a cold stream of water runs down his back. He decides it's time for him to make a one-man hootch.

With rain slowing to a mist, he stuffs a cardboard meal box under his shirt for warmth and leaves. Needing to stretch, he lingers by the canal to watch the antics of several GIs diving and splashing playfully.

Building a hootch attached to his equipment and around a log to serve as a chair, he sets up the bread-can stove for hot chocolate.

"Well, lookie here, a crawdaddy hole," Okie remarks, peeking under the poncho and past a palm leaf. "Ummmmm, smells good. Mind if I moor my Boston Whaler here?"

He and Brown spend the next few minutes connecting their ponchos.

"A real frog-strangler out there," Okie says, settling on the log next to Brown. "Hell's afloat and the devil can't swim." He looks over. "So, whatcha got on the menu there, Brownie?"

He peers at a can of beef stew. "I got some red hot peppers Yamane gave me. We'll have us a real lip-smacker if we mix our cans together. How 'bout it? Mulligan stew."

"That's my last heat tablet." Brown points to the hot chocolate heating.

"No problem, GI. Got it covered." Okie begins fishing through a bulging cargo pocket. "We should write us a cook book." Producing a pale white ball from his pocket, he explains, "It's C-4, man. The guys in the tent are cutting it out of claymore mines."

"But C-4 is an explosive," Brown says wearily.

"I know. That's the first thing I thought." He claps it between his hand. "Compress it while it's burnin' and it'll explode. So don't try to stamp it out. Other than that, it burns just like a heat tab. And nothing bothers it. It could be setting in a puddle of water and still burn. It cooks hotter though, so you have to stir more often so the bottom of the can won't burn."

He places a wad inside Brown's stove where it flames to life next to the dying heat tablet. "And there's plenty more where that came from. We'll use my stove too and heat everything at once and get toasty warm in the meantime."

"Cabloom!"

The report from an explosion comes from the big tent. The occupants spill out, some laughing hysterically and others cursing loudly.

"You nearly put my eye out," one soldier screams wiping his face.

"You dumb shit," Yamane hollers.

From the cursing, Brown figures out that Ziggy had placed an unopened can to heat over C-4, claiming "it'll heat faster". But instead the can had exploded.

Ziggy stands busily wiping food off his clothes. He turns just as a soldier tackles him to the ground. "Come on guys let's get him."

Soldiers converge on the screaming, kicking Ziggy as they drag him to the canal.

"No, no. Not that," Ziggy pleads as he tries to squirm free. "I'll get sick and die!"

With a soldier for each leg and arm, they swing him high and at the count of three let him fly out over the canal.

Dear Ma *23 December 1967*

You asked me what it means to go into the field. This means *we* go out and search for VC. This means we go after them. Dangerous - yes - *nine men* went to the hospital since I've been out.

That Vietnamese money I sent in the mail is worth two dollars. It has a two on the front doesn't it? It's real value is about $1.50 American. That $70 government check you got. That was part of my pay.

About my head. *Great Shape!* No headaches after that first one I told you about.

Man, I wish I could have been in New York with you when you visited Roxanna. Fabulous, great feeling wasn't it. Walking in the rain and paying no mind to anything. I know how you felt.

I wonder if I will like *operas* when I get back. You never know. This not knowing is the good and evil of life, isn't it.

A few days ago we were going through *rice patties* and I fell into a *sink hole*. This is where an artillery round hole hit and it has filled up with mud. I went in almost to my waist. I heard one guy drowned in one. I had to be pulled out. I got to march for a while now.

Well, I am resting again. We just got the *word.* It doesn't look like we will be out of the field for Christmas.

Today is the 23th of December.

We have been in the field for about a week. I haven't had a *dry* night of sleep yet. We also pull guard all night long. All of these days we have been in the field we have marched at night as well as all day. One night we went for *two* miles through *machete* (big knife) terrain.

Last night they *harassed* the village with a 1.55 Howitzer gun battery. We heard a piece of *shrapnel* go through the bushes next to us.

Well, looking at the good things we did. We crossed this river. So we stopped. We all took out our soap and went swimming and took a bath. No kidding. BEAUTIFUL. I filled up my canteens with water. I must go now.

Well, here I am again. Resting! Beautiful! I am making hot chocolate right now. I have a heat tablet to heat up water. *Wow!* Good.

Ma, send me in your next letter two packages of *pre-sweetened* Kool Aid. Grape or lime.

I just got some water out of a local well. Of course I put purification tablets in it.

Earlier in this letter I said we would be in the field on Christmas Day. We are *not!* We are going to climb up to LZ Chippawa for a Christmas dinner.

Fabulous.

These pieces of paper, they are *air dropped*. Have you heard of a program where, if you are a VC you can *surrender*. So, If you are a VC all you do is walk over to the Americans with one of these pieces of paper and comply with the *seven* conditions to the surrender.

These *papers* are only a few of the many different kinds. Well, I will end this letter.

By the way, be sure to send an oil stone so I can sharpen the knife.

Fred Leo

24 December 1967

Chilly monsoon rain made the march absolute punishment for Reconnaissance. Since before dawn the soldiers had been making their way through flooded rice fields, up, down, over and around hills.

Then they came to a deep, fast moving river with a hazardous log jam waterfall. Sergeant Denning had to swim across with ropes. Then after creating a system of ropes and pulleys, the men and equipment were moved across. But near the end, third squad leader Sergeant Muton lost his grip. Sergeant Denning, being a good swimmer, swam out and literally, just before the waterfall, snatched him up and saved his life.

Three hours later finds them again tramping through boot sucking mud and cutting their way through dense foliage impervious to the dull edged machete. For eighteen hours they had doggedly sought their destination, the foot of the mountain range. When the sky cleared momentarily in the evening hours, it came into view. The mountains looked ghostly against a backdrop of gray, mist and rain clouds swirling about and covering its lofty peaks.

It is planned that next morning the soldiers would again rise before dawn and would climb the treacherous mountain in hopes of achieving Fire Support Base, LZ Chippewa. The "carrot" is a mouth-watering Christmas dinner with all the trimmings and maybe a couple of Red Cross girls since "they've been on good behavior".

Nearing midnight, a bone tired second squad shuffles into their night ambush. The only relief is in knowing the 1967 Christmas cease-fire will take effect within minutes. They drop the heavy rucksacks, pull out poncho and liners, and collapse onto the water logged ground. Within minutes everyone is sound asleep, leaving their RTO Brown, alone without the name of the next soldier on guard.

Rummaging through the pack, he pulls out a Pabst Blue Ribbon beer. The day's re-supply chopper had brought out a Christmas present: one Coke and two beers for every soldier. Everyone else had greedily drank their present soon after touching their hot hands. But Brown had stashed one beer in anticipation of this special moment of reflection.

Laying out the sleeping gear, he slips inside. Relaxing his back against the rucksack, he watches the rain flow off his steel helmet, onto the poncho and along a gutter formed between his legs.

Washing off the beer top in the rain, he takes the church key from his helmet and opens the can. Foam gushes and he sucks it all up. *"Ahhh.*

"Here's to you, buddy." He raises the beer in a personal cheer. He takes a swallow of warm liquid. From inside an SP pack, he pulls out a 4-pack of Winston cigarettes. While smoking and nursing his celebration beer, he thinks, "There is no *alone*, like the *alone* you can feel at Christmas time."

His thoughts drifted to a Christmas past, white snow sprinkling through the pines as he and his sisters select their family tree. In the evening he and his sisters Lorraine and Roxanna would laugh as they banter and tease each other while sprinkling tinsel among the blue, green, red and yellow lights on the Christmas tree. And while they work, their beautiful black cat Tinsy with white paws would scurry under foot batting the Christmas ornaments and tinsel. The joyously wrapped presents with their golden laces and bows make the room absolutely enchanting.

"Oh, Tinsy how I miss you," he says taking drink, a tear forming in his eye.

. . .While ten-year old Brown was at church, his father had taken Tinsy and tossed her into a cast iron coal burner. Brown lived with the vision of the door closing and her burning to death.

"How could he have done that?" He sniffles. "I loved that cat."

Finishing the beer, he looks around and saw he now lay in two inches of water. It is past midnight and there has been no call for a Sitrap so that means no one has to be on guard. Reclining against the rucksack, he positions the helmet to keep water out of his face.

"Good night and don't let the bed bugs bite," he says out loud the words his mother would say to him at bedtime.

They wake at 4:30 A.M. sleeping in six inches of water. Assembling gear, they begin moving though the pitch black, zero visibility fog. Although cold, wet and tired nothing can stop the Christmas spirit from pervading their mood. They are thankful for an uninterrupted night's rest and are now intent on reaching their promised dinner.

With the rain subsiding two hours later, dawn's early light begins filtering through to chase after the thick white South China Sea fog. By seven A.M. they find themselves on a half-hour break in a spacious courtyard of a war-torn Vietnamese pagoda. A heavy dew drools from the detailed mouths of the fish heads elaborately carved into the overhanging roof supports. The outer walls are built with mud laced straw.

"Better fill our canteens while we've got a chance," Yamane says. At the rear of the building and in the midst of fallen debris is the local well, easily found because of the concrete thirty-six inch high drainage ring that protrudes from the ground looking like a huge crayfish hole.

"There must be a bucket and rope here somewhere." In the past they usually can find it but after a cursory inspection, they only succeeded in locating an old frayed rope. "They must've hidden the bucket." Giving up the search they attach Brown's steel pot onto the rope to use as a bucket.

"Alright, let's saddle-up. We got a rendezvous with Santa Claus."

They march with muscles still tight from sleeping in the chilly water. The trail increases in elevation till they are again within a dense fog. After two more hours of marching and judging by the how far he leans over, Brown decides they're past the base and are now beginning the actual uphill climb.

"Gimme your hand," Sergeant Yamane offers as Brown crawls over the edge of a jagged outcropping. Safely on top, Brown makes the same offer to Shepard, but he's already negotiating the obstacle. Well, if it wasn't for the extra twenty-five pound radio, he justifies, it wouldn't be no big deal for me neither.

The terrain becomes more and more rocky and treeless with only patches of soil. Second platoon continues to squeeze their way through narrow crevices and pull themselves over mammoth boulders. Several times they have to back track or detour around extremely rugged terrain. Then they walk into a blind alley. To their front rises a sheer fifty foot wall of rock with no way around.

Sergeant Denning contemplates the wall. Coming to a conclusion, he peels off the rucksack, lays down the rifle, and drops the pistol belt.

With no equipment, Denning drapes the rope over his shoulder and does a test footing on a rock. Deciding on a likely course, he slowly claws his way up the sheer face, testing every foot and hand hold. At a threatening gap, he halts pressing his body against the rocks to regroup strength. Then he continues his vertical crab crawl, looking as competent as a professional mountain climber. Finally he shimmies and disappears over the top. A minute later the rope end cascades off the cliff, reaching them with length to spare.

Okie drops his rucksack, slings the second rope and both his and Denning's M-16s over his shoulders. Then he takes a firm grasp of the rope. Okie begins scaling the cliff, using foot holds in the rocks. Near the top he loses a footing, his body slams into the jagged wall. With feet dangling, he clings with bleeding hands to the rope.

"Come on, Okie, you can do it!" Brown encourages. Okie musters his strength and clambers up the last six feet to clear the top.

The second rope cascades down. With a climbers ring, Yamane secures Denning's rucksack with pistol belt and it is quickly hoisted to the ridge. In turn, everyone climbs the rope while Sergeant Yamane and Brown continue securing the packs for hoisting.

"Shepard, you're up."

"Heah, man! Don't rush me. And I don't need no sissy ass rope!" Shepard claims defiantly showing both his stubbornness and strength in equal measure. It seems that if Sergeant Denning can scale the wall, so can he. 'So there.' Taking a foot and handhold, he begins the climb. Near the halfway point, his foot slips and gets stuck in a crevice. His steel pot tumbles off, hits a rock, and bounces past Brown. Without comment, Shepard edges over to the rope and uses it to climb the rest of the way.

Finally it's Brown's turn. He takes a foot and handhold like Shepard and begins to climb, but after a few feet slips and bangs his knee.

"Brown! Come on. The rope!" Yamane yells. "Tarzan of the infantry you ain't."

With rope securely in hand, Brown calls sheepishly over his shoulder, "Just playing around, Yamane. You know me. Always fun and games."

Nearing the top of the cliff, Okie pokes his head over. "Easier than it looks, huh? Should've kept your pack on, Brownie!"

Brown crawls over the edge and lays out to catch his breath. "What a bitch." Wiping sweat from his eyes, Brown finds a sunny blue sky overhead. Sitting, he looks out from their high elevation to a pristine valley below. The partial fog cover has lifted to uncover a crystalline panorama of valley painted in lush browns, yellows and greens. The north end of the valley consists of huge rice field network, connected by a choke-passage between two ridges.

To their relief, the route momentarily levels out. A while later though, they are again trudging up a steep incline. No big outcropping to climb but it is strewn with large rocks that threaten to give under foot.

RTO Brown is now seriously struggling to keep pace. Finally in resignation, he slows with head drooping. His mind becomes occupied with watching his worn boots moving back and forth. In a daze, he notes his foot-strokes are becoming shorter and shorter similar to how a steam locomotive would start to chug going uphill. He is barely able to put one foot in front of the other.

Shifting into his lowest gear, he sucks in the sweat that pours down his face. He constantly wipes his brow to keep the salt from stinging his eyes and blurring his vision. His rifle hand skims the ground with knuckles now bleeding from occasionally scraping on a rock. Then finally, with the incline so steep, he finds it necessary to simply drop to all fours.

Every movement has become a concerted effort as he fumbles onward, a drizzling rain doing little to refresh. Stars twinkle and swirl throughout his vision, then he gives it up and collapses. His heart pounds, his breath thrashes and the weight of the rucksack crushes him mercilessly against the rocks. After achieving a few normal breaths, he pushes himself back on all fours, then to his feet and finally to a wobbling shuffle.

During this time the rest of the platoon, which is now far ahead, is sending loose rocks tumbling back toward him. He makes futile attempts to dodge the rocks and finds on occasion it is necessary to simply lower his head and let the steel pot take the blow. He feels lucky, since all the really big ones have missed.

After six hours, the platoon comes upon a grassy area with a reduced grade. They should rest—but instead—grind on slower, slowww-er and slo*wwwwww*-er.

"Hey, man," comes a raspy voice from up ahead. "Where's top? Sheeee-t."

As pointman, Sergeant Denning stumbles on a rock and wilts to the ground. He rolls around with a lackluster expression and leans against the rucksack. Time to rest. He pulls out a canteen and relaxes. The other soldiers collapse nearby, the air filling with turbulent breathing, moans and groans.

"Ball-buster," someone sighs.

"Why da hell we gotta do this?" Shepard grumbles. "This ain't right."

"Shee-t man, I ain't gonna make it," Green whines.

Everyone drinks long and hard from thirst as well as wanting to lessen the weight on the pistol belt. It takes some ten minutes for Brown to finally catch up and drop next to Yamane.

After a prolonged drink, Brown offers some to Yamane. "Goofy Grape?"

Yamane extends a bruised, shaky hand. The Kool-Aid is emptied in one long gulp. Wiping purple dribbles from his mouth, he hands it back. "God, I need that. Thanks," Yamane says. "You know, my favorite is Loud Mouth Lime. My girlfriend, Sandi, she's the only one who thinks of sending me any."

Brown reaches into his side pocket and produces two packages of Kool-Aid. "Let's say we mix 'em together." Brown promptly portions half Goofy Grape and OJ Orange powder into a full canteen of water. Shakes and serves. As they share, red drops dribble from both of their now rosy red lips.

"I love Freckle Face Strawberry, too."

Yamane drearily looked over his shoulder and notices the soldiers are moving. "Okay," he exhales. "Hang in there, Brown, it won't be long now."

"God only knows."

After seven straight hours of marching, the mountain starts to crown and their destination, LZ Chippewa comes into view. Sergeant Denning radios the base. They direct him to hold-up until personnel can come down and guide them through the perimeter's minefield.

"Ummmm, *ummmmm*, I can smell dem chitlins from here! Mama, I'm a hungry man," Green announces. The elation of almost making-it begins working on the soldiers. "You knows, I love turkey. And I'm gon-na eat everything in sight." Wide eyed Green turns to Brown grinning, his yellow teeth gleaming with saliva. "And I'm gonna eat all yours too!"

"No you ain't," Brown says amused.

Then, in mock apology adds, "A man's gotta do what a man's gotta do. Look out for number-one." In a loud bellowing voice he adds, "And the rest of you turds come last."

"We'll remember that the next time we get into a firefight," Bedford calls out from up front.

"Now, baby, why you gotta go talking to me like dat? All I wants is my turkey cooked *just* right," Green continues playfully.

"I hope they's cooked up the neck," Shepard jumps in. "I love's the neck. You know what I'm gonna do, I'm gonna grab that big turkey leg, a big helpin' of dressing, an dump that goo-d giblet gravy all over everything. Oh, yeah, don't cha know. And a whole loaf a bread just for me, honey," he says with an expansive smile. "Wash all that good eaten' down with lots of cooooo-ol beer. Oh-h yeah. Sure mama, I'll take a helpin' of dem sweet potatoes and some greens, please!" Shepard savors his every word.

"Right. That all?" Brown asks like he's the waiter.

"Don't forget the fried chitlins?" Green calls over.

"Fried chitlins it is. Anyone wanna add somethin'?" Brown continues.

"Yeah," Doc Holliday hollers from point. Brown stares over to the sweat-drenched, pale-face soldier. "Double it, Brown. But I want the heart just for me. Alright?"

Grasping the radio handset he begins a bogus transmission. "Yeah, uh-uhh, and extra giblet gravy on those mashed potatoes. . . no that'll be good on the sweet potatoes, but the gizzard, heart, liver and neck I want put aside special. . . . Uuh-huh, you can give the leftovers to 'Chicken Colonel'. That's right, the mean green eating machines are on the way!"

"Alright, Brownie!" Everyone cheers.

"Lookie! Lookie here!" Green hollers. "I'm even drooling." Green raises his chin to show the others the saliva running down his chin.

"I wish those guys'd get their butts over here before I whither and die like a snake on these rocks," Muton grips.

Moments later, two base soldiers appear wearing open shirts and soft caps—no pistol belts—and carrying rifles. After disarming a few booby trap grenades, they wave "All clear" and step aside.

Nearing, Brown notes the base soldiers are intent on staring at the infantrymen's equipment. He wonders about their fidgeting and decides there could only be one logical reason. Until now, combat to them hadn't been all that *real*. Combat had been talked certainly but like artillery shelling in the distance, it remained just as distant. As Brown and the rest of the platoon clump past, he can see the reflection of reality bulge from their glassy eyes. The reality of War is passing uncomfortably close.

"Well, Sergeant Denning, my compliments," an officer congratulates. "At least now we know we're vulnerable from east. We'll beef up the perimeter with extra concertina wire, pronto," the officer states. "Now you and your men have a well deserved rest coming and a Christmas dinner which will arrive shortly."

A half hour later the familiar pop sound from a smoke grenade followed immediately by a hissing sound cut through Brown's thoughts as he dozes against a bunker wall. He stands to watch a chopper with crossed rifles painted on the nose, the insignia for *Minute Man,* approach with their promised Christmas dinner.

Then clouds of red and green smoke begin spewing from the front of its landing skids and the chopper starts to weave and whirl around. Everyone cheers, laughs and waves as they realize the pilot, Peacock, is trying to simulate Santa's sleigh with the colored smoke streaming through the air.

"Can you dig it Brownie," Okie says walking to hand Brown a beer. "Christmas in Vietnam. A lunatic's dream."

Dear Ma *Christmas 1967*

Did Roxanna and you read that letter about that *dead man*? Well, I am more or less used to seeing hurt or dead men now. We killed another VC a few days ago.

They have a lot of *pot* (grass) over here. Plentiful. I tried it and unfortunately, or fortunately I got a bad headache. So it don't look like I will smoke much. There are a lot of people who *thrive* on it here.

I sent myself a letter talking about the situation I was in this Christmas time. I will open it and read it next Christmas. I also have *thirteen* things I wish to accomplish by next year. Mostly things of *mental* importance.

Don't open the letter. Okay. It just talks about how it rained all night and we walked all day and then climbed a mountain.

Right now I am at an installation called *LZ Chippewa*. It is new and my company was the *first* to climb the mountain to it. We have been in the field for two weeks now. I heard we are now going to "AK-Valley."

This is where A Company got *shot up* bad.

I have a view of the South China Sea from here and I can almost see *Chu Lai*. By the way my base camp, LZ Gator, is just outside of a town called *Nuoc Mau*, which is on Highway One, the biggest and longest road in Vietnam.

Well, I am thinking of applying for door-gunner on a chopper. To do this I will have to extend my tour of duty for six months. But I will get a month off at the end of the regular tour.

If I apply for gunner and get it, then I will be safer in the air than I am now. But I will stay right where I am until I do a little more killing, before I actually take the dive.

Well, lately I have been getting lots of beer. *Bla!* It doesn't taste good. I like *Coke* better.

Wow! *Beautiful knife*. What I really, really needed. But now

I need a small *oil stone* to sharpen it. *Okay*. A small one. I hope I can keep it in good shape because it is hard to keep things from rotting and deteriorating here.

Just finished Christmas dinner. We had turkey, green beans, giblet gravy, dressing and real mashed potatoes. Two helpings and I am stuffed. I am on top of a bunker now with my shirt off and I am getting a *suntan*. But surprisingly enough it gets real cold at night. One day I had to wear my field jacket all day.

From LZ Chippewa I can see abandoned rice patties. They look weird. The whole area around here is a mass of abandoned homes and fields. I have seen fabulous houses. They use beams like they use at churches to support the roof. But this one house had the whole support *beam* carved at each end. Fabulous! There were about three beams like this. The whole house was beautifully carved and put together real strong.

Well, tomorrow we move out off this mountain. So take care and I will write soon.

Your son, Fred Leo

P.S. Send paper and envelopes in next letter. Okay?

29 December 1967

"Right behind you, Yamane," Brown assures him though he's still yards away. Panting, he takes up the RTO position, approximately ten feet behind the squad leader. To get a better grip on the rifle, he wipes his moist palm off on his dirty fatigues.

Lifting the little D-ring on the suspenders, he pulls over the three-foot antenna and secures the tip inside the ring making the radio less noticeable. Outside of pointman who has a life expectancy of one-tenth of a second at the moment of contact, Brown is well aware that the RTO position holds the second deadliest position of two-tenths of a second.

By monitoring radio traffic, Brown concludes that their present mission is to sweep an illusive enemy in the direction of Bravo Company which serves as a blocking force.

Reconnaissance pushes cautiously through thick underbrush and around saplings. It becomes so dense, they didn't notice Bravo Company until a couple of its soldiers pop up, seemingly out of nowhere, their helmets heavily camouflaged with twigs and leaves.

"Hi, guys." They grin. "Come to join the party?"

A buzz of conversation accompanies Reconn into the clearing. However, the conversations are cut short because Bravo receives orders to move-out. In fact, they assemble and move from the clearing so quickly that they appear like strands of spaghetti being sucked hungrily into a vein strung foliage mouth.

A hollow, numb sensation sweeps over Brown as he continues to watch his fellow 'grunts' slip one by one into the expectant jaws. A well-known adage plays in his mind, "while we search for someone to kill, that same someone is waiting to kill us."

The carnivorous trail continues to swallow the platoon whole. When the last strand disappears into the belly, the tongue rolls in and the jaw closes with a satisfying, "*Oooommm*" to leave a crimson sauce dripping around the edges.

The resulting silence tries to convince Brown that Bravo Company has never existed, except a black/white image of the scene has already been burned into the cells of his brain. Along with the trail's lip-smacking smile.

"Quiet!" someone calls motioning toward the trail. "Hear that?"

Their ears quicken at the sound and echo of a single muffled explosion. A barrage of M-16 rifle fire immediately cracks through the still jungle air.

"They made contact," Sergeant Denning bellows. "Everyone get down." Being the nearest RTO, Brown rushes over to pass-off the handset. Denning quickly dials a different radio frequency. "Bravo two-five, this is Romeo two-five on your push. Over." He waits for a response. None. He tries again. Sporadic small arm fire and high-explosive detonations continue.

"Shit!" Sergeant Denning thrust the handset at Brown. He curls his lip while coming a decision. "Yamane! Take your RTO and Doc. They've lost radio contact. And be damn careful when you get near 'em. They might be spooked. And watch . . . the trail might be booby trapped," Sergeant Denning rattles orders. "Bedford, go with 'em. They might need an M-79 man."

The four soldiers double-time into the mouth of the jungle, the sounds of the firefight subsiding. Everyone has left their heavy rucksacks behind, except Brown who carries the radio. He quickly falls behind from exhaustion, his walk barely able to keep him within visual contact. The heavy rucksack and radio mercilessly pounds his back and drains his strength.

Reaching the rear element of Bravo, Brown slowly weaves his way past the grunts who appear edgy and a bit trigger-happy. The tough-faced soldiers crouch among expended brass cartridges, every other weapon aimed toward the opposite side of the trail. Like moments before the firefight, an eerie silence engulfs the area.

"Two-five, two-five, this is two-two kilo. We've alpha. Over." Brown radios back that they have arrived.

Moving along the trail, he comes to a small blackened crater near the middle of the path, where blood mingles with exploded earth and where the air is heavy with the smell of gunpowder and decay.

Pausing to study a boot slashed by shrapnel, his eyes follow a blood trail that leads to a shrapnel-riddled, rucksack-mounted radio. Alongside with eyes empty lay the RTO in a pool of blood.

Yamane, Bedford and Doc Prien begin feverishly working on three other soldiers lying nearby. Brown kneels next to the motionless RTO, the GI he had heard earlier talking on the radio.

"He's dead."

Brown turns to the speaker, a grunt who has

LIFE'S A BITCH
THEN YOU DIE

written on his helmet in bold magic marker.

"Slow Poke is dead, man," the grunt repeats wiping sweat from his eyes. "My buddy bought-the-farm."

"Brown!" Yamane shouts. "Get a chopper in here. We need a medevac. Hurry!"

"You mean. . . ?" Brown says baffled. Although an RTO, he knows practically nothing about how to use the PRC-25 field radio. On top of that, he'd never called *Six*, the call sign for the company commander, and bringing in a dustoff is far beyond his ability.

"Yesss!" Yamane shouts. *"CALLLLL!"*

"Call? Right away." Brown releases the antenna to let it reach full height, then grabs the handset. Boldly pressing the squelch button, he speaks, "Six, this is two-two kilo. Over."

"Two-two kilo, this is six-kilo, I hear you loud and clear. Over," their CO's RTO replies.

"Roger," Brown responds trying to control the jitters. "We got one KIA and at least three WIA. Need dustoff. This is an emergency. We got soldiers dying out here. Over."

"Two-two kilo, this is six kilo, roger," the CO's RTO replies. "Chopper inbound. What is yankee lima? Over?"

"Location? Shit." Brown lowers the handset. "Yamane, where are we? They want our location."

Yamane waves him over. After placing Brown's hand on a bloody bandage wrapping a soldier's wounded leg, he instructs, "Hold it tight until Doc ties it off."

"Oh my God." He swoons with dizziness. Fighting to keep his mind occupied, he turns and busies himself with watching Yamane scan the complex topographical map. He sees a grease pencil mark on the plastic map cover which marks an earlier position.

"Ah, let's say, Tango-nine, Bravo-two," Yamane says his finger planted on a spot. "That'll give us a rice paddy just over there." Yamane nods toward the west. He glares at Brown. "Well? What are you waiting for?"

Still griping the bandage, even though Doc has finished, Brown jerks his hand away and quickly wipes off the blood on some grassy foliage. After the communication, Brown peers around at the other two severely wounded soldiers. They lay in a daze, their blood soaking into the ground, and the bandages oozing more.

"It could've been a train, a car, a falling tree. Right? I mean who's to know," the dead RTO's friend says in borderline shock. "When it's your time to go man, you go." The grunt leans over and pulls the eyelids closed on the deceased. "You know what I mean?"

Not wanting to look at the corpse, Brown stares at the soldier with eyes rimmed in exhaustion-purple, his combat fatigues marked with fresh blood. "It was just time for Slow Poke to go."

Lightning had stuck, and why not? Brown thinks. Makes as much sense as anything else.

"Brown!" Yamane shouts. "The rice paddy is about a half klick in that direction." He points. "Time's short. Better hustle."

"Roger," the wounded platoon sergeant babbles. "That's affirmative. The perimeter is secure. Everything's A-okay."

"Roger that, Sarge," Doc says playing along. "No problem. Everything's shipshape. Got a chopper inbound, so hold on there buddy, you're goin' home." Doc pulls out a syringe of morphine. "Hold him," he instructs a soldier as he jabs the leg just above the wound.

"What time ya got? I gotta give six a SITRAP." The delirious sergeant thrashes his arms as he twists around. "Where's my RTO? Hey, Slow Poke! Where are ya?"

"Relax, Sarge, Slow Poke is busy," Yamane continues to reassure him while lightly patting his shoulder.

Brown turns to face the anxious soldiers of Bravo Company. "Alright, listen up!" He takes a deep breath as he notes the volume of his voice. "We've gotta bring in a Medevac. If you're not needed here, follow me."

Brown starts to push through the brush and after a few yards dares to glance back. With a sigh of relief, he finds the soldiers are indeed following his orders.

Shoving and pushing, he forges a trail through the thick underbrush till he comes to the edge of the tree line. To the front unfolds a horseshoe shaped flooded rice field with plenty of landing space for a Huey. Time is short, so he'll have to throw caution to the wind. With this in mind, Brown does the only thing he can, which is to slide into the calf-deep water and quickly move about forty yards from shore. If the enemy is present, he will surely draw fire. If not then they've found an PZ.

Continuing the air of confidence, he turns to the soldiers waiting his instructions. "All right," he bellows from the middle of the rice field, "I want two of you on each of those land points." He points while walking backwards, feeling the cross hairs of an enemy rifle on his back. "The rest of you spread out along the edge of the paddy."

Near the middle of the rice field, he begins to hand-signal like a traffic policeman to get the soldiers into position. The entire time his skin crawls knowing the impending dangers. "Farther to the left. That's right. Keep it movin'. Keep it movin'."

While directing, he keeps bobbing around not wanting to become, literally, a sitting duck. "Okay. That's fine. Let's keep a sharp look out. You over there," he shouts and motions. "Don't bunch up. Keep it spread out!"

Listening to his even baritone, Brown begins to feel a sense of power. These GIs don't know a thing about him, yet never dare question either his authority or ability.

Yamane, Bedford, and Doc halt just inside the tree line with the wounded. It amazes Brown how they, the four of them, have taken control of the entire evacuation. Without the platoon sergeant's leadership, it appears the entire unit has been effectively paralyzed.

The distant *"whup-whup-whup"* of a Huey's rotor blades cut through the air. A tremor of terror runs through Brown, the responsibility lay heavy on his shoulders. Until arriving at his unit hardly three weeks earlier, he had never even seen a field radio, let along operate one—now this, an entire combat medevac.

The words of the helicopter pilot's vibrating voice blares over Brown's radio receiver. *"Two-two, this is Minuteman on your push, over."* He recognized the voice of Peacock, the helicopter's pilot. He searches the cloudless blue sky in the direction of the beating noise and spots the chopper.

"Roger, Charlie Charlie, this is two-two kilo. Over," Brown replies.

"Two-two kilo what's your lima. Over?" Peacock asks.

"Nine o'clock your location. Identify smoke. Over." Brown tosses a smoke grenade onto a raised dike. It *pops!* and begins to spew its deep red smoke.

"Roger, two-two kilo, I identify choo-choo cherry. Over," Peacock replies in a vibrating voice.

"That's a roger Charlie Charlie. Alpha secure, papa zulu cold. Over," Brown says, verifying the color of smoke and that the pickup zone is secure. Secure? He looks around and mumbles, "I hope."

In an effort to relieve some tension, he stares at the colorful smoke that flows whimsically through the air and thinks he sees the shape of a dancing angel.

"Okay, listen up!" he shouts diverting his attention back to the perimeter. "If there's any VC around, they'll probably open up. So look alive!" The Huey banks and speeds in for a landing. It sends the remaining red smoke either scurrying across the rice field or threading up through its beating blades.

The severely wounded are hurried into the rice field on rifle poncho-stretchers. Following behind are Bedford and another able-bodied soldier who helps a slightly wounded GI with one leg wrapped with bloody bandages. The dead RTO is brought out last. Hustling, his head bounces unsupported by the rifle poncho-stretcher.

Nearing the chopper blade wash, everyone stoops to protect their faces from the high wind and splashing water. They struggle onward with their burdens in calf-deep water, clothes flattened against or furiously flapping around their bodies. Rather than set in the rice field, Peacock hovers the chopper with skids only inches above the water. The medics step off the side of the rocking helicopter and balance their feet on the landing skid while they help hoist on the KIA and WIAs. Meanwhile, the door gunners keep their M-60 machine guns trained on the tree line.

As the last of the dead and wounded are loaded, Yamane hands outgoing mail to the door gunner. The door gunner in return hands off a plastic bag.

Everyone clears away as the chopper blades hit a feverish pitch. The chopper lifts, turns and bounds away to speed low across the open field. Occasionally it jinks right or left to avoid any possible ground fire, then springs up and over the distant horizon.

After making arrangements for a replacement platoon sergeant, the reconn soldiers start back. Moving guardedly over the trail, Brown takes his usual RTO position where he detects the scent of death wafting from everyone's fatigues.

"How can you stand all that blood and guts, Yamane?" Brown asks. "That was . . . well. You know. And when you made me hold that bandage . . . *ugh*."

"It's really not that bad," Yamane contends, without breaking stride. "If a man is dead or wounded, just pretend he's a *mannequin.* Block out any thought of it being real." Yamane, suddenly noticing a speck of bloody flesh dangling from his sleeve. He flicks at it madly as though it were about to burn through to his skin.

Composed, Yamane slows to face Brown, his eyes gaunt, face grim. "Anyway, this's war. That's what it's all about."

Back on the main trail, they silently maneuver around the booby trap's crater, past patches of pulverized bloodstained earth laced with remnants of army clothing, and a shredded boot.

Brown contemplates the place where Slow Poke Kinsey had been killed and others severely wounded. A place, a day and a time that would be forever etched in the forefront of all the participants minds. But from this moment forth, no one who passes here will know what happened at this spot on the 29th of December 1967.

Dear Ma *29 December 1967*

Well, it has been three days since I wrote last. I think. Not too much has happened. I left *LZ Chippawa* and went by chopper about ten miles away. The other squads had contact. They killed a VC medic, or rather a doctor.

They think that there is a company of VC in the area. This whole area is abandoned. *Hundreds* of *hooches* (huts) are torn down around here. Well, I will write again tomorrow.

Today is the 30th of December.

We have been on the move, up to ten miles a day, since we left LZ Chippawa from one enemy confirmation to the next. Reports are daily of contact and kills of VC.

Like yesterday, I didn't even have time to put foot powder on and Yamane, my squad leader, yells, "Saddle-up, we're movin' out."

I'm his RTO and the radio is so heavy, I have to sit and pull on the straps then stand up. Then I take long steps to catch up. I never run because I get too tired.

Well, it is *noon* the 31st of December.

We set up an ambush last night but no one came. This morning we went over to a big coconut tree. We got a coconut down and had some good coconut juice. The thing was green so there was no meat in it.

We cut down some bananas yesterday and they are ripening now. We also found some hot peppers. We put them in our C-rations.

While walking along these trails I noticed some hedge rows, the kind we planted in our back yard. The ones here look as *scraggly* as ours.

They had to turn in my radio and so for a day now I have not been *RTO*. I am recuperating from the weight good.

Bye, Fred Leo

January 1968

Dear Ma and Dad *1 January 1968*

Ma, it seems like I need more things each day. The trouble is I can't buy anything in the field, and I can't get a lot of things here. This is what I need: Some black cloth tape inch-and-a-half wide. I need it to tape the sheath on my knife. It will last longer if I tape it up. I need that oil stone also to keep my knife sharp.

Do you think you could send some cans of fruit. Nothing is ripe here yet. Also, send some dried apricots and prunes too. Put it all in a cardboard box.

Well, right now it is 2:30 P.M. We have been sitting here for about 2-1/2 hours. They are dynamiting everything in the area. Some of the bunkers need a real big charge.

This piece of paper I sent with the letter is a safe conduct pass for a VC who wants to surrender and come to our side. These coins are all *Red Chinese*. I found them on the trail near where the VC doctor was killed.

It is funny the way my *fatigues* get. The pair I have on were brand new three weeks ago and three weeks later they look about three months old. But I have been wearing them all the time.

Today is the second of January.

It has rained for two days straight now so I couldn't write. I received your letter Dad. It gave me a *lift*. At the time I received it I was soaked. It had been raining for days. I felt down.

Ma, I wish you would take better care of yourself, the *flu* is dangerous. Take care, *okay.*

Did we have our own Christmas Party. I would have liked to have been there.

Ma, the *knife* you gave me. I have had many compliments on how *sharp* and good sized it is. I am going to start carving a lot of bamboo for a hobby.

Today we went out and found a lot of VC supplies. We found the supplies in the same vicinity where we killed the doctor. In the supplies we found *six hammocks* (the type you fix between two poles and sleep on) and we also found many ponchos and clothes. We think it might have been the material of a supply sergeant. Besides that we also found—now get this—rice bags. Unused from *New York!* They were produced by *NATO*.

Do you think you could send me some *good* food in the little ten-cent cans? Maybe some soup, beans or something good like that. These C-rations get a person's system down. If you would send some food like that I could bring it in the field with me.

How is Aunt Lillian. Is she feeling the same. Be sure to tell her I am thinking of her.

Well, today I have been in the field for two weeks and three days. We came out the sixteenth of December. I imagine we will be out here for about another week.

Fred Leo

HAPPY NEW YEAR !!!

Say Hi to everyone for me. All Right?

5 January 1968

A man-made irrigation canal looms into view. It appears wide and deep enough to float a shallow keel boat. The broad waterway tunnels majestically through vine covered shade trees that let only a flickering of light sprinkle on the water's marbleized surface.

Ascending fifty-foot mounds of excavated dirt, they find a

depression that serves as a bulwark plus offers a commanding view of the area.

"Man, would you get a load of this place," Okie said, dropping his rucksack. They could see for miles in all directions over the top of the trees. "I knew it. Should've brought my fishing pole and a can of worms. Man." With the heel of his hand, he bumps his forehead.

"What we really need is a canoe," Brown says, lowering the rucksack and resting the steel helmet over the radio. Standing in full sunlight, he massages his scalp while the balmy breezes brush his face.

"Well, first thing I'm gonna do is get these moldy clothes off," Bedford decides reaching for a canteen.

Upstream, Brown can hear soldiers from another company splashing and carrying on as though this were the "old swimming hole" back home.

"Say, Yamane. How about if we take a dip, too?" Brown suggests when he walks over.

"Sure why not. We'll be holdin' up here for a while," Yamane says. "But one at a time. And keep someone on watch." He raises his head to let the sun shine full on his face. "Wash up and have some fun."

"Okie, I'm goin' first, okay?" Brown says without waiting for a reply and scurries off with pistol belt, rifle and towel.

By the time he realizes the incline is steeper than he thinks, he's running at full speed and ready to catapult head over heels. Coming to the flats, he pulls back and skids to a halt, teetering on the edge of the canal.

Looking up stream, he sees other soldiers in the midst of their antics. Without combat gear they appear like a bunch of little kids. They scamper around shirtless. Their snow white skin shows in stark contrast with their tan necks and arms. Like boys at the play ground, they scream, push, shove and chase each other around.

From a rope attached to a tree limb that overhangs the canal, guys swing like jungle monkeys way out over the water. Some playing bombs-away, let go of the rope trying to hit or splash the others engaged in savage splashing and chicken-fighting below. One crazy, screaming boy sheds all his clothes and swings out buck naked to everyone's hoots and hollers.

Soon after his arrival in Vietnam, Brown began to get chafing between his legs. That's when he noticed the veterans never wore undershorts. Now, he didn't either and the chaffing disappeared. So, with time ticking away, Brown strips down to only combat pants then slides off the muddy embankment into the water.

He splashes the cool water over his chest as he continues to walk deeper. What amphibians or strange type of reptiles might be lurking beneath the mysterious surface? To be on the safe side, he snatches a floating limb and swishes it under the water ahead of him. Then, with his body adapting to the brisk water, he settles in up to his neck in the silky captivating liquid.

Sunlight sprinkles through softly swaying vines and coconut palms, glittering like diamonds on the surface. Diving deep into the river's bosom, he swims wrapped within her magic. Stroking, he swims twisting around and around. Taking soap out of his cargo pocket he begins to soap up.

The exotic setting reminds Brown of a river deep in the heart of some exotic African jungle. He half-expects to hear the shrill whistle of the *African Queen* as she rounds the curve to ward off the hippos and crocodiles. Then he imagines the canopy, jaunty mast, black funnel and a steam engine that hisses, gasps and spits like an old percolating coffee pot. He could see the boiler's puffing white and black smoke as the hard drinking rogue Humphry Bogart feeds it coal and dry wood.

On the scruffy wooden deck stands Bogart, a dirty red scarf tied around his neck and a stogy dangling from his tobacco stained mouth. Leaning next to the ancient cast iron boiler, that he enjoys kicking, with oily rag in hand, he says, "Ain't nobody in Africa, except yours truly, who can get up a good head of steam on the old African Queen."

After a swig of gin and a puff on his cigar Bogart adds, "Now, the way I look at it . . . . "

While he jabbers, a composed Katharine Hepburn, who plays a stern and puritanical missionary, sits prim and proper near the rudder while fanning herself with a map.

"What I mean to say is," a shy Bogart stammers in his one sided conversation as he tries to find words that would make him sound *somewhat* educated—maybe even a little sophisticated.

The steam engine also makes tea. "Of course," Bogart said, "it tastes a little rusty, but then again, we can't have everything . . . can we, ma'am." He punctuates the words with a little bow of the head.

Rolling onto his back, Brown lets the current and memories of that classic American movie buoy him.

He remembers how they journeyed down the mythical Nyanga River running into hippos, fly swarms, waterfalls, rocks and storms. His mind fast forwards to the scene where Bogart tugs on a rope hauling the African Queen through a shallow fetid, growth choked delta. With Hepburn's help, an exhausted Bogart claws his way back into the boat to collapse on the floor. Her eyes widen. He groggily looks. His body is covered with large black, blood-suckers.

Bogart screams, *"Leaches!"* Like a crazed man, he grabs and pulls on the leaches. "The little beggars, if the head stays in, they'll poison the blood . . . . If there's anything in the world I hate it's leaches." They both frantically pull the slimy creatures off his body. "The filthy little devils!"

Something touches Brown's leg. "Ahhh!" He cringes. A leach? He thrashes his way back to shore, clambers up the bank. Jumping into his boots, he grabs the pistol belt, rifle and clothes and dashes away checking for leaches.

"It's an experience, Okie!" Brown pants.

"Where's my cut off jeans?" he jokes pretending to search. "Come on Rover, let's go swimmin'." Without further adieu, Okie screeches out an American Civil War rebel's yell, "WOOH-WHO--EY! WHOO-EY! WHOO-EY!" A call that is part hunter's shout, part hog call as he bounds down the hill. Brown stares amused by the comical way Okie runs with shirt flopping, towel in one hand and an M-16 in the other.

The commotion doesn't disturb Bedford who lay flat on his back with chest bare, a towel over his face fast asleep. Pulling his shirt back on, Brown stands bare foot to absorb the quiet beauty of the area.

A few minutes later, a shot from a carbine rifle rings out.

"Incoming!"

More carbine fire, then the afternoon stillness gets shattered by a barrage of M-60 machine gun, M-16 and M-79 fire.

A dripping wet Okie scrambles back up the hill. "You're right, Brownie," he gasps. "You gotta experience it!" Brown and he break into laughter as he dives into the safety of the bulwark.

Still breathing hard, he conveys the story. "I'm in the water, right. Splashing around like a California surfer boy . . . .

"Surfer boy?"

"Yeah like the song, *Surfin' Safari.*" He does a little dance with his hand panning the waves. "Anyway, Victor Charlie opens up." His eyes are shiny as he struggles to get his clothes back on.

"And man, did those swimmers scatter!" Okie continues. "If it weren't so damn serious, it'd be funnier 'n hell. You should've seen the guy *buck* naked, who'd just swung out and let go of the rope. He looked like a worm wriggling in the air. I bet those VC are laughin' their asses off!" Okie giggles. "I know at least one guy got lead poisoning."

Keeping a low profile, Sergeant Yamane comes within shouting distance. "You guys, get over to the LZ! Chopper in-bound. Hurry it up!"

"Go on, I'll watch the gear," Bedford volunteers, sitting on his poncho liner, airing his ghost-white, crater-marked feet.

"How bad are the dogs?"

"Just look at 'em." He raises one swollen foot to show ghastly chunks of flesh with blisters and bleed-lines throughout. "It's this continuous wet that gets 'em. Jungle rot. Emersion foot. I don't know," Bedford says. "We all got it some. I got it the worst."

Unloading supplies, Okie and Brown return with a case of C-rations and mail, to find Bedford still sunbathing. Now his pants are rolled exposing jungle sores, small cuts and a mass of festering insect bites which are inflamed red—obviously not healing properly.

"Life of Riley," Okie says pretending envy. "You act like you're in sunny Palm Springs. But if the CO catches ya, you'll be in bi*iii*g trouble, buddy."

Bedford paws at Okie like a cat wanting forgiveness, then stretches contentedly. The pendent around his neck moves across his strong chest muscles.

"Say sugar, could you put some cream on my back. Will ya hun? It's getting dry," Bedford purrs like a feline.

"Sure, hoochy coochy, honey buns," Okie replies in an extravagant *May West* voice. Silently, he unscrews his canteen.

Out the corner of a eye, Bedford detects movement and flings his hand out.

"Hey watch it," Okie screams splattering water over Bedford. "I was just having a drink." He brings up the canteen innocently toward his mouth then tosses water all over Bedford.

Bedford jumps to run after him but hobbles after a few steps. He gives an ear piercing howl of pain. "I'll get yo*uuu* later," Bedford swears gingerly walking back to his poncho liner where he nurses his feet.

"Oh, poor boy," Okie says walking back.

"Poor boy to you too."

Meanwhile, Brown inserts the three-prong rifle flash suppressor onto the wire holding the C-rations case together and snaps it. He flips the case upside down, tears open the back to show hidden meal labels

"Ladies and gentlemen!" Brown stands pretending to be a carnival hustler. "Step right up, take your chances! What will it be? Will it be Scrambled Eggs and Ham? Beef Slices with Potatoes and Gravy which tastes best cold? Ham-Fried or Beefsteak? Chicken and Noodles? Meatballs with Beans in Tomato Sauce? Or my favorite and yours, Ham and Lima Beans?" He looks around. "Did I forget Spaghetti and Meatballs. Beans and Weiners?"

While Bedford holds Okie at bay, he and Brown grab their four meals and read the contents.

"I love Beans and Dicks," Brown says ecstatic.

"Sheee-t!" Okie protests after taking the last four meals. "I got dog food, man. Ham and Mothers. And what's this? Awww, no way man. Choke and Puck." Dropping to his knees, he clasps his hands together and pleads, "You guys gotta trade. You just gotta. I'll be shittin' like a volcano and barking like a dog by morning." Okie pounds his fists on the ground like a spoiled baby.

Ignoring the pleas, Brown sorts through the mail and finds four letters addressed to him.

"Brownie, I've never seen *anyone* get so much mail. Damn. Could I read some of it?" Okie asks getting off the ground.

"One's from my sister."

"Your sister? Have you been telling her about your fun loving, happy go lucky buddy?" Okie looks around at the two soldiers. "Yeah, I could write her. Really."

Dismissing the offer, Brown reaches inside his helmet liner webbing and pulls out a plastic battery—the only place where things could be keep dry. It has a book of matches, a pen, letters, writing paper and envelopes. Saving the letter for later, he slides them inside and put it back into his helmet.

"How's about some hot chocolate?" Brown asks as he opens a bread can with his P-38.

"Yeah-h, Brownie! You *kno-ow* what I like!" Okie croons.

"Need a church key to make a burner?" He offers a can opener which has "Budweiser" imprinted on the handle.

"You know, when I first saw this little can opener I didn't think it would open even one can." He knocks out the bread from the can. "And look, weeks later it still works like brand new."

With the can opener, he punches holes around the bottom and top rims. He drops a purple colored heat tablet into the *bread-can-stove* and strikes a match. A blue flame dances to life. Next, he fills an empty meal can with water. Using the attached lid as a handle, he sets it on the bread-can-stove to heat. Minutes later the water begins to steam. He stirs in the chocolate powder.

"Hummmm, *so* fine." Brown smiles taking a whiff. Okie holds out an empty can, happy to accept half the mixture.

"Just like a bunch of freeloadin' bums. Drinking from a tin can and liking it!" Okie says.

"Cheers." They click cans.

Sitting cross legged, Okie pulls his towel tighter around his shoulders and pretends to shiver. He cups the can in both hands like he is gathering warmth and takes a large gulp.

"Mmmmm," he coos. "Ooooooh, my, my, my. And what do we have here?" He peers goo-goo-eyed into the can, then reaches with his fingers to fish something out. "A roach practicing the backstroke!" After displaying the imaginary bug, Okie rolls his head back to let the insect free fall into his gaping mouth. He chews with comical exaggeration, then swallows hard. "Ya know, a person's got to have his vita-mins."

Dear Ma and Dad *6 January 1968*

It has been three weeks now that I have been out. Yesterday I took a bath in a *River!* It felt *great*. As soon as I left the water and was under cover some VC Snipers shot it up. No one hurt bad. Just one man wounded in the arm.

Today I was choppered out and am now eight miles from *Da Nang* in the Que Son Valley area. I am one of the seven men picked to be an OP (Observation Post) to guard LZ Center, an artillery position. The artillery positions around here have all been *hit* lately. This place where I am is the only place not hit.

Well, today is the 7th of January.

Yesterday I had a *scare.* They said that we would be in the *thick* of things with the NVA (North Vietnamese Army) Regulars in thirty minutes. Luckily they changed plans. I got a little bright from that scare. I am trying to develop a daily routine of cleaning my weapon and taking care of my gear so if we are put into action I will be ready.

I got a bad case of pimples on one side of my mouth. It was about a week between each face washing. That is probably the reason. Now I take a little water and wash my face each day.

See, *I am learning.* WOW!

I have found that it gets on your nerves listening to rifle fire all day and night. The land is beautiful but you are not looking at the land, you are looking for a *trail,* a place to *hide*, a place to *eat*, and a place for the *night.*

Ma, that knife you gave me! What a *life saver*. I cut down bamboo and did some carving. It keeps my mind occupied and it's *fun*. I am carving a *pipe* we use to smoke *pot* from. I also am carving a holder for it. When I finish it I will send it home. You will be the only family with an official VIET NAM POT PIPE!!!

Well, I will write later

8 January 1968

At dawn's early light, the dark molten sky finishes drenching the mountaintop, its accompanying cold front has pushed the temperature down into the fifty degree range.

A long face Brown stares through the haze while on guard. With poncho wrapped tightly around, he sits on a cardboard ration case with legs pulled tight for warmth while using a granite boulder as a back rest, rifle on lap. An occasional shiver and vaporizing breath being the only signs of life.

It is three days since Brown and six others were loaded

into a Chinook helicopter. Entering though the rear drop hatch, Brown had remarked that it must be how Pinocchio and Giappetti felt when swallowed by that ocean whale. The hatch had clanged shut as the Chinook helicopter swallowed seven grunts from reconnaissance.

They sat on canvas benches along the olive drab fuselage facing each other, while the two gunners stood, manning the M-60 machine guns pointed through dinky port holes behind the pilot's cabin.

Swaying with the motion of the helicopter, Brown relaxed. He needs, they all need the rest. And the vibration of the ride was very, very relaxing.

Check here. Check there. Hurry up here. Hurry up there. The platoon had been on one search-and-destroy after another. "Saddle-up! We're movin' out!"

They were forced marched to near collapse, with cryptic reports bombarding them constantly. Reports like, "The chopper can't evacuate the wounded!" "Chopper's down." Situations that could frighten the most seasoned veteran, "They're surrounded and almost out of ammunition!" And the most mind bending of all, the bogus intelligence reports, "100% alert. S-2 expects contact with a battalion of hard core NVA." S-2 Intelligence were the brainless ones. If you believed everything they told you, you'd opt for a gun to the head.

Every step under the crushing weight of the nearly one-hundred pound radio and rucksack made Brown's elastic-bandaged knees sing with pain. It was mental annihilation as well as bone-numbing to have to keep sloshing through cold water then lay on hard ground for a few hours of shivering rest. His feet were showing signs of jungle rot and at times, just like Bedford's, became throbbing clumps of flesh.

Maybe a bullet would be the best bet, Brown found himself thinking more than once. At least that would put an end to this incessant Chinese style water torture.

If fighting conditions remain this excruciating, he believes his health will deteriorate beyond repair. Already the days felt like they have aged him by years. Demoralized, he knows he won't stand a chance against healthy people. The ones who never crossed a snake infested rivers, plodded through a rice fields with mud up to their knees or humped through a triple canopy jungles of South Vietnam.

The Chinook had dropped them in the Que Son Valley region, a mile north of Fire Support Base LZ Center to take up the OP. They set up three positions in a saddle of high ground heaped with jagged rocks. And the area, as far as they could see, was a desolate, barren rock field.

At their position, Okie and Brown had spent hours piling boulders to form a breastwork.

"I'm realizing more and more what it means to be *combat ready,*" Brown says hoisting another rock out of the fighting-pit.

"I know what you mean. It's like, you'll die for things you didn't think of or from not doing the things you know," Okie agrees rolling a boulder.

"But you know what, there ain't no good way to learn this. . . this war stuff."

"Mean like learning how to stack rocks?" Okie jerks his hand free when a finger get smashed between two rocks. He shakes it then shoves it in his mouth and sucks.

"Okay?"

Shaking his hand, he continues where he had left off. "And we're always trying to dig ourselves out of the worst kind of shit." He looks at his bruised finger in pain. "That hurt."

"Gimme a hand with this rock, will ya?"

As the morning continues to develop, Brown shifts his weary eyes to the east where, through a hole in the dark clouds, he can see long fingers of yellow-blue light beginning to muscle their way up. It appears like the sun, with flashlight in hand, is clawing its way out of a cave.

Three days earlier Okie had asked, "Yamane, what's the deal?"

"It's simple. The CO volunteered us to be OP for LZ Center." He nods toward the beyond view fire support base. "So at the moment, we're set-up in the middle of the easiest access to LZ Center."

"Oh, okay. I get it," Okie said. "So when the NVA come, we jump up and scream at the top of our lungs..."

"They're on the way," Brown finishes the sentence.

"Then we *didi mau.*" Yamane is very matter of fact

"Really?"

"Run? Where to?"

The sheer drop-off to their right could not be scaled, nor could it be used as an escape route, unless as a last ditch "jump for dear life." Toward LZ Center, lay a barren wasteland strewn with loose rocks—ankle spraining, leg breaking, head cracking kind of rocks. The narrow path they had arrived on furnishes the only feasible escape route. The grim reality is they are expendable pawns in the big "Game of War." Like NVA who were rumored to have been tied to trees so they couldn't run, they too, had no possibility of escape. It would become a fight to the finish.

Continuing on guard, the sky clears turning a light blue. And a white rolling South China Sea fog begins moving over the low lands, splashing against the base of the mountain and frothing up the sides like a slow motion tidal wave.

Yesterday four of them had trekked deep into the bowels of Que Son Valley along a zigzag path following a bubbling crystalline stream bed. A path that had quickly brought them into triple canopy jungle.

Reaching the valley floor, the soldiers were treated to rich aromatic smells of tropical plant life. The trail moved through one serene foliage tunnel after another where spiders weaved their tiny intricate webs over the matt of flowers and veins. At different places a yellow-green light would penetrate small gaps in the dense foliage ceiling to dance merrily among the dew drops on the botanical underbrush. At other places weaving vines would strangle the light, transforming the passage into a dank, underground cavern.

But the virtual Garden of Eden doesn't fool anyone. It is snake filled and the soldiers are being drawn farther and farther into its bosom. Far beyond a dare—a double dare. They press onward going deeper and deeper with their hearts pounding out a fateful warning, "Go back. Go back, you fools while you still got a chance. *Get the hell outta here!*"

Brown begins feeling himself pass through a seamless wall to another universe. On entering, an uncanny wind swirls and the opening seals itself off—along with his fate. He dare not turn to look for fear of seeing something or someone he could never be or go back to again.

They follow a jungle trail up the adjoining mountain till they come upon a dug-out staircase. Up and up they go to make a rendevous with a legendary LRRP Team. And like in a training session, all of a sudden this white toothed American soldier is standing there perfectly camouflaged and smiling.

The LRRP is team leader Major Harney. The major wears a boonie hat and arms himself with an Army Colt .45 pistol and a NVA AK-47 rifle. And come to find out, the major had been Sergeant Denning's instructor at the survival school in Panama. As the jovial reunion proceeds, Sarge makes reference to the AK-47.

"It's more reliable than a Jammin' Jenny." He motions to Sergeant Denning's M-16 rifle. Lifting the AK47. "As for this. Throw it in water. Drag it through mud. Spit on the rust and wipe it off. Then pull the trigger and it fires. And . . . since it's their rifle." He swivels his head likes he's trying to find something, "Where's it coming from?"

"You've always been resourceful."

"Anyway, I'm a Night Crawler on my second Asian tour," Major Harney says after reaching their hilltop plateau perimeter.

At camp there are three other team members, who also blend into the landscape like fawns. Brown stands in awe—here before him are LRRPs. "Damn." These highly motivated soldiers are considered by most to be the boldest and bravest of them all.

Brown turns to look at the terrain over which they have traveled and gawks in astonishment. From his perch, the earth drops away giving him a magnificent panoramic view of a mythical Xanadu. As far as the eyes could see lay a pristine fertile valley cloaked in the golden colors of a rainbow. The distant mountain slopes are sliced with tier upon tier of harvest-green rice fields. The snaking terraces, with fresh water running between them, follow the valley walls and out of sight.

A deep breath brings the sweet aroma of a bouquet of flowers. And, while the panoramas takes in acres upon acres, everything appears mysteriously miniaturized. It's as if he can reach out and touch it, like a three dimensional oil painting. His eyes continue to suck-in the sea of colors, that to him, redefines the meaning of beautiful.

"Better take a seat before a sniper puts a cross-hair on ya," Major Harney warns. Brown drops to the ground like a stone.

Being that a soldier is always hungry, they start to rummage for C-rations.

"Trade?" The major smiles at Sergeant Denning. "This here LRRP ration that you can buy at Abercrombie and Fitch, for that can of Spaghetti and Meatballs."

Sergeant Denning pretends reluctance to the swap. He now holds an OD foil bag with **BEEF STEW** printed boldly on the side. After carefully peeling back the top seam, he pours in water and stirs.

"Directions easy enough?" Major Harney laughs.

Gravy forms and he let's it soak for five minutes.

"Tastes great," Sergeant Denning claims while chewing. "Still a bit on the crunchy side, but it's comin' around." He sees Brown eyeing the pouch. "Wanna try?"

"Sure. Why not." This is the first Brown has seen a dehydrated meal. Initially it had the consistency of dry dog food. Producing a dirty spoon, Brown digs in.

"Pretty good. Tastes like real beef stew," Brown says munching. "Wish *we* could get some of this stuff. How about it Sarge?"

"We deal with deep penetration," Major Harney tosses a pouch over so Brown can test the weight. "Can't have a resupply chopper giving away our location. Which means, we carry upwards of two weeks of supplies. This dehydrated food weighs a lot less and takes up less room than those C-rations of yours. But if you don't drink enough water your guts will turn to stone." The spaghetti dinner is hot, so he starts eating.

"It's different with you *Charge that hill* infantryman," Major Harney jabs Sergeant Denning and they laugh. "You can afford to get a re-supply chopper, say every fourth day."

"What's it like, sir . . . sneaking around out here like this?" Denning asks, scanning the mountain and the surrounding triple canopy jungle.

"You mean what's it like trying staying alive in the Valley of Living Death? As the Vietnamese so aptly call it." Major Harney watches the effect the local name has on the soldiers. "Actually, not so bad," the major continues. "Almost like a continuous picnic." He lets loose with a huff of amusement. "But the truth of the matter is this valley is plain mean."

"Sounds like a woman I once knew," Denning says comically.

"We must've met the same girl," the major rejoins and they laugh. "When I say 'mean'. What I'm sayin' is there are the ants, mosquitoes, leaches, snakes, drowning, friendly fire, sickness and diseases, jungle rot or even a twig pulling the pin on your hand grenade. Within seconds . . . this valley could suffocate, skin, turn you inside out and leave ya dangling.

"Did I mention the NVA?" The major raises a calloused, lacerated index finger, and states, "One slip. One mistake. Only one chance out here and it better be a good one." He gives them pause to contemplate.

"We've cut PZs with chain saws that saved our ass by seconds. And other times, Jacob's Ladder was the only escape.

"You have to volunteer to be a Night Crawler and believe me it takes nerves of steel and a keen sense of survival to stay alive for long out here," the major says somberly. With a steady gaze he looks at Sergeant Denning then Private Brown.

"For months the NVA have been moving through here day and night. Like A Shau and Khe Sanh—Que Son Valley is a major infiltration route from the Ho Chi Minh Trail as well as a major food producing area."

Even the greenest soldier knows about the notorious Ho Chi Minh Trail originating out of Hanoi, North Vietnam. A resupply route that stays just shy of the South Vietnam border and makes its way through Laos and Cambodia. A trail that consists of two-thousand miles of snaking paths and, by some reports, in some places a six lane paved highway. The B-52 Bomber and Phantom-4 Jets are constantly pounding it, trying to tear it up and knock out bridges, but supplies continue to flow. If not by truck then by elephants. If not by elephant then by carts drawn by water buffalo or men. If not by cart, then by bicycles with baskets. If not by bicycles, the baskets are carried by men. It appears that absolutely nothing can stop the flow of supplies down the Ho Chi Minh Trail.

"Sarge," the major talks slowly, measuring every word. "There are more supplies running through *here* than we've ever seen. That can only mean one thing. Something's brewing and it's gonna be big." His jaw muscles bunch as he looks guardedly at the jungle. "I can taste it."

"Major," Sergeant Denning breaks in, anxious for answers to pressing questions. "What's been going on," he motions with a hand to mean the Que Son Valley, "out here?"

"It started back about a month ago," Major Harney begins. "B Troop, 1/9 Cavalry, the Blues as we call 'em, spotted an enemy unit and wiped 'em out. Searching through the bodies, they found some maps detailing all the American positions in this region and their access routes. Along with some NVA future positions."

"Strategic maps," Denning says. "Could have come from an

intelligence officer."

"Most likely." Major Harney nods in agreement. "Best we can figure, he was on a personal pre-attack reconnaissance."

"So, that confirms those feelings you've been havin'."

The major takes a noisy breath. "Just after midnight about a week ago, the NVA hit LZs Ross, Leslie and West. And by morning our companies in the field were under attack.

"We've had contact ever since—day and night. Then three days ago, Charlie Company 2/1 was hit and by evening the NVA were in the perimeter."

"Jesus," Sergeant Denning exclaims.

"And it wasn't until dawn that the gunships could fly-in and help out," the major continues. "Now they're rocketing Da Nang along with Charger Hill–the 196th command post." Major Harney stops talking long enough to take a drink from his canteen.

"That's when *we* got the call that Bravo Company 4/31 needed assistance."

"Assistance," Sergeant Denning repeats. "Okay. Now it's all starting to make sense. That's why we were on call for a possible combat assault. But they broke contact, right?"

"Yeah, I guess. If you wanna call it that. Eight out of an entire company walked out," Major Harney says. Crossing his legs, he sits straight and tall. Then with both arms gesturing, he says, "Let me explain something. The field combat rule is 'no more than twenty percent replacements in a company at any one time'. But Bravo Company was made up of a disproportionate amount of NFGs, and a few officers that in my opinion were too gung-ho and on top of that—dumber than dirt.

"Believe me, I know my boundaries and don't put my face where it don't belong," he stares directly at Sergeant Denning. "But for the life of me, why put a bunch of cherries up against a God forsaken valley like this? Believe me, they don't call this the 'Valley of Living Death' for nothin'."

The major's audience nods in unanimous agreement.

"Anyway, to get there quick, we cut through the jungle on some secret trails, ones not on the map, like the one you just came in on. Well, the NVA were thick as gnats. Bump into 'em at every turn. Then we detected this platoon of NVA heading in Bravo company's direction. We quickly radioed the CO to take diversionary action." From his tone of voice it is clear the advice had not be heeded.

"Well, just then the NVA spot us and Jail Bird takes a hit. We had to *didi mau* and when we doubled back, we found him hanging from a tree." The ghastly scene is painted by his expression. "They were waiting in ambush, so we couldn't do anything. He's listed as MIA. But he's dead all right. These NVA don't take prisoners.

"Next thing you know, Bravo Company is in pursuit of NVA crossing this wide open field," Major Harney says with an expansive gesture. "I radioed and warned 'em again. These NVA are solid professionals, and they could be layin' a trap." The major glances at Denning and states, "I know for a fact these NVA have bigger balls than the local VC.

"So picture this, an entire American company goes running blindly across a rice field with no cover." The major is exasperated. "Sarge," he says in a fatherly tone, "you gotta run herd on these young officers. If you don't it spells trouble."

"I know sir," Sergeant Denning assures him. "I've had my times."

"A lot of officers consider this war a way to advance their career. They're a real gung-ho medal grabbing bunch."

"I'll keep that in mind, sir. Thanks, sir."

"Well, the choppers had to come in low to get under the bad weather we've been having. Which made them fat chunks of meat for the NVA machine gunners."

"I bet."

"The NVA corners Bravo on three sides. Then all hell breaks loose. Mortars, machine gun fire, AK-47 and RPGs. By the time we get within range, black smoke is pouring from the battlefield.

"We decide," he breaths through his nostrils, "we weren't gonna join that blood bath," he confesses tight lipped.

"Tough decision, major."

"Yes. It most definitely was." Then Major Harney explains, "But bearing in mind, my primary mission is to collect information, take prisoners, sniper or ambush when necessary. Based on those guidelines, we positioned ourselves along the tree line to sniper and spot for red-leg. Problem was, there were so many fire missions going on it got all botched up.

"So with front row seats we got to watch the hopped-up NVA converge onto the battlefield like crazed werewolves." The color drains from the major's face.

"I watched one kid try to shield himself with a corpse. God."

The major raises his arms into a rifle firing position. "I got a bead on the slop head and blew his brains out."

Brown flinches at the image of a head exploding.

"The NVA began collecting the field radios off the dead RTOs." Looking significantly at Brown, he adds, "NVA learn to kill RTOs first. That way they can break radio communication. It's a big plus if they manage to capture a radio because then they can easily monitor our communications."

With raised finger, he adds, "Never, *ever* call in the clear because you can bet your bottom dollar there's someone listening."

Brown nods his understanding.

"Kids," the major's voice quakes. "Just a bunch of cropped hair kids, trying to die . . . . trying to die like men." His tough facade evaporates, leaving his face ashen.

He spits, then reaches for a cigarette. The color returns to his cheeks as he lights up. With extinguished match in hand, he points at Sergeant Denning and Brown.

With the conversation over for a while, Brown, Okie and Bedford are invited to join two LRRPs on their patrol. They return two hours later after snipered at a VC.

Brown walks back over and sits next to Sergeant Denning. They are again in the middle of a conversation.

"Ever wonder why the brass call this 'Injun country' or why General Custer's unit, now part of the First Cavalry, was one of the initial Army units to land in Vietnam?" Major Harney asks.

"Well, I'll tell ya. The brass honestly believe they can win this war using the same tactics used during the Civil War and the American Indian wars. Simply put, determine how many enemy soldiers there are. Then start taking a body count. When they're all dead you win. That's called *attrition*."

He lets the magnitude of the strategy sank in.

"Do you think we can kill enough people to free this country?" Sergeant Denning wonders.

"People may forget, but we never did beat the Seminole Indians during two Seminole Indian Wars."

Everyone perks their ears when they hear the heavy "*crump*" of artillery booming from LZ Center. They listen closely trying to calculate the proximity of the impact as the explosions echoes through the valley. Moments later, an ominous howitzers fire mission pounds the valley making the ground tremble underfoot.

"Well, I think it's about time you saddled-up," Major Harney says. Then he motion toward the LRRP Team giving them a silent command.

"Yeah, we have a good two hour march ahead of us," Sergeant Denning agrees..

Major Harney gazes for a moment at each infantryman. "I hope you've learned something today," he said fatherly. "And I wish we had more time. But we don't. So I'll leave you with these words, 'Live every day like it's your last, but plan to live forever."

He turns and draw Brown into his hurricane blue eyes. "And the only one who can save you—is you."

As the squad marches from the plateau, Brown turns for a last glimpse. And there they stand in all their glory looking like those American Civil War soldiers. So lean. So unyielding. So, "United we stand. Together we fall."

The sun finally rises over the top of the white rolling South China Sea fog and the eternal beauty of a new day reaches into Brown's drained body to warm and transfuse his spirit.

He raises his arms, bones crackling and popping. A deep refreshing breath of jungle air makes his nose, throat and lungs tingle.

It had been a long night. Longer than most. Why? The moon had been high and bright. And at around one A.M. the LRRP Team had called saying the NVA were on the move. Everyone in the region went on a 100% alert. A firefight in the proximity of the LRRPs ensued.

"Wolf said a crack team of NVA were on to 'em," Okie had said while they stared across the rocky terrain. "He didn't know how much longer they could keep outsmarting 'em."

They had heard a few single shots fire from an AK-47 rifle and the Valley of Living Death went silent. An eeriness had engulfed the area.

When Brown was nine years old, he remembers his fascination with an old Anheuser Busch sponsored lithograph entitled "Custer's Last Fight." He would stand there and stare into the face of every Indian and cavalrymen curious to know what went through their minds at the last moment of life.

Then he thinks about his great Aunt Lillian who lives with them who had been born in 1876, the same year as Custer's Last Stand.

"Lookie here." A groggy Okie had held out a brown bottle with a sitting Buddha on the label. "It's some kind of *speed* they bought in Hong Kong."

According to rumor, the enemy bought their drugs from China. And that one Chinese herbal medicine could miraculously stop the bleeding. Chinese medicine was considered by most to be superior to the American medicine. In fact, the U.S. military was said to be procuring its own supplies of Chinese medicine from neutral Hong Kong.

A shiver goes through Brown as he continues to contemplate the past days. If truly great warriors, like the Night Crawlers perish, what possibility of survival does he have? He could have perished just as easily as any of the hundreds had during the past weeks. But that was the plan—wasn't it. He is expected to die.

Taking a deep breath he tries to calm the jitters that sap his strength. He has to learn how to rest, relax and accept that which is destiny. "God, give me strength. And if need be, give me strength to die with dignity."

Dear Ma and Dad *8 January 1968*

I had a little experience yesterday. Me and four others went over and spent a day with *LRRPs* (Long Range Reconnaissance Patrol). These guys have been here for a long time. A couple are on their second tour. They know their *stuff!*

So, anyway, we walked over to their *CP* (command post). From there two of their best men took us on a *sniper patrol!* We sneaked down the mountain and hid behind some bushes. In an hour we spotted a VC. By the way, they had a *special* M-14 sniper rifle with scope. So, with the sniper rifle he shot towards the VC, but I think he only wounded or missed him completely.

Then we lobbed some M-79 Grenade Launcher rounds over there. After that we ran across a valley and up towards the position where we saw the man. Well, we couldn't find him so we went back. We must have walked five miles. Up and down hills.

Ugh!

The Vietnamese call this place *The Valley of Living Death.* It's pretty scary around here.

Today, I haven't done much. I will write tomorrow.

Fred Leo

10 January 1968

With feet swelling, Brown slips off his boots. He powders and massages his feet and toes, then lets them air dry. The elastic bandages that support his swollen knees have slipped during the night. Unraveling them, he let the sore joints breath.

Relaxing, he casually checks his ammunition and grenade pins. Finding them in good condition, he dismantles and cleans the rifle. Finishing, he re-wraps the knees and pulls on clean dry socks. Taking the boots, he turns them around and checks them. The leather is beginning to crack and the heels are running off one side. With cardboard from the ration boxes, he spends the next half-hour diligently fashioning arches inside the boots hoping his feet wouldn't hurt so badly.

Usually there is a good reason for someone from the OP to walk back to LZ Center. On this particular day everyone is too lazy to find a reason. Undaunted and needing to clear his head, Brown ventures out alone.

A medium gray overcast settles over the mountaintop cutting visibility to fifty yards at best. Brown moves quietly into the fog and is quickly surrounded by a serene, weightless fine drizzle isolating and rewarding him with the blessing of *quiet*.

Absently, he starts kicking rocks to watch them ricochet through the water logged atmosphere. A chilly breeze swirls and he pulls his towel snugly around his neck and tucks it under his shirt collar. The mountain air is invigorating, and the fine droplets feel refreshing against his face.

The heavy atmosphere brings back good memories of times in Florida. He remembers how his parents would take him out of school so they could go fishing. A few times they went to the Everglades

National Park where he'd enjoy watching the grey pelicans swoop and dive for food.

In the wee hours of the morning, he would walk to the docks where the birds perched motionless on posts painted white with their droppings. When it rained, the pelicans would bob in the water, stoically unconcerned about the pelting water bullets. And they never blinked.

They would go fishing all day long around the mangrove trees and return in the evening to clean their catch for the day on special cutting tables set near the water's edge. His parents would allow him to lure the pelicans closer with the fish heads. Once the birds understood there was food, Brown would toss the remnants high into the air to see if they could catch them in mid flight. Whenever it rained, no matter where he was, he'd think of Florida and those grey pelicans.

Brown clears his head, smiles, and then kicks another rock.

The path leading to LZ Center is littered with old, rusty C-ration cans. Veering toward one, Brown takes a short running start and punts it. "Did you check it for a booby-trap?" he asks himself.

"No."

Grabbing a can, he flings it high into the air, then swings the rifle and begins dry firing while it falls back to earth. Just like he had done with his trusty BB-gun rifle.

As a boy he had cherished that *Daisy* BB-gun. With it he fired at tree limbs, cans and glass. Everything was a 'bad guy'. Then one day, killing birds became a big deal among his ten year old friends.

So, on one balmy day, Brown snuck into a prairie in search of prey. Spotting fair game, he sank to one knee imitating his hero, Davy Crocket "The King of the Wild Frontier" who fought and died in 1836 at the Alamo. An unsuspecting Cardinal flies within range, perching on a sapling's branch just within range. He steadied 'Old Betsy'. Holding his breath, he squeezed the trigger.

"Damn! I missed!" he cursed under his breath. Swiftly, he cocked the rifle taking deadly aim once more and fires. Yet, even after two of his precise shots, the Cardinal still perches on the limb.

"What?"

Indian-style, he slithered through the brush until he was in un-miss-able range. Bringing the Cardinal into the rifle's sight he could actually see its heart pounding through the red breast. Then with no mercy, he blasted away.

The harmless creature pivoted its head to stare at the executioner. It's eyes rolled closed and it plummeted to the ground. Brown dashed over to gloat over the fresh kill. But when he actually gazed at the lifeless form, he didn't feel the exhilaration that hunters often boast about. His stomach rose into his throat as he gingerly lifted the feathered creature from the cold ground. He ran feverishly for help, but tripped and fell head over heels.

"God, I just didn't know." He gazed at the bird which now lay in the grass. "I'm so sorry little bird."

A killer is not a soldier and a soldier is not a killer, he reminds himself.

Strange, he doesn't recall seeing or hearing a bird since arriving in Vietnam.

He finds himself standing across from where the Chinook had left them only days before. Remembering the terror on arrival, he immediately crouched. Scanning the area, he searches for signs of movement or hostility, and does not proceed until he feels safe.

As he walks, it dawns on him that this is the first time he has *truly* been alone in Vietnam. The thought is both frightening and, at the same time, exhilarating. He carelessly zigzags in short steps around rocks while rolling his head back to stare into the swirling mountain mist. He leaps and spins like a child at a play ground, till dizziness causes him to slip and nearly fall.

"What are you doin'?!" he scolds. "Does your mother know where you are?" He laughs.

Coming over the rise, he spots the fire support base with its quad-50 machine gun emplacement. The beaten path leads him directly past the gigantic awesome machine of destruction. The motorized weapon is mounted on a huge iron turret set inside a sandbag wall through which its four barrels and thick armor plating protrude. A ladder propped against the sandbags provides access to the massive weapon.

"Not expecting a human wave are ya?" he says to no one.

Near the crown he sees the barrel of a 155 howitzer and a battery of smaller 105s. Close by lay piles of expended brass casings in a net from all the fire missions. Inside a pit protected by thick sandbag walls are the crates of ammunition, and stacked to one side are the canister rounds. The shotgun-canisters are only used as a last resort if the base gets overrun. They lower the muzzles and fire the howitzer at point blank range. Everything within five hundred feet will be immediately vaporized. No burial detail necessary.

At the chopper pad, he deposits his letter in OUTGOING MAIL and makes note of the pile of C-rations. Intent on cannibalizing a case—only taking his favorite cans—he decides to wait. Lounging, he moves past the slick resupply chopper to sit on a sandbag wall and smoke a cigarette.

The pilots approach the Huey toting brown bag lunches like school children. Both officers wear the usual full-body camouflage aviation outfits with dozens of zipper and snap pockets. Brown never could figure out what they use all those pockets for. It's hard not to stare since he seldom saw a pilot outside of their chopper.

Seeing Brown, they nod before climbing into the cockpit to engage in their routine switch-throwing, gauge thumping and checking.

The engine whines seconds before the twin thirty foot blades begin turning. Gaining speed, they start a *patter-patter* type sound that turns into a "Ph-ph-ooop. Ph-ph-ooop. Ph-ph-ooop." A moment later, the tail rotor starts to whirl and the noises coalesce into an air throbbing whi*rrrrr*.

With the helicopter now reaching full throttle, the blade wash begins splashing Brown with muddy water. Seeing his chance, he bolts around the back of the chopper and grabs a case of rations.

As he dashes back around the chopper for the get-away, an unexpected movement catches his eye. He turns just as the Huey's tail section, now thirty feet in the air, drops abruptly, its nose rising in compensation. Then the Huey begins to twist out of control like a spring-held child's rocking horse. The chopper swirls around and begins to lose altitude as it tries to level off. Through the front windshield, Brown sees the pilots frantically clutching the control sticks and slamming switches in rapid succession.

The front of the helicopter shoots into a steep rise looking like it might go over backwards. But at the last possible second, the tail section smashes into the ground with such force that the entire section buckles. The tail lifts six feet off the ground, then it again slams back to earth even more violently while the ship continues to rotate in the air and inch toward Brown.

Like a mighty sledge hammer, the rear section again bashes the ground, the entire rear section giving way. The Huey leans so precariously that its blades hit the ground shattering off four-foot sections.

Twenty seconds is all it takes and Brown finds himself backed against a drop-off. The chopper's left skid collides with the ground collapsing, while the big blade again smashes into the ground, sending more shrapnel flying through the air catching Brown on the left shoulder. With what momentum the chopper has left, it continues a slow spin, as flames belch from the engine's exhaust.

Brown drops the ration meal and springs off the edge of the hill as someone yells, "She's gonna blow!"

Rolling wildly down the muddy incline with rifle tucked close, he collides with a ledge twelve feet below. Clinging to the ledge, his heart throbbing wildly, he grabs his muddy steel pot, places it back on and huddles in anticipation of the explosion.

"Ch-oooooo-sh! Ch-oooooo-sh!" comes the sound of fire extinguishers.

Feeling it safe to return, he claws back up the muddy cliff to the LZ. The wrecked Huey lay on the side of the fractured landing skid, its doors ajar. On the ground near a patch of mud lay a brown lunch bag. Without hesitation, Brown scurries over to snatch the bag. Inside he smells a delicious tuna fish sandwich. Then curious, he looks inside the helicopter's cabin and spots a Playboy Magazine.

"That was a close one." Startled, Brown feels a pilot's hand reach past to take the magazine. When Brown turns the pilot spots the lunch bag.

"Food always tastes better when it's someone else's," he says with a smile. "Keep it, soldier, this here's what's important." He opens the page to reveal the heart throb centerfold of Miss November 1968. "How about that!"

Brown stares speechless.

"The rotor quit," the pilot explains stuffing the magazine inside a cargo pocket. "There's no way you're gonna keep 'er steady without the rotor."

Listening, Brown stares at the reflection in the pilot's aviator sunglasses. The reflection of a mud-caked beggar holding another man's food.

"I'd say we're pretty lucky just to be standing here." The pilot lifts his hand to sweep off the glasses and wipe ripples of sweat from his brow. Behind the sunglasses are bulging, blood-pumped eyes encircled with thin purple crimson skin.

"We should be making *love* not war, like those long-haired hippies back home."

Dear Ma *9 January 1968*

Last night we were put on 100% alert because they spotted a large force of NVA approaching our OP. But nothing happened.

Today I walked the mile between our OP and LZ Center. At the landing pad, I saw a helicopter *crash!* It was about thirty feet from me. It lifted off okay but then the tail dropped and hit the ground. Then it started spinning in the air and the big whirly blade hit the ground and the copter almost tipped over when it crashed. It almost *blew up!* Flames were coming out the back of it. That piece of aluminum (sent inside envelope) is part of its whirl blade. The aluminum is honey combed. It is real, real light.

Later on I saw the wreckage of a helicopter on the ground. It was shot down not far from where we are now. It was demolished beyond repair.

Tell Uncle Raymond I really miss his *hash and eggs!* I sure would give a lot to have one of his breakfasts. Tell him I think of him every time I drink coffee.

It is bad news on this hill. It has rained bad almost all night and is raining now. That is why my pen is *skipping*.

Ma, do not send watch!

When I go to Japan, I am going to bring about $600. I will have you send me a money order from my pay. I then will buy everything real cheap.

1 - Long Wave-Short Wave FM-AM Radio
2 - Portable TV
3 - Watch
4 - Small but real good Tape Recorder
5 - Real, Real Good Camera.

I will then send them all home, so when I get home I will have some basics for a *new start* in Life.

I can hardly wait. I should be able to get a $1000 worth of

things for half the price in *Japan*. I will write later on. Okay.

Today is the 10th of January.

Nothing has happened. It looks like I will be on this hill for at least another four days. I have been out for twenty-five days now.
I received a pair of socks and the oil stone. I didn't get the package of socks because they will not deliver them into the field. I'm real glad to receive the envelopes and paper. I had only one sheet of paper and two envelopes left. Well, I will write soon. Bye for now.

Your son, Fred Leo

P.S. At Eulers Hardware they have the 'Sabre' brand pocket knife. Would you send me their three-blade one. Remember the one I had a year or so ago. I can carve little things with it.

P.S. I am all your failures. I am all your dreams. I am your only hope. I am your child.

Dear Ma *14 January 1968*

I stopped by base camp, *LZ Gator,* yesterday for a few hours. While I was there I picked up the package of socks and the Readers Digest. I also put on *clean* clothes. The first time in a month. By the way I got off the mountain in the *Da Nang area*. I heard the full story of how about a hundred men were killed and even more wounded. It gets pretty gory and merciless at times. The NVA are a rough bunch!
When the fighting was going on the 198th (me) was called in. Fortunately they had the fighting under control before we got there. *Close one!*

Well it is the 14th of January.

We haven't slept at LZ Gator since the night of the fifteenth of December. It will be at least two more weeks before I get in. Or rather it will be February before I get in.

Guess where I am right now! I took a chopper and they flew me over the China Sea and what a view. I saw *"Sam Pan"* boats. Also fishing boats and fishing going on. The chopper landed at a camp which we are protecting which lies right along the South China Sea. The *fresh* clean air is beautiful. It was a clear crisp night. I woke up to the sounds of a *motor boat.*

I am located really close to *Chu Lai*. When I walked around last night I looked over the water and saw the lights in the town. I saw big rocks like in San Francisco Bay area protruding from the water. And I heard the sound of waves gently washing up on sandy beaches.

There is *no* (as close to safety as I ever will be) danger here. In my bunker I have an M-60 machine gun, eight claymores, twenty hand grenades and all kinds of M-16 ammunition. A whole Brigade of NVA wouldn't be able to take this place.

This lined paper is nice writing on. Send it instead of the unlined. Okay.

I have the Kool-Aid in my hand right now. I have so many envelopes, I can't believe it.

By the way try and send envelopes and paper in a regular envelope. When I am in the field they won't send out those big *brown* flat envelopes. I received that one pair of socks in the field. So the envelope can be big as that one.

Tell everyone to hold on. I will have time to write to everyone. When in the field I was down to only one envelope. I had to save it. Now I am loaded.

I am thinking about taking a *shower.* How about that. What luxury.

My location on the mountain was thirty miles southwest of Da Nang and eight miles from a place called Tam Ky. We were supporting the 196th. The 196th was the people who were hit.

Sounds like Dad is going to have a lot of fun in Florida. I imagine he will be home by the time you receive this letter.

Well, I am around a lot of interesting things. So I will write again in a day or so.

Take care, Fred Leo

Dear Cousin Karen *14 January 1968*

I received your letter *today.* It takes about a week to get here.

Well now, what is my favorite cousin doing. It sounds like you really enjoyed this Christmas.

These *South Vietnamese*. Bad news. They don't know what is happening and what's more, they could care less. The Popular Forces, Puffs for short, as a whole—stink. They run when they are attacked.

I was at Bien Son Bridge right after it was overrun by a VC Company. One night we were to be hit by 300 VC. The VC were said to have wanted to destroy the whole town of Bien Son. That night all but a few Puffs took off including the Puff Lieutenant. Last attack only two Puffs stayed to hold the bridge. The others ran.

Everything seems so useless.

Karen, the guys in RVN (Republic of Vietnam) do have their own ideas. Most of us are disgusted. We clear a valley one week and the next week the VC are back. But last week your best friend was killed securing the valley. But all in all, the difference between RVN guys and others is just plain *WAR!*

Karen there are too many rules to the *war!*

A few days ago we saw a man farming. We couldn't shoot him, or we shouldn't shoot him. But later the same man was seen in the hills. We shot him but he got away. Why not kill him in the rice patties?

We must stay clean *shaven*. We can't roll up our sleeves. We have to wear a steel pot. We have to wear certain field supplies. Too many rules.

I have been in the field since the 16th of December and I will be out another two weeks at least. We have visitors so I can't take my shirt off in the little free time I *have!*

Gripe. *Gripe.* *Gripe.* Huh!

Well, I am glad I'm in the warm sun and not the cold.

I have heard about how bad the winter is in the States. Try not to catch a cold.

Karen is my brother Wes the same as he was? Did he change to the better. I never hear from him. We just never hit it off. If he has changed maybe I should drop him a line. What do you think?

Well I have had some hairy experiences but I am still alright. I have been managing to be at the scene of the action just as it ends.

Wow! Sweat that one.

A helicopter crashed twenty feet from me a few days ago. *Bla!*

Well, I will write. I just got my hands on some *envelopes*. Well take *care*. Tell your folks I said *HI*.

Your cousin, Fred Leo

My time: Viet Nam 6 P.M. 16 January 1968
Your time: Chicago 8 A.M. 16 January 1968

Dear Ma

Received your *Goody* package. Guess what I will have for *breakfast*. The package opened a little and the *apple* was *squished!* The Orange is good though.

We have a couple of Vietnamese kids around here. I gave one of them a few prunes and he really liked them. These people do not get much variety of fruit. The fruit is ripe only for a time and then if the fruit isn't near, they will not go get it. The people love the fruit that is in our C-rations and our *Goody Packages*.

Ma, I will send some cloth material home. Okay. I haven't been in a village that had bolts of it for over a month but when I do I will send some home. Then Lorraine can sew-up Danny something. Maybe you could hang the material on the wall. If you have any left give it to someone at the store.

Did I tell you I met a guy who knows our stores? He lives behind Southfield Shopping Center. He said he saw us all over the place around Chicago. Well, now we are known in RVN.

Is the weather typical winter? I imagine it is. Wrap up to stay warm.

From where we are now, I can see a hospital ship in the South China Sea. It is like the hospital ship *Hope*. It is about three miles out to sea.

Well, I will write tomorrow

Today is the 17th of January.

I had some vegetable beef soup. Wow! Fabulous. Really tasted good.

Right now the 198th battalion commander is inspecting where I am. We have been cleaning up the area for the last couple of days. Luckily he isn't coming to my bunker.

The boats over here are called *Sam Pans.* They have a 2-1/2 HP and some have a 5 HP outboard engine. The people leave their boats anchored in the bay and they have these round baskets boats that they row to shore. It looks funny seeing these round boats. Some of these little baskets have sails. They are big enough for two but one man is best.

Dad, I saw some beautiful wild parrots. It seemed funny seeing them free out here. There are reindeer here but you don't see many. I have been in places that used to be farms but are now abandoned. I have been in some wilderness but I haven't seen any animals. Heard some monkeys though.

By the way the last paragraph was in answer to your letter, Dad. I received it today. How did you like that house boat? Thinking of getting one?

Well, not much is happening here. I am resting and recuperating. Could you buy me that 3-blade knife, made by *Sabre*. Remember I used to have one.

Ma, I forgot to tell you. Since I spend a lot of time in the field and packages will not be sent to me out there, you have to send food that is canned or *non-perishable*. Because by the time I get it, it might be a month old. Okay.

By the way, I receive mail *every* day by chopper if I am in the field. That is one thing they do in the Army over here.

They know we need our mail. Well, so long for now.

Fred Leo

P.S. This is a parachute used with flares. The flare shoots out and it floats to earth as it burns.

Dear Ma *18 January 1968*

This is part of the whole *Stars and Stripes*. I sent in three separate envelopes mailed at the same time. Put it together and read it. It's interesting.

Fred Leo

P.S. Received the tape. It really helps.

Dear Ma and Dad *22 January 1968*

Well, since I last wrote not too much has happened. We were *probed* once by sniper fire, but that was all.

I finally made it back to Nuoc Mau. I always go to this one *shanty*. The people have a young girl, Lan. Remember she gave me the Montagnard bracelet. They also have *cold* beer and a good many things to buy.

So, daringly I bought Roxanna a *skirt*. I wrapped it and turned it into the orderly with some money. I don't know how it will get there yet. I also found a baby shirt or jacket and mailed it to *Danny* (baby) with his name on the package. I am looking for something good to send *you* and *Dad*. I told you I was going to send you some cloth, Ma, but maybe that's not a good idea. Don't worry. All of a sudden I will see something really great to send.

I am still carving something to send home, but it will take more time. Maybe by June. I received a letter from you, Ma, and also the package from Lorraine on the 21st about 8 P.M. my time.

Well, today is the 22cd of January, my birthday. Funny I only feel a day older than 18.

It doesn't rain so much anymore but it will be a month or so before the monsoon season will officially be over. Sounds like the Chicago winter was worth missing. *Burr!* It's cold huh? Right now at this very moment I am on my bunker with my shirt off trying to get a suntan. But it is really too windy and those clouds keep getting in the *way* of the Sun.

The sea is so *blue* today. The sky has hint of green and far out in the sea is the hospital ship. The boats, or junks as they say, are staying in the bay because it is too rough out to sea.

Well, I had a jacket made to hold fourteen M-16 magazines. But the jacket will not last long. I need something stronger. Well, I was thinking of the Levi Blue Jean jacket I have there at home. It would be just the thing. But it has to be *dyed green* (dark) or olive.

It must have a camouflage color to it. I think the jacket is in my laundry bag, you know the one in the closet in my old room. You might have to take some dye out of it to dye it *dark* camouflage. Okay. Send it as soon as you can. I am going to bring it to the village and have them make me a real strong magazine jacket.

Also, did you find the knife I wanted? The Sabre knife (pocket size) I think Eulers Hardware has it. I am not sure. If you can't find it just get a good knife. Well, I will write tomorrow.

Today is 23rd of January.

Good News! I will be at River South—that's the radio name of the place I am at—until the 13th of February. By then I will be going on my third month here. Sounds good. I get my *C.I.B.* at the end of three months. Then if I go back to the states, proving I have been here three months, I will not have to come back. CIB = Combat Infantry Badge.

Well, try and get the Blue Jean jacket fixed up and get the knife. Okay? So good-by for now. I must get some sleep while it's nice and warm and sunny. I am getting a suntan and trying not to get a sunburn.

Fred Leo

24 January 1968

Early in the morning, Brown walks over to Okie's bunker but stops short when he hears someone talking. He peers through the entrance to find Ziggy adoringly holding a *Playboy* centerfold at full length. "Oh my God, you must drink a lot of milk to have a body like that. Oooow-we-baby. You know-*wwwww* what I like!" he croons.

Brown walks through the entrance. "Morning."

He wipes sweat from his steaming brow. "I'm gonna write her a letter," Ziggy declares pointing at the Center Fold. "Lookie here." Turning the picture he reads, "'Enjoy today, trust little to tomorrow. This she interprets as a call to the active pursuit of pleasure.'" He eyes Brown. "Unbelievable. Yeahhh, man!" he shouts excitedly.

"And there's more. 'Just a girl who wants to live life to the hilt . . . an outdoor girl.'" Ziggy glances over wide eyed and bushy tailed. "Shit man, that's all the stuff I love too!"

As he reads on, Brown gets an eye full of a tall, tan and gorgeous blond who is sumptuously endowed.

Brown thinks back to 1965 and the first time he had looked at an entire *Playboy* magazine. It was visiting his sister Roxanna in New York City. At the time Roxanna was bartending at the Crazy Horse Saloon in the New York City World's Fair.

Lounging in her apartment, he began investigating the reading material and stumbled upon a stack of *Playboys*. A virtual bonanza for any sixteen-year old male. When Roxanna walked into the room and saw the expression on her brother's face, she shrugged. "Those are all my roommate's. She likes those, and also those bottles of baby food in the refrigerator. She eats them for snacks. I think she's a little shocking sometimes, but okay." Her girlfriend turned out to be as liberal as the magazines indicated . . . .

"Ohh-h yeah, that body could start ya dreamin'," Ziggy professes. "Make ya dizzy with all the possibilities, huh?"

"Yeah, it sure does." Brown smiles meekly. "Think she'd really write ya back? Ya know? I mean she's a celebrity now. Probably got more guys hanging around now than she can handle."

"Brown. You ain't listening, man." He leans into Brown. "You just ain't listenin'. " Shirtless, he stands broadly, although he is shorter than Brown. With a statuesque pose, he runs a hand through his short dishwater blond hair and stares with dreamy blue eyes. He begins to strut his stuff trying to look the model of masculinity. Rocking his head back he flashes an alluring eye. "Believe me, baby. She'll write."

He relaxes back on the bunk. "She'll write, that's for sure. But what I should do is slip in a photo of myself in my dress green Army uniform," Ziggy decides. "I got what it takes, Brown, believe you me." He spread the centerfold neatly out on the bench and takes out a pen and paper. While speaking aloud, he writes:

"Dear Gorgeous Blonde,

I'm a young, well-built, Vietnam infantryman and you're the only one that stands between me and death. I'm gonna go into Dead Man's Alley tomorrow, and for good luck, I'll put your picture in my pants.

But before I do that, I'll put my love and kisses all over it and hopefully your body will be next to mine real soon.

I'm forever the savior of your liberty and always in pursuit of your heart, body and mind.

P.S. This virgin might be dead before you can write, so write back quick as a bunny!

Signed,
Private First Class
Handsome As They Come.

Finishing the letter, Ziggy looks dreamily outside the bunker. "And if that don't work, I'll dress up in some hot threads. Take her to an late night flick. Roll some Acapulco Gold. Then I'll drive her down Sunset Strip in my *hot* red Corvette Stingray."

"*Hot.*" Okie, only half conscious, rolls over in his bunk. "How much hotter can it get? What the hay!" He rubs his eyes. "If that works, I'll write a letter, too! Maybe she's gotta girlfriend."

Okie throws off the poncho, sits and wipes his sweaty brow. "Hell, man, I'm all tuckered out just listening, let alone thinking about what would happen if she were here. Read that again," he begged, "but slow*www* and with more feeling, please."

Like a movie star, Ziggy dramatically pulls out a cigarette, flicks open his Zippo and takes a puff. Holding the centerfold at arms length, he drops to one knee. "Miss January, Connie Kreski. I will do anything, anything, baby for your love."

"Come on, Ziggy," Okie breaks in. "That ain't no way to talk to a lady. You ain't got no finesse. Let this country boy have a look at those gazzongas." He snatched the centerfold from Ziggy.

Okie straighten his spine, as though Connie is staring back.

"You know, Nam can make a guy go a little crazy. Especially when he get a load of stuff like this."

"Lemme see that *Playboy* magazine." Brown reaches over.

"When you're finished I wanna read the editorials.

"Yeah I heard they're *really* pretty good."

"Tits and ass," Ziggy says, smoking. "Tits and ass. That's what I miss the most."

Dear Ma *24 January 1968*

Remember the last letter? I talked about the *Blue Jean* Jacket? Just two days ago one man in my company had his life saved because of it. They are *very, very* useful. This is the reason I am asking for the jacket. The people over here make *bad* jackets. They wear out fast.

We might be moving to Tam Ky in March. If we do I will never have a chance to get another jacket made. If the one I wear, wears out I will go without it. It could save my life. See what you can find.

Well, nothing has happened. I will be where I am till the eleventh of February. Well, good-bye for now.

Take care, Fred Leo

P.S. Write and tell me if you get this letter. It is important okay.

Dear Ma *25 January 1968*

Is Betty receiving any letters from me. I wrote her at least three letters. *Ask* her. Okay? I would like to hear from her.

Remember that poster I bought for Stanley. The one from S.F. (San Francisco) which said "JOIN THE ARMY". Did you give it to Stan?

Wow! I got a lot of mail yesterday. I got the socks and knife. Wow! I felt like I was back in the *States*. But I'm not and I shouldn't fool myself. *UH?*

When is everyone's birthday? Maybe I can get something for everyone on their birthdays.

Ma, I like the way the college sounds that you are going to.

Well bye, Fred Leo

Dear Uncle Ken, Maude and Karen *26 January 1968*

Received your letter. Don't fool yourself. You do more, much more than I do. Those calendars you sent, everyone wants one. I am giving them to only my squad and close buddies. Thanks.

As for being close to a town. I am surrounded by two towns. One is a settlement village for former VC. They try to convert them to our side. Oh well, we'll see. The other village is *friendly*. I will be at this location, River South, until the 11th of February if everything goes well.

It is beautiful here. I overlook the South China Sea. By the way, these people celebrate New Years from the 29th of January to the 2nd of February. Everyone is automatically a year older. The people are real happy. They bang on drums and the kids run around blowing off fire crackers and the Popular Forces (PFs) fire their weapons all the time.

Some villagers were smoking pot last night. I almost got *high* just breathing the air. I heard it is illegal for them, but the law probably isn't carried out much.

Well, I come home the 27th of November 1968. I have ten months left. It is only a year overseas tour of duty.

Well, goodby for now.

See you, Fred Leo

P.S. Your cards and letters really made my birthday happier.

Dear Ma and Dad *27 January 1968*

Today marks my second month in Nam. Well, I am at the same place. I can see the *German* hospital ship from here.

I heard about *Korea!* It looks pretty nasty. Wonder what they will do.

I hope your winter has let up a little.

Tomorrow is the start of the Chinese Lunar New Year. Everyone automatically becomes a year older. All the people are getting ready to feast. Us G.I.'s are giving a lot of C-rations to them. All the boats are out today. They want *boo-coo* (boo-coo = much) food. The PF are shooting off their guns all day long and the kids are blowing off fire crackers. The barber came to the perimeter to give hair cuts. He knows we just had our hair cut. I wonder what he wants!

There are two villages around my perimeter. One village is a VC work project. They are trying to convert them. *Ha, ha*. The village on the other side is a *friendly* village. They are supposed to be law abiding people. Maybe they are. Who knows?

I saw a South Vietnamese Army gun boat. It looked like a customized Sam Pan. They are made out of wood. One thing I noticed is each Sam Pan has a pair of *eyes* on the *bow*. They must be religious symbols.

Did you know the PFs are drafted. They are in the Army for six years. Their pay is bad and they get very few benefits. The boys old enough are grabbed right off the streets all the time and made PFs.

The PFs hate the army. They want to get out. So there are lots of deserters. Worse than our Army by far.

Well, today I got hold of a mail bag. They are made of nylon. When you cut the seams they are big enough to use as a hammocks. They are real light and weigh next to nothing. Now, I can sleep in the jungle relaxed and off the ground. *Wow!* All I have to do is camouflage it. It is RED. Do you think a magic marker could do the job. Well, I have a black one. Maybe you could send me a brown one or some color that will mix with red to make brown or olive.

Did Lorraine get the present I sent for Danny?

About the jacket. Can you send some waterproof nylon thread that is thin and strong. I could have the jacket sewn with that type of thread. Send lots if you find some.

I received the knife. *Wow!* It really is good for carving I took a lot of time sharpening it. One of my *high* buddy—from Brooklyn, New York—who smokes grass all the time, really liked the knife. His people back home don't help him. I guess that is a good reason to stay *high*. Maybe you could send him a knife like mine. But wait! Maybe he can get one for himself. He is going on R&R in a few weeks. Forget it. (Oh, my - jibber, jabber). I get a lot of Coke here. Beer too, but only when we are around permanent installations.

Bye for now, Fred Leo

28 January 1968

While eating lunch inside Okie's bunker, the soldiers detect something in the distance that resembles a slow, steady gong beat. They discount the mournful noise until it grows louder and is accompanied by jingling chimes.

"What's all the racket?" a shirtless Okie peering out through the front rifle slit. "Sounds like some dink Rock 'n' Roll band or somethin'."

"You know," Ziggy says, "the more you know about their ways the crazier it gets. I swear to God, the whole dink village was high on grass last night. You only had to whiff the haze to get stoned."

"Does that mean you didn't smoke last night?"

"Say, there's something goin' on out there." Okie races out the back entrance in his socks.

Everyone scampers from the bunker to see a procession of Vietnamese coming from one village along the path that connects to the other village. They scramble up the ladder to the rooftop for a better view.

"A funeral?"

"Yeah," Yamane confirms. "I'd say."

The funeral cortege is led by four flag bearing men and an older man shading himself with a black umbrella. Next comes the gonger-man with a leather mallet. He carries the back end of a pole over his shoulder, another man supports the front, with a large metal gong suspended between them.

Next comes two miniature wooden religious houses, one draped with a Vietnamese flag, also carried on poles. Then the chime jingler and two others, hoisting dragon-like flags. Men carrying a red lacquer coffin is next in line with a man walking beside, waving incense over the top. Two men carrying a second bamboo pole coffin take up the rear.

The procession keeps pace with the gong and chime dirge, "PUM, PUM. CHING." The people surrounding and carrying the coffin appear to be the immediate family and close friends of the deceased.

The interlopers continue to stare but receive not so much as a glance from the Vietnamese. Not far beyond the base of the hill the funeral procession veers off taking the road that leads to the graveyard.

Never has Brown felt so alien. The Vietnamese are enveloped in a sacred Buddhist ritual and his mere presence is probably a mockery to that rite. But still he stares unable to pull himself away.

At the grave site a dish of food, flask of water and rice bowl are placed on a bamboo mat. The final joss sticks are burned and the widow has to be restrained from throwing herself on the casket as it is covered with dirt.

From what Brown has seen, dirt will be mounded over the coffin and a channel would skirt the grave. The final resting area will resemble a Martian flying saucer. As a final touch, a large stone is set at the foot of the grave and another at the head.

The dirge is soon replaced by the more familiar sound of squealing pigs. Chow time.

"Instead of staying here another week we might be moving to Da Nang," Sergeant Yamane reports. "There's been some heavy fighting going on up north around Khe Sanh. The Marines were attacked a few days ago on the 21st and it's getting hotter by the hour."

His eyes drift to the Vietnamese mourners straggling along the path on their way back to the village. "I'm not saying it wasn't convincing," he turns his attentions back to the soldiers, "but if I were of a suspicious sort, I'd wonder whether that casket may have been full of weapons."

"Really?"

"Yeah really," Yamane affirms. "There should've been some money scattered along the way and the widow should have kissed a portrait of the dead person."

"We'll keep watch on it," Okie says.

"Chu Lai and River North have been mortared. And the battalion has taken some casualties in both Sniper and AK Valley just west of here near LZ Chippewa."

"I thought we just cleared that valley," Okie comments.

"It's kinda like we gotta keep taking the same place over and over again," Shepard remarks in despair.

"It doesn't make sense," Brown enjoins.

"No shit," Ziggy agrees sprawled in the hammock smoking. "I thought all along the plan was for us to join hands and start pushing the VC north back across the DMZ."

"This whole war is a bit crazy if ya ask me."

"And for that matter, I hear there's more deserters than soldiers in the entire South Vietnamese Army," Ziggy contends. "And no one can tell me those Puff's ain't VC at night neither."

Ziggy sits in the hammock, now fighting mad. "What the hell are we trying to prove over here, huh?! Their own people don't care, so why should we? This whole thing is beginning to piss me off royal."

"Remember that dink barber who came up here?" Yamane asks with everyone nodding. "Well, the MPs tell me they saw him talking to some VC." Everyone's interest peaks. "And there's more." He looks at everyone. "Some dinks were caught letting loose helium balloons near the Chu Lai ammo dump."

"Balloons?" Brown questions.

"Pretty slick," Ziggy says. "That way they can pinpoint everything inside the ammo dump."

"Exactly," Yamane confirms. "Also, orders from the *top*—keep all gates closed and all civilians out. Completely out!"

"Just this morning, I saw those MPs peel the village kids off the gates."

Brown happens to notice the *Stars and Stripes* newspaper that lay next to him and muses about the irrelevance of the headline, "Girl in Convent—by Choice or Spell?"

"Yamane," Brown says, "do we get the combat infantry badge after being here three months?"

"Either that, or sooner if you get shot at."

"Hell, Yamane," Ziggy sputters, nearly falling from the hammock. "We've been shot at! Quite a few times. Why just last night. With all those firecrackers going off most people can't tell the difference . . . but *I* can! A bullet hit the bunker I tell ya. Not just one, a couple of 'em, too. We can go out front and check for holes?"

"Oh, before I forget. The CO dropped off fragmentation jackets at the CP. One for everyone. And from here-on-out don't be caught without it."

"No way, man," Ziggy cries. "That thing weighs a ton."

"Orders are order. And I want more sandbags around these back entrances. So start shoveling. And one more thing. Division found a cache of C-rations which means the civilians are collecting cans for the VC. No more rations for the Vietnamese," Yamane says slowly. "Got it?"

"Yamane, how long we got?" Okie asks. "Before we move-out?

"Realistically?" He pauses to measure his words. "Things are changin' by the minute. They could call us up within the hour and we'd be in deep shit by nightfall."

The answer is met by silent stares.

"I'd say, clean your rifles, get your gear together and be ready to move-out at a moments notice. As for right now. Go check your field of fire to make sure the claymore mines haven't been turned around. Then, just to be on the safe side, put one right up against the front of your bunker," Yamane advises. "Alright, party's over. Let's get to work."

Tension permeates the air, the kind that has been absent since their arrival at River South two weeks ago. This was a virtual island paradise with beaches, ocean air and the rhythmic sound of gently lapping waves. Without further encouragement, everyone jumps to the task.

After manicuring his M-16 rifle, Brown lightly oils and reassembles the weapon. While rearranging the rucksack and pistol belt, he hears, *"Knock, knock, knock."* Elliott, the MP from the river guard bunker stands at the entrance.

"What do ya got there, Brown?" Elliott points to the fragmentation jacket.

"Orders are we gotta wear 'em from here on out."

"Say, I gotta a couple flares." Elliott raises the aluminum cylinders in his hand and grins.

"Got a lot to do," Brown says curtly going back to work. Since arriving at River South, Brown would pull his first guard on the bunker roof. Knowing this, the MP Elliott would come on over and keep him company. It was very heart warming to have someone to converse with while on guard duty, and they got along famously. And whenever Brown had detail, Elliott was right there helping him fill sandbags, clean up garbage, and even helped him pull the drums from under the outhouses and burn-shit.

Elliot also had access to an M-37 truck which they would drive around and once went back to LZ Gator and the village Nuoc Mau. That's when Brown, once again, presented Lan with a bunch of wildflower. Lan was special and he always thought of her when he looked at the Montagnard bracelet on his wrist. And, Elliot also had the means of getting his hands on the little things like extra socks, pens, fresh lobsters, or extra C-rations.

In a nut shell, he and Elliott had become good buddies. But two nights back, Elliot had crossed-the-line and made a sexual advance. This had stunned Brown. And he had told Elliott to leave.

They hadn't talked since. But Brown had to admit, he misses his buddy. He missed their nightly conversations and laughter.

"Come on, you can finish that later," Elliott. Let's have a little fun."

Still reluctant, Brown set his pistol belt on the wooden bench and stares.

"The war will be here when you get back."

"Yeah," Brown says, caving in, "probably will."

They leave the bunker shielding their eyes from the intense afternoon sunlight. Elliott moves immediately to the middle of the clearing that serves as the LZ. He pulls off the cap, slides it over the back and gives it a whack with his palm. The flare fires rushing against the wind.

"Whoooooosh-sh-sh, pop!" It explodes into a brilliant white phosphorous light and dangles from a small white nylon parachute.

Elliot hands a flare to Brown. They prepare to fire by making adjustments off the first flare so that the parachute would land nearby.

"Whoooooosh-sh-sh, pop!" They fire them low and off to the northeast noting the wind has carried the first parachute out into the middle of the river.

"Got it," Brown runs to snatch the parachute off the barbed wire gate. In the meantime, Elliott hurries to the river and out on the wooden pier.

With two silk parachutes in hand, they unravel the string and cut loose the remains of the flare. Securing rocks to the strings, Brown folds the chute carefully and tosses it high into the air. It opens with only one string hanging up, and begins to slowly drift toward the water's edge. He runs dizzily after the chute, hoping to catch it in mid air. The ground slopes downward while he keeps pace, and he finds himself in ankle deep water when it lands in the river just beyond reach. He snatches a tree branch and fishes it out of the water.

"Kids love these little things." Elliott tosses his high and the strings tangle as it plummets to the ground.

"I bet they do." Brown gets his ready for another launch. "I think I'm getting the hang of it." He chucks it into the air.

"Dinks will trade for most anything." He looks over with a wide grin.

"Catch it, Elliott!" Brown yells jubilantly. The wind quickly carries his chute toward the minefield. Elliott grabs a stick and snags it in mid-air just short of the concertina barbed wire.

"Ta-daaaa!" He raises the stick with parachute to punctuate his feat and bows. "Caught in midflight. That's one out and bases loaded." He jogs to the middle of the helicopter pad. "Say, I got an idea. Let's see who can keep theirs in the air the longest."

They both ready their chutes. "On your mark," Elliott starts the count down. "Get set!" They both wiggle around making last second adjustments. "Goo*ooo!"*

They fling their chutes with all their might. A suspension string catches on Brown's and it crashes into the side of Elliott's head. "Hey! Just because you can't win, don't mean you gotta kill me!"

"Wow, I'm sorry, man," Brown laughs. "You should've been wearing your steel pot, after all this is a combat zone." He runs over, snatches the chute and without folding it, catapults it into the air. At twelve feet it opens.

Elliott grabs a handful of rocks and starts bombarding it while Brown whips up the ever present M-16 rifle and pretends to shoot it down.

"Brown," Elliott says, suddenly serious. He stares at the black assault rifle. "From what I've heard, you'll be leaving here real soon now."

"From the sounds like it."

"I don't know how to say this. Aaaa*ammm*. I wanna apologize for what I did." He fidgets with the rocks still in his hand. "I know . . . I . . . well, listen. How about us being friends again? How about that?" He stands dejected, eyes downcast.

"God, Elliott. Listen, you're the best buddy a guy could ever ask for," Brown blurts. "And I mean it." Brown's green eyes meets his and neither look away.

"You'll be in the killing fields soon," Elliott motions to the assault rifle. "And I don't think I could live with myself if I . . . ." He stutters then chokes with emotion. "Oh hell, man." He licks his dry lips. "I just wanna wish ya all the luck in the whole wide world, buddy. And I really mean it."

He reaches and pulls Brown into a bear huge dropping his head on Brown's shoulder. Brown, unsure of the expression, lightly places his arms around Elliott, while searching to make sure no one is looking. Then he too, sucks in a breath, but unlike Elliot who cries, he holds back his feelings—like he thinks a man should.

This is the first time in his life that anyone has cried so openly, with so much heart felt concern about him. And it touches him in places he never knew existed.

"Listen buddy," Elliott collects himself and pulls back wiping away tears. "I wrote something." Sniffling, he produces a piece of paper. "It might sound a little sissy, and all, but I feel real deeply about it." He scrunches his lips. "Here goes." Elliott reads aloud:

INFANTRY SOLDIER He has stumbled into a land of grief, where barbed wire strangles the earth, where madness is ablaze, and where an infantryman can plod to his destiny. Darkness crawls over him and brings with it lost dreams, memories, and appalling reality, while impassionate storms of war strip him of youth and bring the prospect of a future filled with emptiness. In the end, the land will sleep to await its rebirth. The soldiers who fell will be just bones of the past. The survivor's heart must not be strained anymore, but somewhere in his grey vault, all is

remembered. And the

love *he once knew.*

Signed,

Your River South Buddy

"These last few days have been really hard on me," Elliott claims with a quirky smile. Without another word, he hands the folded poem to Brown, turns and slumps away.

"Elliott," a mournful cry passes from Brown's throat. "I . . ." Brown is at a complete loose for words. "I'm . . . ," he says to the wind as his friend vanishes inside the MP bunker.

Brown now understands the choke hold the past has on him. In the present, he struggles to maintain his humanity, while the future fills itself with life threatening perils. And at this moment there is precious little standing between him and the secrets of the forever after.

With loneliness eating him away, Brown trudges back to the bunker and finds a letter on his gear. Like usual, he stuffs it safely away leaving it for a better time so he might enjoy it more fully, and goes back to preparing for combat.

That evening, he climbs to the bunker roof. More and more he's been spending time alone on the roof—where he can sit unnoticed and watch the world go by.

Taking off the steel pot, he notices an old letter from his father. He opens it and begins to re-read. But now as he reads, Brown questions the contents of the nicely typewritten letter which uses words so commonly found in a dictionary. Words that roll so pleasingly off the tongue but do they really mean anything? Do they have a soul? Should he search for a deeper meaning among the mush of words? A sign? No, he thinks not.

"It's all really a bunch of bullshit. Isn't it?"

Sitting there alone with a towel draping his shoulders, he decides that a person should be judged by what they actually *do* versus what they *say* or write on a white piece of paper. For instance, his father was actually the one who got Brown fired from his job. It was his father who never really talked to him about life decisions. Oh, but he certainly did talk *at* him a lot. Brown vividly remembers being so distraught by what was happening in his life, that he went out and joined the military. But he didn't just join. No. He could have opted for an occupation, but instead volunteered for combat in the Vietnam War. Now that was a *death wish* if there ever was one.

His father would keep up his usual mealy-mouth talk that translated to "Do as I say, not as I do". Lots of empty words spilling from a man who's only real concern was, "me, me, me me." How he loves himself.

There is something very dark about that man, Brown thinks. He can't put a finger on it, but for whatever reason he found himself becoming more and more angry—violent towards his father. A father that represented a bogus authority figure.

So here he is preparing for the fight of his life and his father is talking about his last fishing trip/vacation. Talking about a new boat motor. Talking about which friend just bought a new Mercedes Benz. Or a new location for a store. Nothing was ever said about *him* caring to do anything for Brown, his own son. "Me, me, me, me." It was always all about him and his needs.

Brown lay the letter on a sandbag, noticing that date on the letter is January 15, 1968. "Wondering if he realized that my 19th birthday was just a few days away?"

Sitting cross legged on sandbag, he swoons under a drizzling rain and enters a dream-like state.

Adjoining his sphere of worldly thought is a swirling mist. The mist solidifies and turns into a second worldly sphere. Now, confronting him are two complete worlds—incompatible in thought. An electrifying battle of reason rages between them, until Brown's old world begins to break apart. At that moment a span of light appears and he finds he has no choice but to run for the new world.

"Welcome," a Civil War general greets him on the otherside as he slows to a walk. This rugged officer is obviously a person who would lead his men into battle. The wily sage image puffs on a cigar. Brown looks over his shoulder to find both the bridge and his past have vanished.

"Yes, as you can see, there is no way back." Following the general, he enters a fog bank.

Till now, Brown's brain has been an organ upon which others would imprint their beliefs, but were ultimately not his beliefs. He now understands that to survive, he must use his brain as a claw or fang. He will have to accept as truth only that which is demonstrated. To disregard his past imprints and old world convictions.

"I follow my soul for I know no other way. Touching the morning sun is easier that way," the general confirms. He stops and turns to face Brown. "Use your intelligence to see clearly. To visualize where you must go." A dark cloud sweeps over them and the general disappears.

The fingers of the storm strip Brown of his youthful clothing. He continues in a loin cloth, coming upon a peaceful serene region within which, silhouetted against a tranquil reddish sky, is a hunter-gatherer seated solemnly beside a wood fire. The primitive man probes the glowing embers with a blackened tree limb, his back to Brown.

He wonders if this ancient soul knew the laws of life and is wiser than all others. Perhaps through simplicity, he knows the secret of enduring the unendurable.

Sparks fly as the man continues to jab at the burning embers, his back muscles twitching obviously conscious of the intruder. Brown moves opposite of the man and like him sits cross legged to stare at the dancing flames amidst a pregnant silence.

"I am what I am. It is what it is. My soul is not for sale," Brown finds himself chanting. Then he raises his eyes and stares into . . . .

A distant rifle discharge brings him back to find himself watching the ink run off the drizzle soaked letter from his father. He places the letter on the sandbags to let the paper clean itself.

Laying back, he contemplates the swirling black rain clouds and feels as if he were falling into them . . . and into sleep.

Dear Ma and Dad *28 January 1968*

Well, last night the whole area was *mortared*. But not me. See how safe I am. We only get sniper fire and a few grenades here.

Well, the people are getting keyed up for the New Year party. It starts the 29th and ends the second of February. I could smell *pot* from my bunker. They must have blown their minds last night in the Village. Most of the shops are closed today because they are cooking. *Yum Yum*. They can cook some good stuff.

A couple of families had a race in their Sam Pans this morning. They really paddled hard. It is nice to see these people having fun. I didn't know it existed.

I've seen a lot of funerals in Nam. Though I've never seem them so elaborate as they are right here. The people are buried above ground. I think that is the way they bury people in New Orleans, above the ground.

Well, I sunburned myself yesterday. Not too bad though. I hate telling you about how warm it is here.

Well, I will write later today and tell you what is happening.

Well, I just ate lunch. We had Ham. A buddy of mine had some Heinz "57" sauce which I put on it. I was eating it, then all of a sudden, it tasted like shrimp sauce. *Wow!*

Well, the Vietnamese people are real happy. They walk around and try to walk through our perimeter. They bang on drums and yell and scream. The people are playing around in water at the edge of the bay.

In my last letter I wrote about the PF's. The PFs (or Puffs because they are as threatening as a cream puff) are compared to our National Guard. The PF's protect their own little village. I am not sure how long they are enlisted for. The South Vietnamese Army is a lot better and are called ARVN (Army of the Republic of Viet Nam).

Well today is the 29th of January.

Starting at five A.M. I heard pigs *squealing*. They are cooking them up. *Yum, yum*.

Guess what I am doing right now. I am sitting in my mailbag *hammock*. I cut it open and strung it up this morning. Really comfortable. If I bring it into the field, it will keep me off the ground.

Well, try to find some nylon thread. And send me black magic markers so I can camouflage the hammock.

Hurry with the markers. I will go into the field soon now. Okay.

By the way, could you get the address of *Colt*, the rifle people. They have a 30-round magazine for the M-16. Maybe you could ask about it at the gun shop. I know they have them. It is a matter of getting them. It would be a real handy thing to have when the going gets rough. There is a real good gun shop at Southwest Highway and 95th Street. It is on your right. Okay?

Bye for now, Fred Leo

Dear Ma *30 January 1968*

Received your letter from Florida, glad you made it. You should get a house down there to relax. Think in private and get things straight. Business or such. Sounds good huh? Anyway, you should spend more time down there. Well, I know you're trying. I hope maybe I will get a house and you can come see me and stay there.

Well, Anton Bridge manned by the other half of my platoon has been hit two nights in a row. Mortared the first and assaulted the second.

Well, today was the big day of the three-day Chinese Lunar New Years. It started the *29th* and ends the *31st.* The 30th, today, was a real big day. The women had on perfume and the regular silk oriental stuff. I don't like oriental clothes much. But there was the *Western* civilization trend. Some girls had on slacks and a *shirt*.

I noticed the husband always walked ahead of the family. The kids of the same ages got together. That was nice but you don't see guys with girls. I saw two couples but they didn't have their arms around each other or anything. I notice how many young people have European faces. One guy reminded me of my buddy Ray Blais. Some real cute and even good looking young women too.

The South Vietnamese men are so skinny. All the people really! We Americans look like another *species.* Maybe not that far. In other words you can tell a Vietnamese from an American real easy. I've heard the North Vietnamese people are bigger.

Slept in my hammock last night. I am trying to find out the best height.

Well, this day has come to a close. Tomorrow is the 31st of January. *PAY DAY. GOODY! GOODY!*

I drove a 3/4 ton truck a couple of days ago. Wow! Fun. I love to drive trucks. Well, bye until tomorrow.

Well, its happening, today the 31st of January.

We are moving to *Da Nang.* The whole 198th Light Infantry. You know where Da Nang is? I am not there yet so it isn't confirmed until I write a letter from there. You may have heard the 198th was mortared real, real bad. I haven't heard much about the dead or wounded but three men were killed in my platoon. One a very good friend. I haven't heard all about it yet.

They rocketed the Chu Lai ammunition dump and it blew up. We could feel the explosion and see the black cloud from here.

Two hangers *blew*-up last night too. A couple of valuable planes were burned and a lot of helicopters. River South, where I am, was the place not flattened. They even hit LZ Gator with mortars.

I don't know anything about Da Nang. I might have to get rid of a few things I carved but I will get more later.

Well, I feel *messed up* and I guess I need sleep.

Always remember, if you don't hear from me in two weeks something has happened. But that doesn't mean anything more than that. It just means something is wrong.

Well bye for now, Fred Leo

P.S. I am not at Da Nang yet. I may not go. But this will be the last time to write for the next few days, if we do go.

Dear Ma *31 January 1968*

We are going to be hit tonight. I am as sure as sure can be. They blew up the Anton Bridge and they are trying to overrun it.

Three men killed and seven wounded out of my platoon. I was friends of all three. I don't have a platoon anymore. I don't know what will happen.

Confirmed. Going to Da Nang. My whole battalion.

Ma, did you receive my allotment to you? You can send me a money order in April or May without problems can't you? What about my Income Tax. Can you take care of it. I don't know anything about it.

Well by for now, Fred Leo

February 1968

Dear Ma and Dad *1 February 1968*

Everything is okay. We didn't get hit. It was real *hairy* around here yesterday and the day before.

The VC or *NVA!* have rockets. They shot point blank at the bunkers and blew them away. When the GIs ran from the bunkers, the NVA would throw grenades. This is how two of my friends got it.

In broad daylight there was three-hundred NVA on Highway One. But by the time the choppers got here, there was only seventy-five and only a few of them were hit.

Anton Bridge was being mortared from about six P.M. on. I haven't heard anything more this morning.

I am not in *Da Nang* yet. I heard we were going today. But it is 10:30 A.M. and I am sitting on my bunker and am not completely packed. I'll continue later when I should know when we are going.

By the way, Da Nang is real big and I should be able to get and do anything I did here around Chu Lai.

Well today is the second of February.

It looks like we might *not* go to Da Nang because things are hotter in the Chu Lai area.

Right now, I am at the same place, River South. We only had a little contact last night.

There are VC recruiters in the villages surrounding us. They come in at night and recruit the people. It is a good way. It isn't too hard to sway the people to become VC because they don't see the whole picture, or is it *we* don't see the whole picture.

No one is allowed on Highway One. There is a *curfew* out. Everyone must man their station. People in Saigon had to be escorted to work. Saigon, I think, was about the worst hit.

I took a shower last night. Man did that feel good. It has been a while. We had beans and hamburgers for supper. Tasted real good.

I don't know if I told you this before or not. But the only confirmed VC are dead VC. We came across three VC awhile back and we killed one and captured two. The one dead was classified as a confirmed VC. The other two were set free as innocent civilians. My whole battalion is getting tough. We don't take *prisoners* anymore We learned not to.

The GIs that were real, real close to the men killed have no mercy left in them. They want payback. Kill, kill, kill!

Well, I don't know what will happen. Where I will go or what I will do, but the whole area is *HOT* and we will be doing something real soon.

Bye for now, Fred Leo

3 February 1968

Inside their barracks at LZ Gator, everyone huddles around Sergeant Yamane. For the last half hour they have been intent on his every word.

Yamane takes a grisly draw on a cigarette. "Da Nang right now?" he pauses, "it's still anyone's guess. Best bet is be ready for anything including getting mortared as we speak."

The enormity of the events of the last few days were tracking deep in his forehead. Yamane's face no longer possesses the youthfulness of just a few days before. Pulling out a canteen, he sits on the bunk. After a long drink, with water slopping down his chin, he says, "This water tastes like piss."

"How about some Loud Mouth Lime," Brown offers. Lately

Brown has been Yamane's RTO, but this morning was assigned to the position of platoon RTO. "Or, tell ya what," he digs into a side pouch of the rucksack, "I got some Choo-Choo Cherry. How about that?"

"Got any Freckle Face Strawberry in there?" Yamane drools with anticipation. "That's my favorite."

"Ahh, lemme see. Well, here's a Goofy Grape." Brown displays the package. "What's your pleasure?" Yamane decides on the Goofy Grape Kool-Aid and Brown tosses it over.

Yamane tears open the package and pours it inside the canteen. Swishing it around, he takes a long satisfying drink.

"Remember that dink we killed in the wire at River South?" They nod. "He was a Chieu Hoi," Yamane explains. "We know that because he had *Sat Cong* tattooed on his chest."

"What's that mean?" Green questions.

"What I mean is, the dink had surrendered a while back. Came over to our side. But just to make sure they don't go back on their word, the ARVNs tattoo *Sat Cong* on their chest which means Kill Communists. The point is, every dink in these parts—no matter what—seems to have turned against us."

"But why?" is the question that no one can answer.

"The good news is our Battalion kill ratio is nineteen dinks to one GI," Yamane says of the empty achievement.

"Who's going to Saigon?" Okie asks. The defenses in and around Saigon are so thin, they've asked every squad in I Corps to give up one man.

"I don't wanna go," Green says, making a stand.

"I've already sent-off one of the new guys." Yamane stands abruptly. "I gotta dee-dee."

With his departure, their attention swings to Bedford. The muscular six-foot dishwater blonde haired soldier has the look and sometimes acts like a hooligan blasting down a highway on a Harley Davidson chopper motorcycle. His unbuttoned shirt exposes a thick gold chain, taped dog tags, and a pendant. The aviator sunglasses and the beard stubble give him a gruesome appearance. He sits on the bunk petting the smooth wooden stock of the M-79 cradled in his lap.

Bedford had been on a perimeter bunker at Anton Bridge, code name River North, located just north of Chu Lai. He is the only one out of fifteen soldiers who survived unscathed from the night attack of January 31, 1968 when their position was overrun and the bridge destroyed.

Everyone hunkers around Bedford like they would a high school stud ready to brag about his very, very *hot* date. The contents of this episode would be different, but to them no less tantalizing. Bedford had been the first to go face to face, hand to hand in combat. He survived and now has center stage.

Bedford draws the hunting knife with folding blade that can also be used as a hatchet. Then he begins to sharpen the blade on an oil stone. *Strop. Strop. Strop.*

"They'd been toying with us for days," Bedford says in a deep baritone. "Sporadically. You never knew when they'd drop a mortar or take a pot-shot. At first that's all it seemed." Bedford holsters the knife. "Maybe they were showing us for-once-in-their-life, they had some balls."

He removes his aviator sunglasses to wipe sweat from his brow. Without glasses, they can detect something *different* imbedded in his once soft blue eyes, eyes streaked with lightninglike jagged veins encircled by pale blotchy skin. His right cheek is swollen and yellow-purplish in color apparently caused by some kind of nasty blow. Scabs are forming on his left inner elbow and on a group of small purplish lacerations. The left hand is wrapped with an elastic bandage, apparently to support a sprained wrist.

"We figure the dinks in the village just on the other side of the river were in cahoots," the detective in Bedford assures them. "I know it's true because every night the dink girls would come peddling 'souvenir boom-boom. Numba-one me no lie,'" he says in a high pitched Vietnamese voice. "Also, next to the village and the bridge was the MP's bunker. Those guys would actually take turns spending the night in the village.

"So here's how I figure it," Bedford begins to surmise. "The girls were sent to distract us so the VC could swim undetected to the bridge and set the charges. You know, come to think of it," Bedford begins combing his hand through his short hair, "yeah it all makes sense because the girls left just before it all happened." He's pleased by how the pieces were all falling into place.

"So, I'm on guard and it's about midnight when I hear this faint 'poof' somewhere off in the distance." To demonstrate, he raises his head to listen. "Szzzzz! Ca-blooom! I wasn't overly concerned about just one incoming mortar. From 6 o'clock on they'd been doing it. So we just figured maybe a dink was continuing his target practice." He reflects. "Ya know now that I think about it. That probably was the signal for *charge!"* His audience gives a resounding grunt of understanding.

"Because it wasn't more than a couple minutes when I hear the first volley." He puts his lips together, "Poof. Poof. Poof. Poof," he mouths the sound of mortars being fires.

"Doc Prien and his buddies weren't taking it too serious. Instead of lock and loadin', they clamor up that fifty foot wooden tower next to the command bunker to watch the fireworks. Cause that's what they thought it was. More fireworks." He forms a bugle over his mouth, "Come on up,' I heard 'em yell, 'the show's better from up here!'"

"Even before the first volley hit, I could hear another series of mortar poofs. I mean we were definitely in deep, deep shit and headed for a pucker factor of ten. And then it really began to *rain,* man. Mortars started hittin' nonstop. They poured it on. The ground shook so hard it felt like a California earthquake.

"Then our bunker starts takin' hits." Bedford is no longer calmly telling a war story. "I mean the sandbags begin breaking up covering us with dust to where we could hardly see. Between that and the smoke we near choked to death.

"Right then and there, we decided we'd have to make a run for it. Get back to the command bunker. Then we spot movement. I mean it was like the ground was beginning to crawl. We shot off a flare and it dangled, lighting up the whole rice field. And Charlie was everywhere and comin' on."

This first person account has his eyes blazing. Sweat shows through his shirt. His face has turned white and he now grasps his M-79 launcher tight like a club.

"We opened fire with everything we had, man," he screams with foul breath. No longer sitting, he stands crouched, eyes darting. "A murderous hellfire that we thought would *for sure* cover our getaway. But no way, man."

Bedford's blue eyes seize the soldiers. "No, not by a long shot. I mean we dropped plenty of 'em. Staggered 'em. But they somehow absorbed it. We watched as they just picked themselves right back up off the ground and starting coming again. Some crawling some running like madmen. I mean, I couldn't believe my eyes. They were running against us and right through their own mortar barrage! Closing fast. Big time."

"O'Connor, Mango and me , we just keep pourin' it on as fast as we could lock and load. Blow the claymore! I yelled. *Blam!* Slowed 'em some. But didn't stop 'em."

Bedford wielded his M-79, pretending to recoil after firing. "Booo-oom! Tataatat! We Rock 'n' Rolled 'em nonstop for what seemed like," he pauses, "God only knows. Blew all three claymores right in their faces.

"They were getting around us so O'Connor jumps off the front and dee-dees to check out back. Caablaam! A mortar explodes throwing him back inside against the wall." Bedford throws his hands and rocks his head to demonstrate.

"Shrapnel chewed him up bad. Blood was all over the place. He was dazed, but still holding the rifle which he swings up and begins blastin' away. Before he passes out, a dink plops in dead, eyes wide, a satchel charge in his hand.

"Mango grabs the charge and flings it clear just as it explodes. I turn back around as this sapper, dressed in black shorts and web gear not twenty yards away is ready to hurl this Chi-com stick grenade. I fire Thumper and the round explodes wide staggering the dink sending the grenade spear wide. Somehow the hopped-up gook gets back on his hands and knees, and starts for me again."

Bedford flicked open his M-79 grenade launcher, dropped out the round and re-loaded faster than anyone could imagine possible. "Blam! I fired point blank right into his bread basket. But it didn't detonate cause the round hadn't rotated enough."

"I threw in a canister just as Mango comes back on line. He lets loose with a burst and drops three gooks just short of the bunker. Then one of the dink explodes from the satchel charge strapped around his waist, sending his guts splattering all over the place."

Bedford slumps and sits on the bunk taking several, deep calming, breaths. He stands again ready to continue.

"That's when a dink swings through the back entrance and grabs O'Connor's rifle. Mango swings around and they pull their triggers at exactly the same time. The dink hits the bunker wall and drops ready for a dirt-nap."

"Then without so much as a word, Mango steps over the dead VC and out the back. Cabloom! Mango staggers back in, his body just blown to bits and drops dead right on top of O'Connor and the dink."

Bedford glares with sweat pouring down his face choked with emotion. Everyone waits in the pregnant silence hoping he can regain his composure. He takes a series of calming, deep breaths.

"Water?"

"No I'm fine." Raising the grenade launcher, he continues. "With Thumper and Mango's rifle and three magazines stuffed in my pocket, I made a run for it. Screaming at the top of my lungs, I ran outta that bunker just as it took a direct hit by a rocket. I skid around the side headed for the command bunker when I see this MP running like mad toward me on the bridge. Apparently, they'd already overrun his bunker."

"Boom!! Whoosh! Loudest noise I've ever heard. The whole bridge lifts right up sending the guy flying. Then it buckles and crashes down into the river. Last I saw of that MP."

"Then, I see Blackjack behind an embankment trying to hold off a bunch of VC. I yell 'Come on man!' and let loose with a canister round and a burst from my M-16 to try and cover our escape. So, I kept weaving back and forth." Bedford pauses nearly drained, he holds his chest, sits. This time he takes the offered canteen and drinks.

Everyone else feels exhausted, just from listening.

With a totally unexpected movement, he stands with muscles glistening with sweat. "I blasted, and blasted, and blasted 'em. I don't know how I did it but I fought my way all the way back to the command bunker and dove inside."

Looking through them, he says, "I should have been dead. I wasn't.

"So, I'm sprawled on the dirt floor when here comes the tower party. The first guy in says, 'What's all the hullabaloo about?' Doc Prein pushes past and stops dead in his tracks. He stares around. At first I don't think he knew what was going on. He just stood there looking at all these bloody guys.

"Meanwhile, two guys are firing out the front, the wounded feeding 'em grenades and magazines. And I'm holding down the back way.

"Then Doc shouts, 'Shit man, I forgot my medical bag.' He bolts out the back and half way to the tent, he takes a direct hit by a mortar.

"Then everything goes quiet. You know, like someone turned off the noise. Even the wounded guys stop moaning. I slide out the back and look around. Nothin'.

"Ya know, that's the worst. Because you get a chance to realize what's going on. And there is this weird feeling you get when you start looking around to see who's left."

Everyone sits breathless as they grasp the enormity of the narrative. Like a "tall-tale" story or "the fish that got away" story, this was big, bold and outrageous—and totally true.

Bedford's sits with an occasional body quake. Was there something else? Brown wonders. Something he should have done? Could have done differently? Or maybe, he's blocking something he didn't even want to admit—even to himself.

The poise of Bedford's body is of a man who has reached beyond the normal sphere of physical and mental endurance. The gaze is clairvoyant but enormously lonely. As Brown watches he knows there is something else etched in those eyes.

Then it dawns on him that Bedford had tapped into his animal survival instincts. The battle wasn't about the red-white-and blue, about America, it was about saving himself and his buddies. "Incredible."

With jaws hung, Bedford walks out.

Dear Ma *3 February 1968*

Well, I got paid $223.85 this month. I am up for SP/4 but that will not come for a few months.

I received your letter from Florida and your letter with the scene of our lawn. It is a real good picture. It carries my mind half way around the world. Only a good photo could do that.

Well, I left River South. I am at Base Camp. I had a whole *night* of sleep! The first *real* one in about two months. We were supposed to be going to the Anton Bridge or Da Nang or Tam Ky soon. They have put us on alert.

I woke up this morning *refreshed!* Then I hear eight men were killed from their own claymore mine. It got turned around or something, anyway it blew up.

Reconnaissance has three platoons. Reconnaissance platoon has seven men left. First platoon has thirteen and second platoon has twenty. We got replacements now so the numbers are up.

We have about thirty men killed or wounded. That is half of the original men before the 29th of January to second of February.

I have been real lucky. I hope it keeps going.

Man, between the stores, your personal needs, and the those around you *plus* mine you must keep real busy. I wouldn't ask for the things I do but they're not a luxury. They will help me make it back alive. I am not trying to keep you busy but they are important. *Okay.*

Ma, you're the only one who will help me like this. *Thanks.*

I hate to say this but soon I will need a pistol. I am not sure of the best kind. I want to bring it on R&R so it must be small. I also need it for tunnel rat patrols. Also, if I am in real close combat, I can whip it out when I run out of M-16 ammunition.

I need one on R&R because a lot of men were killed in Saigon who were on Incountry R&R. They didn't have any weapons. You have to check them in. A pistol might have saved their lives.

Maybe a derringer would be the thing. A two-barreled derringer that I could put in my helmet. You might see about it when you ask about the magazines.

Well, it's high noon. Chow time. Great. I will write after lunch.

Well, it is 1:30 P.M. now. It doesn't look like we are going out today. Some guys are leaving for Anton Bridge now but I will stay.

Well bye for now, Fred Leo

Dear Ma and Dad *4 February 1968*

Well, guess where I am. Half way between Chu Lai and Tam Ky on Highway One. Ten men, including me went out yesterday in the back of two M-37 trucks. We are attached to two Armored Personnel Carriers.

Coming out here last night, we passed *River North*—Anton Bridge—where the other half of my platoon was. This is where three men were killed. The bridge had collapsed so we crossed on a pontoon bridge.

Now the reason I am here is because a *tank* fell through a bridge here. We are protecting the bridge and tank until they get it out and also get the bridge situation taken care of. All day they have been working on a pontoon bridge because the old steel bridge the tank fell through is obsolete.

By the way *don't* send any camouflage markers for the hammock. It isn't practical bringing it into the field.

Be sure to see about the 30-round M-16 magazines. I could use twenty or more but a dozen will do for the present. I need more because I might loose one or bend or break one. Okay.

About the *derringer,* make it a 38 cal. two barrel. Be sure it is utterly dependable. That means, the firing pin will never ever miss or get fouled up. Also a small holster to carry it. Take your time on this. No rush. I will carry it on R&R and when I am not an RTO. An ounce means a great deal when you add it to this heavy radio. Send a box of shells with it. Tell the gun seller, it is to *kill people* not for target practice. I don't want a good looking gun. Be sure it is strong, dependable and rugged.

Well, looks like we have company, two more APC's . I don't know if they are staying.

Well, they just turned and left. *Oh, Well!* I'm going to eat now. I will write tomorrow.

It is later on the 5th of February 1968

Right now, I am back at LZ Gator. As soon as I stopped writing we left for Base Camp. I still do not know when we are going to Da Nang, but soon.

About that M-16 30-round magazines. Send five of the *aluminum* version. If you can't get them aluminum don't get them. I will test the 30-round magazines before I decide to use them.

They got the pontoon bridge up. They also got the tank off the old steel bridge.

Ma, could you send me a few more *Brown's Fried Chicken* patches.

In a year or so I guarantee we will have men from RVN who will remember me from Nam. Good advertising *Hu!*

I wish I could write better. Half the time I am rushed and am writing in wind, dirt and have no backing. Maybe I should *print.* what do you think? Maybe I would spell better if I do.

Well, I have started taking my liver and iron pills and I also have a lot of salt tablets.

I got Linda Key's letter. I will write her. I think I will tell her to join the *Red Cross*. The women in Red Cross come around and talk to us in hopes of making us feel good. If Linda wants to join something the Red Cross would probably be best. The WACs and Waves? I don't think that would be very good. Too much like the Army. You know. Write me and tell me if you think I should tell her about it. College does seem to be next in line for her. She has got to *live* and *help* before she can get all she should get from college. Agree?

Well, nothing happening now, so good-bye

Fred Leo

Dear Ma and Dad *6 February 1968*

Back in the groove now *hu?* Tell me about Florida Dad. Was it worth while? Was the house boat as clumsy a fishing boat as you thought it would be? Like your new car. Why don't you and Ma have a picture taken. I would like a picture of you two. Okay. I'll wait if you make sure it is a good one.

I left LZ Gator last night. It was about four or five P.M. We got to our night ambush at 10:30 P.M. I was the only one who had a good radio. All the others were messed up.

Luck was with me yesterday. I just got back from taking a cold shower when they gave us the word to move-out. The magazine vest I have helps. I am able to carry twenty ammunition magazines. Before I carried only ten to fourteen magazines.

Well, I am drying my poncho and poncho liner out. I will continue soon.

Right now, I am waiting for re-supply. We get C-rations and any other things we might need.

From here I will go to my night ambush.

The reason we are here is because we are trying to find out where the NVA mortars are. So far we've found nothing.

We are located about six miles from LZ Gator. I don't know when they plan to send us to Da Nang. I might be leaving the infantry soon. A new company is coming over from the States. Then E Company will be disbanded except for Reconn Platoon and Mortar Platoon. So I might go into the mortars. Time will tell. I have no definite word on it.

Well, I will write tomorrow

It is the 7th of February 1968.

Good morning. Here I am on a mountain. I can see LZ Chippawa, LZ Gator, River South and the whole Chu Lai area from here. The South China sea is all blue in the distance.

Fred Leo

Dear Linda *7 February 1968*

Linda, I heard you were in a play. I wish I could have seen it. You were the lead weren't you? Linda you don't give yourself enough credit. That was a real great achievement. But you were too modest to mention it. *Huh*. You didn't think I was going ask my Ma about you, did you?

It is good you quit work at the store. Try and take it easy. Get more rest.

I am real sorry about your grandmother. I met her and I truly liked her. She is happy where she is and she is also happy you are where you are. I am too. You have a lot of people up there in Heaven pulling for you. Remember that. Your Grandma and Pa all know you love them. They could feel it. You didn't have to tell them, they know who loves them same as us.

Don't feel sorry about writing me, or sorry about anything. Okay. A person must not be sorry about who they are or what they do. You are you and there is nothing to be sorry for or about.

Just let your sorrows pass and try to avoid them the next time. Okay.

Don't ever feel guilty that you are where you are. Do what you can do and be at ease with yourself.

You asked why I gave you a cross. If you don't know I could never tell you.

You asked if the praying hands you gave me are doing any good. Whenever my life looks like it is over, my hand goes to my rifle and my necklace.

Linda, don't promise me anything. If you want to write. Write. You know I am on your side. I know you are thinking of me. You don't have to write.

You wrote, "I'm closing now hoping that you'll answer my letter soon." You know I will, don't you?

Broad, life is too, too precious to bring yourself down. Enjoy life. Don't let it get to you.

You had better get to a dance now. Say to your Ma, 'I'm going out to a dance." Tell me about it. I miss them. *Wow!* What am I saying. I dance with my rifle all the time.

Keep Cool. *Ha, ha.* Send me a picture of you. As soon as possible. NOW! Don't wait. Okay.

Fred Leo

7 February 1968

Brown jumps off the chopper to find LZ Gator in a profoundly different mood than that of just yesterday evening. The soldiers hurry about consumed with dead serious preparation because on the morning of February 7th, the 198th light infantry has been called to battle. The soldiers are mobilizing for the inevitable fight.

As the bustle continues, Brown realizes that battle can purify the soul. That battle has the ability to strip a person of identity till they are again virtuous as a child. One who's never been taught to discriminate because of religion, creed or color. Never been touched by greed, jealousy or hatred. The whole atmosphere leaves no room for racial or cultural differences. A camaraderie among the soldiers is being forged, that will become as strong as steel, as enduring as time itself. All brought about by the understanding that they must act as one if anyone is to survive.

The soldiers prepare for destiny as the age old questions linger. Questions like: Who among them would be the first to draw blood: The first to cradle a mortally wounded buddy: The first to lay inert, eyes glazed, body shattered?

"Brown!" Yamane yells over the commotion. "As soon as you're ready get back to the chopper pad. We're headed to Da Nang." He rushes away.

Today is the day Brown has been preparing for his whole life. The rifle is already clean, everything is already packed, and his mind is combat ready. So, what else should he do? A short scavenger hunt might shake-off some anxiety and might produce something of worth.

The temperature has been dropping steadily and then it starts to rain. Brown wraps his towel tightly around his neck to keep out the chilly water, then leaves the barracks. While meandering, the rain increases. Not wanting to get soaked, he ducks inside one of three vacant tents.

In the dingy light, Brown begins to rummage through ammunition cans, C-ration boxes and anything else laying about. Next to a folding bunk, he spots six discarded M-16 magazines. "Bingo." He snatches them and concludes four are worth saving.

"What do ya need?" a demanding, though not unfriendly, voice trumpets. Brown spins around like a thief, but there is no one in sight.

"Yo!" Brown calls trying to flush him out. "I'm lookin' for some ammo." He waits for a reply or a hint of the whereabouts of the interloper. "Can't seem to find any though." Brown hears rustling in the next tent over. Kneeling, he lifts the canvas flap of the adjoining tent and spots the boots of a soldier.

Crawling between the two tents Brown finds the soldier sitting alone working on his equipment. "Gettin' ready, huh?"

"Yeah," the soldier nods. "Grab some ammo if that's what you need. I got more than I can ever use." The soldier motions to two ammunition cans filled with M-16 bandoleers.

"Wow!" Brown glows with appreciation as he sits on the adjoining bunk.

The soldier has just finished assembling his rifle, the smell of fresh oil lingering. He works the rifle's action. Satisfied with the movement he carefully leans it against the bed.

Empty magazines lay next to him on the bunk, and M-16 bullets litter the mud around his feet. He grabs a sling of ammunition, attaches a formed piece of metal to a magazine and begins to feed the bullets in, along with intermittent red tipped tracers.

Brown has seen these magazine loaders before but never has he seen it so adeptly used. "What do they call that thing?"

"This?" the soldier asks, holding the molded metal. "It's called a quick loader. You oughta have one, might save your life." He tosses it over. "Don't say I never gave you nothin'."

The soldier reaches into the ammo can and grabs out another quick loader and again starts filling magazines. Brown takes one of his magazines and empties the old rounds onto the floor.

"Here," he reaches, "Gimme that magazine." Brown hands it over. "Lemme show ya somethin'." He takes a bullet, inserts it at the back of the magazine and the cartridges spill out. "See. Lickety split. Whole thing's done. And while the magazine is empty check the spring. Make sure it's got good tension, ain't tangled or sometimes you'll find 'em broken."

Following the example, Brown empties two more magazines, the rounds piling onto the hundreds already collecting in the mud. "Seems like an awful waste."

"Yeah, sure is," he agrees. "But if a dirty round jams, you bought-the-farm. Besides there's no time to clean 'em."

As Brown starts to re-load a magazine, the soldier hands him a box of tracers. "Here ya go, buddy. Now remember, tracers build up deposits in your barrel. Make it hard to clear. So the best way to load 'em is—first two rounds tracers. Then every fourth round and also the last one. That way, when you see two red streaks in a row, you know you're outta ammo. Time to reload."

The GI takes a leather strap with double row of holes and brass hooks. He threads it into the rifle loops and sets the length. Brown has never seen such a handsome rifle sling.

"Oh, yeah, one last thing. When you finish filling 'em, tap the back," he demonstrates by tapping a magazine against the side of the bunk, "to make sure all the rounds are lined up."

"So who ya with?" Brown asks wanting keep the air filled while they work.

"Alpha kickin' A Company. You know about us?"

"Yeah, sure. I've heard all about you guys," Brown says, though a little unsure of the soldier's meaning.

"We're the Gunfighters, Dealers of Death," he puffs full of pride. "We been kickin' alpha. Got myself four kills so far," he says with a wink. "After the last one they started calling me, Bull. Like strong as a bull. Least, I think that's what they meant by it. Though it could mean, bull-headed or a bull-shitter." They both chuckle.

"No matter. I plan to get some ears in Da Nang." He produces a playing card which he spins into the air with it landing in Brown's lap. The card has a grinning skull and crossbones within an Ace of Spade.

"We drop 'em on our kills. That way the dinks know who done the honors." He said it with such cold indifference it made Brown's skin crawl.

Bull snaps a full magazine into his finely tuned rifle and, lightning fast, pulls the charging handle manically back and forth ejecting gleaming brass round after round into the air. He does it so viciously, so expressionlessly cold, and so dead calm it makes Brown feel the need to head for cover.

"Someone's gonna get wasted," Bull hisses, his eyes wide and dark. Sweat breaks across his brow as he gazes at Brown. "It could just as well be you . . . or even me." His eyes narrow as his ears perk. "Hear that?"

"The shots?" Brown says hearing the report of a distant rifle.

"Yeah, man. That's what it's all about." He leans forward. "Reality. The primal simplicity of kill or be killed. Ain't nothing complicated about it. Not like back in the World where as soon as you turn your back your best buddy is boom-boomin' your girl. Back in the World where gossip and rumors can strip you of your self worth and integrity. Back in the World," he continues to philosophize, "where they think the amount of money they got has something to do with high moral, values, principles or how *right* they are. But it ain't so.

"Yeah," he looks around, "over here we all bleed red and we don't leave our buddies behind."

"Well said."

"Thanks." Written on Bull's steel pot is:

LIVE BY CHANCE
LOVE BY CHOICE
KILL BY PROFESSION

"How long you been incountry, man," Bull asks.

"About . . . little over two months now."

"That's respectable. That means you know that when you land in Nam the first thing you do is write yourself off as dead," he says all-knowing.

"How so?"

"You gotta have nothin' to lose," Bull fixes his eyes on Brown. "Then you might have a chance." He swings the rifle like a gunfighter might and dry squeezes the trigger, mouthing, "Blam." He lowers it. "Gives ya the edge. Does no good running around yellin' 'I'm gonna die. I'm gonna die.' If you do, you'll die a thousands deaths.

"I ain't afraid of dying," Brown says straightening-up as he tries to act brave. He has been near the-edge on occasion but nothing like Bull who's been swimming with the sharks.

"I hear ya." Bull senses his young listener is still basically an NFG. "Let me put it to you like this. In war to have a commitment to kill is to have a commitment to live."

"Yeah, I think I know what you mean."

Bull gives him a fraternal nod. Reaching he grabs a can of fruit and begins running the P-38 around the edge.

"What's it like," Brown asks, moving to ground zero. "To kill a man?"

On hearing the question, Bull tightens. Taking up the rifle, he ejects the empty magazine and clears the weapon. Then slowly, almost mechanically, he lifts his head to where Brown can see a volcanic eruption taking place within the abyss of his dark orbs. "It's great, man." He stares through Brown. "Best high ya can ever get," he says with no sign of remorse.

Brown nervously taps the magazines while Bull's hot moldy breath continues to spill.

"It's like . . . ," Bull pauses in deep thought. "It's like ya got this control over life and death. And when ya do the honors." He looks wild. "Wow!" Bull calmly, returns from the vision which had ignited his soul.

"Shit, you need to let off some steam? Just go into the bush and blow someone away. It don't get no better than that." Bull takes a dirty spoon from his pocket, and digs into the can of peaches. "Want one?"

"No thanks. I'm fine."

Bull is truly a unique soldier. The kind that could hardly wait to get into a firefight. He appears very intelligent, very cunning, and with a four day old beard—which he has no intention of shaving—Bull appears like a natural born warrior.

Brown wonders how straight-shooter Bedford would stack up against this one? Which one would be more prepared to do battle? Who would be the tougher, braver, unforgiving?

Bull seems to have a special brand of courage, persistence, optimism, and a single minded purpose, "more war please." And remarkably, he seems to view it romantically.

"That's my babe. We're thinkin' of gettin' married when I get home," Bull says proudly with peach juice oozing around his smacking lips. He hands Brown a small, frayed around the edges photograph, the kind taken in a dime store photo booth. "Fox, huh?"

"Oh yeah. You're a lucky man, Bull," Brown says agreeably, handing back the photo. "Can hardly wait to get back, huh?"

"Yeah, I guess," Bull says smiling at the photo. He fondly slips the photograph back into the wallet. "I'm gonna ask her to meet me in Hawaii on R&R."

Standing, he hoists the rucksack onto his back. He puts on the helmet and Brown reads the girlfriends name, *Elana* penned on the camouflage cover.

"Say, never got your name," Bull asks politely.

"Brown." He quickly stands.

"Glad to meet ya, Brown." Bull salutes with a tilt of his head. "Guess I better get a move on." With a slight limp he makes his way to the exit. "Catch ya in Da Nang, Brown."

"Good luck, Bull. And thanks. Thanks for everything."

Bull walks past the tent flap and out into the rain.

America was built around the courage of men like Bull and Bedford. Men willing to give it their all. Brown remembers seeing the old movie *Titanic*. And since then always wondered what kind of person would willingly face death by staying onboard while the ship sank? Willingly give away their tomorrow so that others might see the light of day. That question has just been answered. The Vietnam infantrymen has that kind of courage. The courage to sacrifice oneself for someone else.

"God bless."

Realizing he's lost track of time, Brown hurries to his barracks. He stuffs the four newly acquired magazines into his rucksack, flings it onto his back and rushes to the LZ.

He's immensely relieved on spotting Bedford near the landing pad, sitting slump shouldered on the wet ground. Brown lumbers over and takes the space next to him. Soldiers are scattered all around waiting in the mud and cold rain. Small groups are thick in conversation, but for the most part, soldiers are listless or dozing.

One chopper after another came in low under the dark storm clouds to load-up while the cold downpour continues. When Bull climbs aboard the platform, Brown stands ready to wave, but he doesn't look his way. Bull just sits there within himself appearing so alone, so vulnerable. Then the chopper yanks him into the black night.

"Alright, listen up!" Yamane calls walking over. "Go back to your barracks and get some rest. We'll try again in the morning. The weather's grounded the choppers."

8 February 1968

"Bravo Company is taking heavy casualties," Sergeant Yamane trumpets. His eyes move slowly across the faces of the soldiers of his squad. "Apparently the NVA are taking them head-on." He refers to the ensuing battle with its sound rumbling through the air and shock waves vibrating the earth beneath their feet. The battle rages across the rice fields at the Catholic village of Lo Giang. It had started early that morning as a running firefight and is now moving into its fourth hour.

"Charlie Company was sent to left flank the NVA, but are now getting hit just as hard as them. As I speak, the Alpha Gunfighters are moving in to try to get behind the NVA, trying to cut-off their retreat." Yamane pauses. "We're moving in to reinforce the Gunfighters."

"Brown!" Sergeant Denning hurries over, "you'll be with the lieutenant as the platoon RTO." Denning moves to address the soldiers. "Men, listen up! Fix bayonets!" Everyone's face goes slack as they draw the cold steel blades, knowing full well the hideous implications.

"Yamane," Brown calls.

In mid stride, Yamane turns and with a glint of a smile asks, "You ready?"

"I guess?"

He motions to his heart and swallows hard. "I'll see ya on the other side, buddy."

"Reconn! Saddle-up. We're movin' out!" The command reverberates through the air on the wings of destiny and the doomsday troops obey.

The wide village main street is lined with curious Vietnamese civilians who have been waiting patiently for the advance. Intermingled among them are a few Marines who stand well back within the crowd, apparently not wanting to appear conspicuous.

Tailing the platoon leader, Brown's eyes sweep over the spectators. Spectators that understand the procession is heading into what, for some, will be certain death. His eyes drift over a little boy and wonders what thoughts are going through his head. Is the boy trying to detect something about a soldier that might foreshadow his imminent death? In a bizarre way, Brown realizes this is probably entertainment to these people. Like gladiators going into the coliseum to fight to the finish. The point is, these villagers are not going to miss the cryptic excitement.

A huge bomb explodes making the earth quake. Electric cannons from gunships chatter and F-4 Phantom jets engines screech overheard on bombing runs. The noise and vibration come together in a mind shattering crescendo that envelop Reconn as they enter the mouth of a rusted French built plank bridge. Beyond the steel structure, they can see black smoke billowing over the tree tops.

"Napalm," someone remarks.

"They say that if you're close enough to the explosion, it'll collapse your lungs and kill ya."

"And it sticks to you like glue not like willy peter. That phosphorous stuff will burn a hole right through ya."

"Wouldn't wanna be on the receiving end of that," another soldier groans.

Sergeant Yamane, who volunteered as pointman, turns left into a ravine on the far side of the old bridge. Moving through a tree grove, a chopper zooms low overhead and someone shouts, "There goes Crazy Peacock heading right into the thick of it."

"Go get 'em Peacock!"

At the edge of the tree line, reconn has a panorama of an expansive rice field a good mile-and-a-half across which extends in width beyond view. The roar of a Phantom Jet catches Brown's attention. Silhouetted against the clear sky, it banks and swoops around for another bombing run. Brown follows the F-4 Phantom as it goes into a steep power dive, pulls-up and screeching at tree level flings two napalm bombs.

The bombs erupt on impact sending voracious balls of fire vaulting vegetation to engulf a swath of trees over a hundred yards long and fifty yards wide. The engines roar as the Phantom banks and skyrockets, leaving behind an area billowing with black smoke. Another Jet sweeps in firing rockets that send shrapnel exploding across the terrain, its 40mm cannons whirring.

Reconn moves into the rice field in wide fire-team formation. In the distant smoky haze, they spot A-Company Gunfighters in the maelstrom of battle. Closing, they realize Alpha is in the midst of fierce hand-to-hand combat with a horde of NVA. And are virtually encircled by exploding enemy mortars, mortars intent on cutting off any chance of retreat but also indiscriminately killing friend or foe. Meanwhile, a murderous barrage of enemy rockets and small arms fire pour into the Gunfighters from the distant tree line.

Crouching low, Reconn double-times with their equipment bucking against their backs. On spotting the reinforcements, the few NVA left alive suddenly disengage and try to escape. They become fair game for the Gunfighters that don't let a single enemy soldier escape.

Reconn advances as fast a possible plodding through thick mud and calf deep water that sucks on their boots. Finally they begin passing among the muddy, blood-soaked, scraggly survivors. Gunfighters that are still mobile, help drag along the wounded, dying and dead.

A dazed shirtless soldier with a taunt face struggles past, his chest and side wrapped tightly with a dirty, blood soaked bandage. Another soldier, who carries a wounded comrade over his shoulder, struggles through the mud with the enormous weight, gasping for air with every step. Two more soldiers pass struggling with a lethargic WIA in a rifle poncho.

"Come on . . . come on, man. Hang in the*rrrre!*" Throughout the battlefield, medics and comrades with bloodied hands are desperately applying tourniquets and field bandages. "You can do it. Hold in there. Come on. Come o*nnnn,*" a bandaged medic entreats, to a pain-delirious soldier with the pallor of death creeping over his face.

Like a witch's caldron, the bubbling death brew spills forth steaming war. It is a mixture of fermenting mud, pulverized vegetation, flesh and bone, organs, and the aroma of fresh blood pulling it all together.

Brown agonizes, when the blood soaked battlefield suddenly becomes reminiscent—one he had seen before? In a photograph? At the movies? Even more than that. It holds such potency that it could only have happened for real. But when and where? Letting his mind float, he views a past life. He's a soldier moving across a Civil War battlefield.

Wheeeee-*aa!!!* A Jet comes in low for a last murderous heartbreaker and disappears in the blue sky. The Huey gunships, that have been pounding-away at a safe distance till the Phantoms were finished, now launch their attack.

The throbbing noise reaches a crescendo as the gunships vomit more death from their rocket launchers, electric flex guns and machine guns that pummel every square inch of the terrain just within the tree line. The gunships strafe back and forth over the area with serrated overlap.

A Huey goes for a low level pass dropping from either side fifty-five gallon drums of tear gas that detonate and create a huge swirl of white smoke.

The gunships meanwhile methodically work their way to the left, probably following the NVA escape route.

On reaching the epicenter of doom, reconn finds it strewn with countless corpses. One GI sprawls face down in a puddle of water, his arm draped over a dike still clutching his M-16 rifle. The leather strap on the rifle is familiar. "Bull? God, I'm sorry," Brown says under his breath.

Almost completely submerged in the rice field is another American soldier who lies on his back, eyes wide and gaping mouth full of mud. Brown's eyes travels the dead soldier's foot trail of terror, until he sees where his life first began to ebb. Reenacting the event, Brown visualizes the soldier crouching while frantically blasting away. Then hot lead catapults through his skin, slicing away his vital organs. He doesn't know it at first but he's suddenly becoming dizzy. Looking down he cries, "Oh my God! I'm hit!" His hand tries to stop the bleeding but nothing helps as the blood pumps between his fingers till they drip with crimson red. The soldier turns to run but, as though caught in a nightmare, moves in slow motion. But this is no dream. There is nothing to awaken from. It's real. He tumbles. Twisting and falling dead before he even hits the water.

Looking around, Brown noting that the Reconn soldiers are swinging wide of both American and NVA KIA.

With no body near, an M-16 lays in a fresh pool of blood that the mud had yet to absorbed. Yards away lay an NVA, whose ruptured cranium spills forth gray matter. Brown believes this is the last enemy kill of the now missing American KIA.

Approaching the tree line, their senses tingle with anticipation. Without hesitation the Reconn proceeds through the underbrush, working their way over previously trampled vegetation till they come to a well traveled dirt thoroughfare. To their right and on the side of the road is a bullet riddled Marine Jeep with shattered windshield. The seat is blood stained and a blood soaked GI jungle boot lay nearby. No Marine bodies.

A hundred yards further up the road, leading to the rice field, lay a dead water buffalo. The carcass is so bloated that the skin is banjo string tight with fissures ready to rupture. The flies swarm about in preparation for the feast.

Reconn veers to the left and makes their way toward the main village in the middle of a palm tree grove.

A helicopter lands in the rice fields and a few minutes later a television crew comes crashing through the trees. The trio went directly over to Reconn's lieutenant.

"Sir," a commentator asks, holding a microphone, "what's the situation at this moment?"

The lieutenant stares perplexed, at a loss for words. The camera remains on the platoon leader. "Well, ahhh," the lieutenant fumbles with words. "We've, ahhh . . . dealt the NVA Division a decisive blow and ahhh." He looks over at Brown. "It looks like we have them on the run."

The television crew begins dogging the lieutenant for more information. "From what we've determined," the lieutenant continues, "the NVA moved in here last night and killed the two Marines at the village outpost. That's their jeep over there at the edge of town. Then we know they rounded up all the villagers but we're not sure what happened to them. But we have located a mass grave."

"How many civilians were massacred?"

"Could be as many as . . . two-hundred-and-fifty. We engaged them late this morning and have taken light casualties."

"Light?" Brown blurts pointing toward the rice field.

"Does it appear you'll be making contact?" the commentator continues the interview with microphone again thrust into the lieutenant's face. The officer seems reluctant to answer so remains mute. "Okay," the newsman says, "we have enough here. Let's get back to the field for some footage."

Hours later

Reconn soldiers are sprinkled throughout the rice field as they back-track across the bloody battlefield. Overhead, the sound of a commercial passenger jetliner catches their attention as it rushes to cruising altitude. Then as if by command, the entire platoon comes to a halt and shifts their eyes skyward. "Freedom bird," someone says with the words echoing across the field. Their eyes follow the flight path, and Brown could almost hear the stewardess asking the passengers in a sweet feminine voice, "Coffee, tea, or me?"

The soldiers file into a graveyard where they set-up a perimeter next to the rag-tag remnants of A-Company Gunfighters. Reconn CP, where Brown will stay with the radio, is positioned behind a headstone with a commanding view of the battlefield.

Brown lowers the heavy rucksack. With urgency in the air, there is no time to rest. He unfastens the entrenching tool, unfolds the sandbags and begins scooping out a foxhole. By the time he reaches knee deep, he is exhausted. He plops onto the rim of dirt, takes a canteen, wipes off the dirt from around the mouth and drinks in earnest.

With a rubbery arm, he again takes up the entrenching tool and holding a sandbag in the other starts filling. For the next hour he alternates digging, then sitting and filling sandbags. At the four foot mark, he hits spongy ground. Raising the entrenching tool over his head he slams it harder into the ground hoping to dislodge the object.

"Oh no." He stands back with shovel in hand gawking at the ruptured human rib cage. Then the wrenching smell comes rushing out. Quickly, he shovels dirt back over the corpse and compacts it with his feet till the smell abates. He re-sets the entrenching tool into the chop-position and begins to widen the foxhole in the hopes of having time—strength enough—to dig clear of the corpse.

Drenched in sweat, Brown sits on the dirt rim and takes another drink. Then notices a few Gunfighters talking quietly amongst themselves. They keep staring at something on the ground near the rice field. Curious and in need of a back stretch, he decides he has a few minutes to spare.

When the soldiers move clear, he notices a rifle standing vertical from the ground with a steel pot resting over the butt. That ain't no way to treat a rifle, Brown thinks. Still unable to see what's so interesting, Brown buckles on the pistol belt, grabs the rifle, dons his helmet then ventures for a closer look.

Now that he can see the rifle plainly, he realizes its affixed bayonet has been run through a battle scarred boot and the helmet is shrapnel riddled. "A Field Cross," Brown says under his breath. "I should've known." The Field Cross, built with the equipment of those who have given the supreme sacrifice, is intended to pay tribute to the recent KIAs.

Brown's attention moves to a grieving soldier who is half kneeling, nestling his face in wrapped arms. At his feet lies a KIA with a leg and arm extended in an unnatural positions locked tight by rigor mortis. His buddy.

Then the scene opens full force. A fusillade of horror rushes through his spine. A spike thrusts through his heart. His jaw drops. His eyes bulge. He freezes in place. To the front lay some twenty American soldiers acquiescing to their fate, all in a row that reaches to infinity.

The corpses lay silently naked, quietly exposed, the only thing protecting them from the chilly ground are muddy, blood drenched ponchos that had been used for transportation.

Two GIs move among them, one busying himself with checking dog tags attached to KIA boot laces. He calls out the name of the deceased, detaches one tag and leaves the other. The second GI carefully checks the KIA's name on the roster. "Tagged-and-bagged."

Brown stares at the dog tag dangling from a KIA's boot lace. The tiny piece of metal with the soldier's name, identification number, religion, and blood type crushed into it.

Needing to find Bull, Brown slowly proceeds along "Dead Man's Row." He studies the mud covered, crusted faces of the KIA in shredded clothes, clothes that appear like another layer of ripped flesh. The tears expose a mass of blood, bone and gut but most importantly—the hole from which life has escaped.

He stumbles to a halt. At his feet lay a familiar soldier. "Bull?" He stares with tunnel vision, everything in perfect focus, at every frightening microscopic imperfection of flesh. The view burns itself into his subconscious.

With eyelids drawn, Bull's expression is curiously tranquil. During his short life, Bull seems to have understood and in some ways relished the fact that the deck had been stacked against him. He knew and now Brown knows that he didn't have a prayer in the world of getting through this war alive. Soldiers born to protect, like Bull, seem so much more *real* in death.

Bull, like a legendary gunfighter of the Old West, understands his ilk. In a way it's as if God came down and asked, "Bull. So, how ya wanna go?" And Bull replies, "Well, if it's time, I wanna go with my buddies on a battlefield."

Bull got his wish.

BULL

H e r e,
in the land
of war, will
I be forgotten
on its battlefield,
as soon as the
grey light of dusk
creeps across m y
blood, and my remains
are washed away by wind
and rain? Is my loss seen?
The grief seems s o cold.
Death is different here, not so
easily understood. Please, let
m e be remembered. L e t m y
legacy be passed on. Pray for me
now, and I'll pray for you later, because
the thirst of W A R has n o t been quenched.

Dear Ma and Dad *9 February 1968*

Well, here I am. I can see Da Nang from my night position. By the way it is eight P.M. at night. I can't see the lines on the paper.

I am sorry I haven't been writing the last few days but you'll know why when you read this letter.

I was in the field the seventh of February and they choppered me back to LZ Gator at about five P.M. I was then put on the chopper pad until 8:30 P.M. It was too dark for the choppers to land so we went and slept at our barracks. In the morning we choppered to a place a few miles from Da Nang. They gave us bunkers that were demolished. I worked most of the day building a strong roof because they get mortared often. When I finished the roof they pulled us out and set us in some different demolished bunkers. We were building a roof when we got the word to move into the field.

On the way to Da Nang I saw a couple of Navy *Destroyers*. They use them for fire missions along the coast.

Well, don't be alarmed. My whole 1/6th battalion came here. *Bravo* Company was hit hard, so Charley Company went to the rescue. But then Charley Company started getting mortared. Then A Company went to the rescue. A Company got mortared and so we came in. A company lost eighteen men dead, fifty wounded. Charlie Company lost all of its officers. Come to find out the village they were trying to go into had 1200 *hard core* NVA Regulars.

A couple of days ago a little U.S. Marine Base Camp was overrun in the village. So the village was hit with an Air Strike and an artillery *barrage*. Then we closed in .

All the ground we covered was blood stained. I saw four American soldiers dead, lying where they died. One soldier had an NVA laying next to him with his head broken open. His brains were falling out. The whole area was ghastly. I saw one blood trail that was small, then all of a sudden there was a puddle of blood.

We moved into the village. There I seen a lot of NVA equipment, pistol belts and a NVA beret.

These pictures I found in a house. Last night we dug in because of so many mortars around. A chopper saw us, so he opened up on us with Machine guns and Grenades. I dove into my hole just as a grenade went off a few feet away and the machine gun bullet zipped by my head.

One of my good friends was killed. Another man was hit. I don't know if he died or not.

I am learning about how it is here. I am in a real *HOT* area. I feel God is with me. If anything should happen, I am never really gone.

The last two nights I have slept in grave yards and have seen many dead men and dead animals. It doesn't seem to bother me much. I guess I never knew them when they were alive.

Well, I will try to keep writing. This area is different and mail is harder to get out.

Hey, I might be on T.V. An ABC newsman was with us when we searched the village. We found rifles and everything.

I will start a different letter starting with tomorrow morning.

Well, bye for now, Fred Leo

P.S. I received your goody package and I ate it all up except for one can.

Dear Ma and Dad *11 February 1968*

Well, not much has happened here by Da Nang.

Yesterday we heard there was VC or NVA in a village. So they bombarded it. I almost came home early. A three inch piece of shrapnel missed my foot by two inches. If it had hit, I would probably be on my way home.

We carry more weight here than in Chu Lai. I had over 60 lbs. on my back. I could barely lift it to get it on my back.

The weight is too much and I am continually *swearing*. If we get mortared like A Company I wouldn't have too much of a chance unless I dropped my radio. It has a quick release on it. I have seen so much the last days! I realize many more things than before. About all things.

Could you send me a picture of you and Dad. Okay?

Viet Nam has taught me so much about the ways of life so quickly. Well, right now I am in good shape. Everything is a little confusing. The Company is trying to get organized. I hope I will be able to get more letters written.

I will write tomorrow.

Well, it is eleven P.M. but the moon is out. I am on guard. Every night we sleep in a grave yard. It is good because the mounds will stop shrapnel from mortars.

Ma, send me *thicker* socks, like the ones you sent me before. Okay. Also a *pen*. Maybe two. Okay? This pen is running out of ink and I will not be able to get one out of my foot locker. Thanks!!

Well I guess we saved Da Nang from an attack. There was over 1200 NVA in the area. We have already killed about 300. We put them off balance for now.

Well, it is morning of the 12th of February.

We are going into the LZ (Landing Zone) where we came from when we hit Da Nang. The trucks will be here any minute. When we get to the LZ we will leave right away on another mission. Probably a lot hotter than this one.

Just found out we are going near Tam Ky. You know how Hot it is there.

The weight is so heavy I got rid of my poncho. We dig in every night.

I heard this was a real big operation. It was called Operation "Miracle." ABC has films of it. I am in it. Maybe it will be on TV.

Here are the trucks....

Bye now, Fred Leo

P.S. I am the lieutenant's RTO.

Dear Ma and Dad *12 February 1968*

Well, I am at LZ Baldy. It might be misspelled, but it sounds like this. We are going to carry more than ever before. Things I carry:

Fragmentation jacket
Helmet
27 magazines of ammunition
Radio with extra battery
Gas mask
3 fragmentation grenades
five smoke grenades
100 rounds machine gun ammo
five meals of C-rations
four canteens

M-16 rifle
Poncho & liner
and a few other things.

Entrenching tool
Ten sandbags

BLA! That is weight. It is nearly a hundred pounds. *UH !* My aching back as Uncle Raymond would say.

By the way I picked up a light weight poncho.

It is real *Hot* here so I will need everything because the NVA shoot lots of mortars.

I took two showers in an hour. I just can't get clean enough. It feels great. I love to get clean now. I brushed my teeth about four times.

I have learned to take what you can get your hands on. Act like the Army owes it to you and you will make it. So I got a lot. I took Jelly, Peanuts and I took the shower in a *Personal* shower of a top medic.

I heard a little about what happened at the village of Lo Giang in Da Nang. There was a Marine camp in the middle of it. The NVA came and the PF's hid their weapons and ran. So then the Marines came with twenty-five men in a truck. The truck was blown up and they were all killed.

The NVA were going to cross the river and attack Da Nang!

Well we are supposed to go out tomorrow morning. I will write and tell you if I do. See you tomorrow.

Well, today is the 13th of February.

Got a lot of sleep. I feel pretty good. I am pretty sure we will move out today.

By the way the reason we are here is that the NVA in the area are trying to get back to Cambodia. We are trying to stop them before they do.

Well, I am skimping on the weight. I am going to carry only two meals. We might go out three days before re-supply on food, but I would rather go hungry than carry the weight. Well, I better close. By for now

Love, Fred Leo

Dear Ma and Dad *15 February 1968*

Well, I am out in the field. It is one A.M. The moon is just bright enough to see. Well, I am going to be transferred into another company. "D" *Company.* Don't change addresses yet but soon.

We have had slight contact with NVA. We took pot shots at a platoon of them. But we couldn't hit them. So we called in artillery. Also we called in tanks and tracks. But before we got zeroed in on them they took off. The next day we went mountain climbing. We are now located in the middle of a ridge line of them. For two days we have humped them. It is horrible. Down one valley and up the next mountain. Our lead element killed four and captured two.

Tonight we seen some movement and we called in artillery. We didn't see any more movement.

Guess what. They got new C-rations. More fruit and better meals in each unit. They added another spaghetti and ground beef. I haven't had it yet. I can hardly wait to try it.

Well, I heard we were going into LZ Baldy today. I hope we do. I can't last much longer in these hills and with the weight.

I got the shoe dye. I couldn't carry it into the field, so we all dyed our boots Black. The boots had turned white from wear and tear. I decided not to bring the hammock in the field, so you don't need to send any more dye.

Ma, I still have the picture of you on the advertisement. Could you send me a regular picture of you. Okay? Try to get one of Dad too.

Ma. send me a $100 *bank draft.* I heard they can be cashed easily, but not personal checks. Send it right away so I can find out how to cash it.

By the way, my 'high' friend Ziggy, he was the one killed at Da Nang. I didn't see him after the chopper shot him. I am glad. He was mangled. Well, I will continue tomorrow okay. Then I can see the lines.

Well, today is the 16th of February.

We are not going in yet. We are about to go on a Search and Destroy Mission. The silly thing is there isn't going to be any action. There are no NVA in the area. They cleared out. But we keep on humping the hills. If we would find something, I wouldn't mind. But as it is, it is useless. Well, when I stop to rest I will continue this letter.

Well, I can get this mailed, so I will say good bye

Your son, Fred Leo

16 February 1968

An exhausted Reconn moves over the mountain crest in the late morning hours following an infiltration route of the Ho Chi Minh Trail. Last evening they had bumped into the rear of an NVA squad. After a short running firefight they'd killed one. Then, as a precaution against a much larger enemy force, they doubled back and hurried off on an obscure side trail that went right up the side of the mountain. Once clear of the area, they brought in H&I artillery to cover their escape.

Late in the night they had stopped along the trail and rose at first light. So without much rest, they push past limbs and underbrush covered with dew and begin snaking their way through triple canopy jungle along a rocky dry stream bed.

"Is it always like this?" Doc Labarbra, their new medic, sighs as he trudges behind Brown, the platoon RTO. "I've only been with you guys a week and we haven't stopped humpin' yet. And I've already seen enough war to last a life time," he groans. "Is there some way to turn off this bad movie?"

"Yeah," Brown pants, "we need to find some dinks to kill so we can get a three-day pass like those guys did on those tanks."

"How do ya do it?" Doc asks breathless.

"Don't think about it. Just keep movin' and keep yours eyes off the ground," Brown advises. "Remember, if you let your eyes drop, you'll drop next."

They'd been descending the mountain for hours when they rounded a bend. The jungle suddenly thins and to their amazement are greeted with the panoramic view of a lush green valley floor. The view is so intoxicating that Brown loses track of his footing and nearly falls over a root. The fertile lawn gives way to irrigation canals carrying water to a network of rice fields that stretch to the horizon.

The soldiers enter in awe, their senses imbued with the tranquility and aroma of the a region that could easily pass as The Land of Milk and Honey. They march light on their feet, momentarily ignoring their advanced state of exhaustion. They come to a grassy parade size lawn large enough to assemble an entire battalion of soldiers. Skirting its edge they set up a perimeter and break for lunch.

"Ain't hungry?" Doc questions, opening a can of spaghetti and meatballs.

"Had to make a choice. Can't carry this weight," he motions to the equipment, "along with food too," Brown tries not to sound too pitiful but pitiful enough to get food.

"How can you carry that thing?" Doc motions to the field radio. "You got more weight than anyone."

He offers Brown the spaghetti. Brown whips out a spoon, licks it clean and spits out the dirt. Then he digs in like a starved animal.

"Tell ya what, Doc," Brown mumbles with mouth full. "I'll repay you with some hot chocolate."

"Got a question. What's all this "so called" military intelligence? I mean intelligence says 'this'. You know. Then a next day intelligence says 'that', he shrugs. "If you really listened to that crap you'd go nuts."

"If you ask me, I think the whole group has a lack of Intelligence. Hump here. Check that. Hump there. Then chase up the hill. Run around 'cause intelligence has a hot tip. They don't give us no rest."

"Okay, men, let's go," the lieutenant calls, "let's search the area."

"Sir, can I use Brown?" Yamane requests. Receiving approval he signals for Brown to hurry.

"I'm comin'," Brown said happily. "Sir, can I just carry the radio?"

"Sure. That's fine." The lieutenant turns his attention to Yamane and the other squad leaders. "If we find anything, maybe they'll let us hold up here for a few days."

Searching for about fifteen minutes, Yamane shouts, "There. In the clearing!"

Bedford fires his M-79. Okie and Sergeant Yamane open up with their M-16s. However, the VC is already out of range bolting the last few yards to disappear in the foliage beyond the rice field.

Bedford squats and hand signals toward a tunnel entrance. It leads under a hill that has collapsed after taking a direct hit by an artillery round. Next to it is an array of broken bamboo tables and shelves.

Yamane, Okie and Brown shed their gear. With rifle at the ready Okie goes first with a flashlight shining through the entrance. Crawling twenty feet they arrive at a large underground room with a five-foot ceiling. While Okie explores a connecting tunnel, Yamane moves the light beam around the soot covered walls. Along the wall sets a lantern on a bamboo table. On entering there had been a foul odor, now inside they realize this must've been the local infirmary.

"Lookie here," Okie says showing up with a prisoner. He flashes the light onto a slender Vietnamese.

"Well, I'll be damned" Sergeant Yamane says leaning for a closer look. "A nurse."

Thirty minutes later back at the perimeter, a Huey descends through yellow marker smoke. Their re-supply is unloaded and an ARVN liaison jumps off. Following a short conversation with the lieutenant, the ARVN re-boards with the prisoner.

"I pity that nurse," Sergeant Yamane comments in dismay when the chopper lifts off. This unexpected revelation causes Brown to follow the departing chopper. Interrogating, the ARVN leans over the nurse shouting while he gouges her face with a Colt .45.

"I hope she doesn't try to escape," Brown says.

Yamane looks at Brown knowing his meaning. In December they had turned over three prisoners to the ARVNs. Yamane, Brown and Okie then witnessed the prisoners getting thrown one-by-one from the chopper's platform. The radio communication that followed explained that the prisoners had "tried to escape."

"Our job is over," Yamane says.

Next morning, Brown woke behind a hedge row to the luxuriant rays of the sun spilling through the tree leaves and sparkling off the crystal mist. The filtered yellow light creeps across the parade ground that reminds him of the parade grounds at Morgan Park Academy. . . .During eighth grade Brown boarded there and every morning they would raise the American flag and say the pledge of allegiance before dashing off to breakfast.

Grabbing the empty canteens, Brown heads over to the local well. The ground surrounding the well is trampled clear of vegetation and has several distinct paths leading toward the mountain trails. A bucket and rope sets nearby.

Obviously the area had been heavily occupied by the NVA, but there is absolutely no remnants of tossed equipment, garbage, or so much as a cigarette butt. It is immaculately clear and pristine in every possible way.

"Go-o-od morning, Brown." Doc is cheerful after a good nights sleep. "Guess intelligence had it right about this place, huh. Obviously a training and processing center. The lieutenant said the nurse told 'em the last of the NVA moved out of here not more than a few days back."

"Brown," Sergeant Yamane calls. "After breakfast load up some lunch. The lieutenant wants this area combed inch-by-inch." Yamane moves toward the next position wearing only a pistol belt, helmet and fragmentation jacket, rifle in hand. "Travel as light as you can."

Following a hasty meal, Brown takes his entrenching tool, digs a hole, drops the cans inside and covers them thinking, he'd be as tidy as the NVA. Brown unstraps the pack and hoists the radio attached to the aluminum frame.

"Brown! Don't forget your Daily-Daily," Doc warns, holding out the malaria pill. "You've been taking your weekly one too, right?"

"Thanks Doc." Brown shrugs, then tosses the pill into his mouth and chases it with water.

"You don't wanna get malaria."

"I know," Brown says feeling like a little child. "Say, it looks like it's gonna be a good day, today," he comments pleased with the light work load.

"Alright, stay alert. Stay alive. This area might be booby-trapped," Sergeant Yamane warns as they assemble. "Keep your eyes peeled."

Green, Shepard, Okie, Bedford and Brown follow their squad leader in the general direction of the main village. In a short while they come to a bamboo bridge that spans a ten-foot irrigation canal filled with slow moving water. On the far side are several typical straw and mud huts. Bedford cautiously crosses the bridge. Safely on the other side, he moves over to a tree for cover and gives the "ready" signal.

Being the last to cross, Brown stops in the middle of the bridge to watch the sunlight glisten off the clear water. Just below the green surface, weeds waft lazily with the current flowing languidly into the expanse of rice fields. The colorful scene framed by a blue sky, is so vibrant that it seems as though it is actual a living organism.

"Dung lai! La dai!" Yamane bellows taking aim at a pregnant woman carrying a small naked boy that has steps into view. Okie hurries past to check the hut from which she came.

"Papa-san, can cuoc," Okie calls from inside. An old man appears in the doorway with identification in hand. Okie and Bedford are ordered to continue sweeping through the immediate area.

"Dung lai! La dai!" Bedford shouts. They dart away and begin firing their weapons. Both Yamane and Brown listen, but hear no return fire.

"Born in 1882," Yamane reads the man's ID card. He looks back and forth between ID picture and the shriveled figure that stands before him clothed in only black silk shorts.

"Is it him?"

"Yeah. I guess."

"Well," Brown figures out his age, "that makes him 86 years old. Yamane, why is so many of these of men born in the eighteen-eighties?"

"You tell me."

"Old men and pregnant women," Brown says as he walks over to a hedgerow. "Babies and little kids. That's all we ever see in these villages. And yet the fields are planted and . . . " while talking, Brown shuffles his feet and inadvertently pushes away some dirt to uncover a piece of plastic. "What's this?"

Yamane comes over and kneels to investigate. "Well, a trap door of some type. Too close to the hooch to be a booby-trap." He stares from the woman to the old man to see if there are any signs of trepidation. Seeing none, he draws his bayonet and probes around the wooden cover. Finding nothing unusual, he slowly lifts the cover to expose a ceramic storage jar brimming with rice.

"Rice."

"You know what's really bizarre," Brown says. "Just a few days ago the NVA were standing right here on this very spot. And these people were catering to them."

"Yeah," Yamane agrees scooping out a handful to let the rice stream through his fingers. "But these people are really just trying to get along. I mean this is their home, right?" Both of them find themselves sympathetic to the old man, woman and her infant.

"Bet that's an NVA baby," Brown says.

"She's an enemy factory."

"A wartime baby-factory," Brown says picking up on the gallows humor.

"Ah, shit!" The cry comes from Bedford who had stumbled over a bush and lay sprawled on the ground. Okie steps over him without an offer of help and comes over.

"Bedford!" Yamane laughs. "Let's keep the racket down."

"He got away," Bedford informs them, brushing himself off. "But Okie tripped on some buried crocks full of rice."

"Tripped?" Yamane asks.

"That's the only way a guy like Okie could find anything," Brown jokes knowing that's the way anyone ever found anything. By tripping over it. Just as he did too, a few minutes before.

"Does the rice mean anything," Okie wonders.

"Think so. I think maybe S-2 was right for once," Yamane remarks. "Did you find anything else?"

Okie reaches into a pocket and produces a handful of expended AK-47 casings which he places in Yamane's hand. Yamane analyzes them. "Not very tarnished."

"Probably were having target practice out in the rice paddies," Okie speculates.

Yamane takes the radio handset from Brown and has a short conversation with the lieutenant. Signing-off, he says, "Alright let's continue to comb through just this immediate area."

Since the battle of Lo Giang, Brown has been developing a grudging respect for the enemy. Their dedication was truly phenomenal. Curious, Brown takes one enemy AK-47 casing knowing it has touched the hands of the formidable enemy. He walks over to the canal and under the shade of a banana tree slowly rolls the brass casing back and forth in his open palm. The cool solid brass gives him a vision.

. . . . A young Asian soldier, both physically and mentally challenged after a three month, seven-hundred mile journey down the treacherous Ho Chi Minh, is greeted by fellow combatants at the staging area. After a meal, fit-for-a-king, of chicken and rice, he lays out his sleeping gear for a well deserved rest. After a few days of refitting and getting his new issue of equipment, he walks onto a jut of land surrounded by the flooded rice fields. He takes a seat to rests under the shade of a coconut palm. Complacently, he gazes over the endless sea of green rice sprouts and marvels at the sky that has begun to dispatch rain clouds to nourish the agricultural valley.

The soldier leans against the palm, a rice sprout stuck in his mouth. The placid landscape causes him to ponder and nourish his will to defend the leadership, their doctrines and beliefs with his own blood.

Soldier to soldier, like Brown, his ultimate goal is also peace.

A colorful butterfly alights on the muzzle of his AK-47 that sets propped against the tree trunk. After a few seconds of exploration, the creature takes flight on a warm tropical breeze.

BEAUTIFUL BUTTERFLY

Oh, fly, fly away beautiful butterfly. Fly away to the
enemy camps. Ask them, Why must we fight?
Why can't we have peace? Let us all go
home to plant our rice. To kiss the
girls. Give
us back days that we may
cherish. Oh, fly, fly away beautiful
butterfly all the way back to the ones I love. Tell
them to say a prayer, for I shall not be coming home.

The wind builds to swirl and knead the darkening clouds that begin to move faster and faster causing the suns light to flicker like fleeting butterflies across the fruited plains. At dusk the sun slides behind black mountains of clouds and the rains begins to patter.

A barely perceptible glimmer of light shows on the horizon to announce the dawning of a new day. In the secret valley far below, a young Asian soldier awakes. He stretches and takes a deep breath of aromatic lush jungle air. Rising to his feet, he marches to the call of a distant battle.

Dear Ma and Dad *18 February 1968*

About the men that went to Da Nang. We lost a few but we have gotten a few recruits since the first of February. I doubt you could find *River South* on the map. It is just a call sign. It is south of Chu Lai.

I am waiting for a chopper to take us back to LZ Baldy. Well, I will finish now. I will wait till I can sit down and write without a pack on my back. See you on the other side.

I walked over to the *well* and washed my face and hands.

The chopper isn't here yet.

Well, what have I done in the last few days. Our platoon has been looking for rice. The Company has over five tons of rice. I found over 800 lbs. myself. The whole area used to be a NVA stronghold. We discovered an underground Hospital. We found stretchers and some other stuff in it. It was about a 1/4 mile long, let alone all the little wings and stuff. There are rooms where you can actually stand.

There are only very young or very old people in the whole area. They start crying and carrying on when we break up their house and take all the rice they have. It is cruel. You can look at their faces and see the agony they endure.

All the people are doing is helping their own kind. It seems bad that we must punish them like we do because they can't see why. Sometimes I don't either. But many people's lives are hurt by Revolution and War. I hate to inflict it on the people. Yet that is war. Some of the men get pleasure, some don't. Yet the ends are the same.

One woman tried to stand up against us. We pushed, hit and kicked her. She didn't bother us no more.

The woman said, "Baby Son no chop chop."

We said, "Shut up."

Woman said, "But Baby Son no chop chop."

Then we push and shove her.

You know the strain, the utter strain these people are in. Similar to our American Revolution isn't it?

I guess those people would not lift a hand to help us, although we supposedly are helping them. "America the mighty." What is wrong? The whole world seems to think of *Us* as the Vietnamese do. Well we Americans have ourselves. Isn't that horrible.

I got some fresh garden onions for my C-rations. They make a fairly good meal. Oh, well. The people gave them to me in hopes I wouldn't take their rice. Too, too bad.

Ma, you got to send me a picture of you and Dad. As soon as possible, alright? Candid, not in a studio. Okay. Candid pictures are great.

I wrote to Wes. It takes two weeks to get there.

I had my first ripe banana here yesterday. Wow! Did it taste good.

I got a letter from a buddy in the Cavalry. He had a 500 body count on one of his missions.

The men we have killed have been eighteen years old or so. One Leader we killed was about 21 or so. Very young.

I built a hootch last night. First time I have had a roof over my head for a long time.

I am no longer the Lieutenant's RTO. I am back with Yamane the second squad leader.

Well, I better say bye. The chopper should be here soon. I give my mail to the chopper gunners. That is how I mail my letters in the field.

Tell Aunt Lillian I have not forgotten her. Okay. This is the truth. I hope I will see her again. Say Hi to Uncle Raymond. Did Raymond receive the letter I sent him a long time ago? I hope so.

Well, good-bye take care, okay. Say Hi to the people I know at the store, Betty, Dave, and all of them. Bye now.

Your son, Fred Leo

Dear Ma and Dad *19 February 1968*

Well, here I be. I am at LZ Baldy. As soon as I landed they had hot chow. Shrimp!! How is that.

My watch busted. The crystal broke and then it got dirty and stopped running.

They put me in a command bunker. I am in charge of the whole bunker line. Everyone calls my bunker and tells me if everything is okay. As soon as I got to my bunker, I hurried down the hill to an area some troops just moved from. I scavenged up all kinds of food. I got a mirror, hair cream, after shave cologne. I got all kinds of stuff. I got toothpaste and shaving cream. That is the only way you get things. Look for it. Right!

I also got an air mattress. That is what the Army gives you in place of a box spring mattress. Right. Now it is 2:30 A.M. I am on watch for two hours.

At 6:30 A.M. we are going on a Road Mine Sweep. The sweep is six miles. When we get to the end we get a ride back. They don't even give us time to clean up. Maybe when I get back I can get to a shower.

Be sure to send me a $100 Bank Draft. I need to see if I can cash it easily, or maybe $50.00 Bank Draft would be better.

We almost went back in the field tonight. An airplane crashed and we were going to guard it. But they got the men from the plane out okay. So they gave us a night of sleep in a bunker! Ain't that fabulous. We might as well be in the field.

Well, I will continue tomorrow, or rather today again when I get off the mine sweep. By for now.

Ma, change of address. Instead of "E" Company it is "D" Company. Okay. I am now in "D" Company

Fred Leo

Dear Ma *20 February 1968*

Well, it is about 10:30 AM. I just finished the mine sweep. It was about 10,000 meters. I am setting here securing part of the road. There is a big truck setting next to me that was blown up. I don't know how long ago but it is completely ruined. Behind me I have a tank. You're pretty safe around a tank.

Yesterday the mine sweeper was attacked. The enemy VC threw hand grenades. Two men were hurt bad and two injured.

It looks like I will be going back into the field soon. Real soon! They don't give a guy a break. You have to make your own breaks. It looks like we might make it back for Lunch. Wow! What a Luxury.

I just got word to put my steel pot back on. We want to look "good" for the Colonel. *Ha, ha* It sounds silly, and it is.

I found a brand new pen yesterday. A-ha! One of my two pens ran out of ink, so I am all set, for a while.

Our ride back to the LZ will be here in a few minutes, so I will write later.

Ma, by the way, be sure to tell everyone I have a change of address. I just don't have time to write everyone all at once. Okay. Real Fine.

By until later. I am still waiting for the trucks.

Guess what. I received your package from the 28th January or some time near that. I also received the package from the fifth of February. Also a package from Roxanna, February the 13th. All the same day. Weird!

I have good eating. All the food. Wow! That goodie package and food was fabulous.

Well, I am going to be here at least another day. You know it feels fun walking over a mined road. By the way, we walk in front of the mine sweepers. Bla! Nothing ever happens so I guess nothing is going to happen.

Bye for now. That food is appreciated by my squad and me.

Take care. Keep cool. Keep learning

Your son, Fred Leo

Letter From Father

Dear Fred *20 February 1968*

I have been reading all your letters and the mama says she is filing all of them away. They portray a side of the war over there that is not read about in the papers. Your knack for seeing the things and conveying the picture there is remarkable, so graphic in portraying things as the soldier over there sees and feels that quite possibly they can be of considerable value to you, looking back as the years pass.

I can see from reading your letters that you are developing a philosophy which combines all of the best things for which idealism is supposed to stand. There are a fortunate few who can, when the going gets tough bring from their experiences a deep sympathy and insight for facing challenges. Who also develop a genuine and unselfish concern for the well being of others. Through this understanding they are much more likely to enjoy a better life, because they are more likely to attune themselves to an understanding of what motivates those around them, with whom they must work.

I have the new Oldsmobile, a Cutlass, and it's a peppy little car that rides almost as good as the mama's Toronado. Went out with it to look at locations for new stores. We will probably try to start about three this summer.

I was talking to Betty and she said you wrote to (her daughter) Linda. I was also talking to Jody. She gets better looking every day.

I was down in Florida from January to February. I went fishing ten of those days and the rest of the time I was helping Don. We put some checkers on the building, did some fresh painting, and we are having some lighting put on the building to brighten things. Don is selling about 500 chickens a week which is making a small profit. I think he will come along in a steady gain now. The main trouble has been that he hasn't been able to maintain sufficiently high quality, mainly because he didn't have a clear idea of what to shoot for. I hope he has now. But if he hasn't he's come a good long way.

I bought a new 100 horse power motor to replace the 90 horse one on the boat in Florida. It seems almost twice as powerful. It has a new type of transistorized ignition which eliminates the old troublesome condenser and increases spark plug life from the 20 or 30 operating hours I used to get to about 200 operating hours. It will throttle down so slow that I have no trouble counting each firing of a cylinder. For one reason or another it uses much less gasoline. Mr. Hambrick and I were out with it for three days and a half. We went up the Shark River, Board River, Harney River, Lostman's River plus a bit of traveling from one fishing spot to another and when we got back to Flamingo we still had 25 of the 65 gallons of gas we started with. It uses between a third and a quarter less gas than the old motor.

Tony Digrando went ice fishing a while back and when we started to drive onto the lake with this truck the front end broke through the ice. He had to call a tow truck to drag him out. Frank is getting a new Mercedes Benz car and getting rid of his Buick.

Let's see what else might be new to you. I'm going to write the Caines in Tennessee and tell them you are in the Army. I'm going to take a trip down and see them one of these days soon. I'll give them your address so they can write you.

It's pretty cold here right now. But spring is on the way. It's already whispering down in Florida to the birds and the cypress trees. In the more protected spots the cypress trees that drop their leaves through early winter are already putting out their lacy bright green leaves. And the birds are beginning to sing a lot more. One kind of Wood Ibis, I think it is, has a strange way of showing off for his prospective mate.

The mama says I must finish this letter so Helen can bring it to the post office. So I neither have time to rewrite or finish. However, I will try to write to you the next day or so to continue my observations about spring emerging in Florida. I try and say a prayers a few times each day for your well being. From your father who is very proud of the thinking and self analysis, the searching for essential truths, which your letters convey, and hopes to see you again in the not so distant future.

John

24 February 1968

Reconn settles on top of four APCs with revving diesel engines, and wait for the order to move-out on the search-and destroy mission. The 'aluminum boxes' were easy targets, and all it takes is a nervy NVA with an armor piercing rocket. The rocket would pass easily through armor and once inside explode turning the APC into a virtual coffin.

The armored squad they travel with has seen action, probably a lot, if the burns and dents on the APCs were any indication.

Anyway—they would ride on top with sandbags serving as meager cover.

"Hope we don't have to make a jump-for-it off this monster," Okie mentions, looking twelve feet to the ground. "Especially you Brownie," he motions, "with the radio."

"First the radio, then I jump," Brown says. They lean back using the rucksacks as back rests with their arms clear of the shoulder harnesses.

"Anything beats humpin'," Doc Holliday interjects.

"These little straps all we got to hold on to?" Brown wonders as he looks around for a better hand-hold.

Vroom!

Vroom!

Vroom!"

the engines rev.

The tracks quickly gain speed as they rumble from LZ Baldy through the North Gate. Moving at a brisk thirty miles per hour it feels like being on the a roller coaster ride.

Brown tries to synchronize with the rhythmic romp of the machine like a rodeo cowboy might, but he isn't getting the hang-of-it. He continues to be jolted around on the hard steel surface. Then suddenly the lead APC veers hard to the right and off the road. All the tracks follow through a trough, down . . . up . . .and out . . . then they take off running across the field.

Brown's APC closes on large dike, it decelerates slightly then accelerates to power jump. The soldiers bounce, their feet shooting high into the air. When the APC hits hard on the other side, it catapults Brown off the side.

"Uh!" Brown hits the ground with one foot and rolls over. "Hey, wait up!" he yells, back on his feet. He dashes after the APC, and similar to catching a moving train, grabs the rear hand bar and shoves his foot into the step hole.

As Brown climbs back over the top and back to his position. No one even offers to help because they are breathless from laughter. Okie is holding his stomach with tears streaming down his face.

"Goddamn buckin' bronco," Brown complains over the noise. They hit another dike, their legs fling back into the air. However this time, Brown leans back in anticipation of the drop.

"Yeee haaa!" Okie yells in fun.

"Yipppee ki aaa."

"Ride 'im cowboy."

"These guys always drive like maniacs or is this just for our benefit?" Brown gripes.

The APCs move parallel to the main road over both dry and mushy rice fields, apparently wanting to avoid any landmine. Then they veer slightly to the right heading for the tip of a tree covered peninsula.

"Joy ride's over, grunts," one of the cavalrymen yells when the APC's came to a halt just short of the village situated on the green oasis peninsula.

"Let's move it out. Come on. And keep it spread out!" Denning shouts over the noise of the diesel engines. "One round could kill ya all."

When Reconn is clear, the APC's move off driving through the village gardens that circumscribed the hamlet.

"All right listen up. The APCs are moving into a blocking position. Sweep the village in the direction of the road," Sergeant Yamane commands. "And stay alert. This is a known VC village."

"Hey, good job of cultivating the garden, huh," Doc Holliday jests at the obliterating vegetable gardens, and how they almost run over a Vietnamese who was relieving himself.

"The Vietnamese never plant land mines in their gardens," Yamane calls over.

Reaching the village, Sergeant Denning pulls out a machete and closes on a banana tree that is ripe with fruit. "Eeeee, ya!" he yells and on the first swipe goes half way through the trunk. On the second hack the plant falls and he grabs a bunch of little banana.

"Want one?"

"Thanks," Brown says putting a little bunch into his cargo pocket. Drawing the hunting knife, he makes a few chops at another banana tree, then hurries to catch Sergeant Denning.

Coming around a grass hut, Brown spots an old Vietnamese man sitting cross legged among a pile of bamboo shoots. Sergeant Denning checks the man's ID card. Walking closer, Brown sees a pile of wood shaving and to the left a large wicker tray brimming with lengths of spear pointed bamboo.

The Vietnamese picks up—what appears to be a booby-trap pungi stick—and points toward the outskirts of the village. Then he begins to use sign language.

Sergeant Denning takes the bamboo stick from the man's hand and checks the sharp tip. "He claims they're for keeping animals corralled. The irrigation ditches are lined with these. But they could easily be turned into booby-trap pungi sticks."

"Hey, Sarge," Billy calls. Billy is well known as the bad boy of the platoon. "Pungi sticks, huh. The slant-eye must be making 'em for the VC honcho. Let's do the hut."

Billy pulls out a stainless steel Zippo lighter, pops open the lid and thumbs back the flint wheel. A spark hits the wick which flames to life. Daringly he holds the yellow flame under a grass roof. Eager for praise, he turns on his trademark grin. "How about it, Sarge?"

"Billy!" Yamane call. "Get over here and give me a hand with these people." Billy clicked his lighter closed, but not before leaving a small section of the roof afire.

Continuing to check the village for weapons or contraband they come upon more huts that are in flames.

"Well, Sarge," Billy says showing up, "those dinks oughta think twice before working with the VC. Right?" Beyond Billy and between them and the main road, Brown can see a half dozen huts burning out of control.

"Let's get out of here," Sergeant Denning says. The three soldiers begin running through the smoke, dodging the flames that engulf the village.

At the head of the trail leading to the main road, three Arvan's are questioning the villagers and pulling aside ones they want to interrogate further.

Meandering past the interrogation scene and to the main road, Brown arrives at an APC where he props the rucksack against the tilted front. Leaning back, he takes a swig of cool water. Then splashes some on his face and wipes off the salt with the towel that drapes over his shoulders.

Turning to the commotion, he sees the cavalrymen have separated a couple young girls from the main body. Both of them have their arms pinned behind their backs. One is released and gets shoved back and forth around the perimeter of cavalrymen. The antics are followed by a lot of rowdy laughter.

Then a cavalryman begins to fondle the young girl. Alarmed, she crosses her arms as she shuffles backwards trying to resist. She screams as a guy comes from behind and lifts her in a bear hug. With her feet dangling, she's suddenly dropped to the ground. Words are exchanged as she tries to scurry away but is tackled by another soldier. Lifting her up, they rip open her blouse. There is a roar of approval.

A cavalryman they call "Carp" runs his hands along the side of her face and down her neck. She kicks and the audience laughs. They drag her over to the grassy side of the road and wrestle her to the ground, while Carp unbuttons his pants.

With one knee on top of her chest and the other on her neck Carp instructs them to pull off her pants.

"Stop your kickin' bitch. I'm gonna give her the fantasy of her life! I'm gonna convert her to democracy," Carp billows.

As the wrestling match continues in the dirt and sweltering heat, Brown's temper reaches boiling point.

"Crocodile GI! Crocodile GI!" the young girl screams in protest. "You numba ten GI."

"Shut up, bitch! You're gonna be screamin' numba one GI in a minute," Carp says to cheers and laughter from the audience.

"Hold one, Carp." One of the soldiers has a camera out and when Carp smiles he snaps a picture. "Now how about an action shot?"

This type of thing happens often. Brown knows this. Knows that there is nothing anyone can do. Everyone is loaded to the teeth with weapons and ammo. If he makes a move to protect the girl they would probably kill him. After all this is war and in war there are no rules. The law of the land is written in lead. So maybe he did try to stop it. Next time there was a firefight they would kill him. Who would know? Right?

But Brown is much wiser than people take him for. He knows that if he just stands there and does nothing it will rot his soul. That even if he pretended not to see—he did see.

And after all, who are these APC guys, anyway? They hadn't put their lives on the line going into this village? So what right did they have to do this? Brown's anger reaches eruption. Before anyone can stop him, Brown moves through the outer circle and is standing over the couple on the ground.

"Hey!" Brown shouts enraged.

"Hey to you too. I'm first'," Carp replies comically thinking it a joke. "You get sloppy seconds." But the joke goes flat when he feels the cold steel of a rifle's muzzle against his head.

"What?" Carp turns in shock. "Who are you. A grunt?" The

girl sees her chance tries to shimmy out from underneath him.

Staring down at Carp, Brown remembers all the punks he's had to cower from in his life. All the bullies who would push everyone around, everyone laughing at their pathetic jokes. All the people that made fun of him. Everything was a joke as long as it was at someone else's expense.

Studying the antagonist, Carp has second thoughts. Slowly he releases the girl who grabs her clothes and scampers away with the second girl to the safety of the other villagers.

Brown steps back with his M-16 rifle angled upwards.

"Carp," someone calls. "What do you say?"

Carp stares hard and mean as a snake. Brown stares back cold and deadly. There is a Mexican standoff as Carp transforms into Brown's father.

"It ain't worth it. He's one of those crazy grunts."

"He'll be dead in a week," someone else joins in.

"Yeah Carp, don't waste no time on a Dink lover."

"I hope you step on the booby trap that bitch sets," Carp spits. "Grunt!"

Before anyone could make another move, Sergeant Denning showed up. "Brown," he calls.

"Yeah, Sarge."

"Call all the squads and have 'em load up."

Yamane walks over. "Sarge, something's fishy."

"You mean about this being the wrong village?" Sergeant Denning asks.

"That yes. But I know a little Vietnamese and these people are telling me they didn't pay their protection money last month. So, they got reported as being VC sympathizers."

"That's not my problem. We have orders to move across the road to the next VC village."

"Sarge, this isn't a VC village and the one across the road isn't either. They're using us to shake these people down. I saw the ARVNs taking money from the villagers."

"Brown," Billy says coming over. "Don't so look worried. The people won't hold it against us. They'll still love us in the morning."

Dear Ma *24 February 1968*

Well, I am still at LZ Baldy. We went on a *S*earch and *D*estroy mission today. We went on five Armored Personnel Carriers. First of all they told us to search the wrong village. We burnt down three hooches. We burnt them down for no real reason at all. And we harassed the village by collecting them in one area.

We went to another village which was supposed to be the right village. It was not. We found propaganda signs at this village. Well, not too much has happened. I went on sick call. My legs got hurting again. But they are in good shape now.

I was real glad to get your letter. I am so happy and proud you are on my side. Some men here have parents who are against them being here. It puts a real big strain on them. It is hard enough without that. Other men are strained because their people don't write and help them face the next day. I can honestly say, my parents behind me. I can face the next day knowing tomorrow I will be with people I love.

Keep cool. I will write soon.

Bye for now, Fred Leo

Dear Uncle Ken, Maude and Karen *24 February 1968*

Well, I have been here three months. Nine to go! I have been at LZ Baldy for about a week. I will be going out real soon now.

I received the fudge. That really hit the *Spot*! Maybe you could send some more. Okay? Everyone had some. It was great.

I haven't been doing much. I was just on a routine Search and Destroy mission yesterday. Nothing came from it.

Then we went searching around for NVA on an Armored Personnel Carriers. It was Fun! The APC went up and down huge dikes. One time when an APC went down on the dike it almost flipped over. The driver fell out and did a flip in the air and landed sitting down!

Everyone thinks the heat is horrible here. It is cold. I have a sweater and am going to use two covers. One reason is because it has rained all day. I imagine this summer will bring the heat.

Karen, so how is the motor cycle. I don't imagine you use it much in the winter. Well, by for now.

Keep cool. Okay

Goodby for a while, Fred Leo

Dear Ma and Dad *28 February 1968*

I have been in Nam three months and one day. I am entitled to a Combat Infantry Medal. Uncle Raymond knows how they look.

Well it looks like we are going to the field today or tomorrow.

I have learned that a man must not be afraid to die. He must let luck and destiny do it's work. If a person does not do this he is not a man! If I let myself be selfish with my life, I will be dead in spirit. If God wills, I will come home a man. I will never come home a coward. If my life ends here, let it be as a man! My least concern is to come home. Not that I don't hope that someday I will. But if I worry about going home alive I will merely get frustrated.

I know you understand. I hope some day I can let the philosophy *ride*. But it serves its purpose now.

I was almost hit by sniper fire three times. By inches it missed my head. And by inches it hit the ground next to me. Since then, to keep from getting nervous, I have had to develop the philosophy above. See, the RTO is the first person *shot* at.

While over here I have noticed some men turn sort of animalistic. I have known these people for months now. One such person is our Platoon Sergeant. He is helpful, kind and worries about his men. He has a beautiful wife and is happily married. When we go into the village he cuts down banana trees and burns houses and breaks houses up. On one Search and Destroy mission I found myself doing what he was doing. We are good friends. He helps me out personally. This is why I lost control of myself. Instead of finding satisfaction out of it I found dissatisfaction.

War, here has brought out the worst parts of man. The *ID* is dominant. You have heard of the Ego, Super Ego, and the Id. The

Id is the inner self. You must suppress the ID, but in War the Id is uncontrolled. This I have noticed in many, many people.

It is of some satisfaction to meet people who are unselfish to you and the Vietnamese. Of course no straight humanitarians.

Everything I have said can be read one way or the other. Also they can be disputed, but every idea or sentence has something to stand on!

While I have been writing this letter I have been in the midst of a Road Sweep. I have continued the letter about four times.

John, from the store, sent me the pistol. It is just right. I am going to put notches on the bullets so when it hits something it will splatter. Have John get me a few more magazines for my 25 cal. Astra pistol.

I am almost to the end of the road sweep. When we get to the end I will open my C-ration and chow down. I have a can of beer so I should have a good meal.

Well, I will finish for now. I will continue after the road sweep is finished.

Well, I will close. I will write again tonight.

Bye for now, Fred Leo

March 1968

1 March 1968

That evening Brown is assigned to second squad bunker.

"Scotty . . . believe it or not, this is the first time the lieutenant has spent a night on the bunker line," Brown tells the NFG who has been in Vietnam for only a few weeks, and has been assigned to the Lieutenant. "So, don't feel sorry for him. And when it's the lieutenants turn on guard, give 'im a shove. Alright?" Brown keeps encouraging Scotty until he finally smiles.

"I won't be far." They walk from the CP bunker. "I'm just down the hill. That's my bunker right there." Brown points. "So, call me on the radio if you need anything. Anything okay. Just call."

"Okay," Scotty is still doe-eyed, still unsure of himself as platoon leader RTO.

"Everything will be fine. See ya in the mornin'." Brown waves as he moves down the hill.

"Bright and early?"

"No rest for the wicked," Brown shouts back grinning as he remembers those first few days with Scotty.

All the Delta Company NFGs were milling around the CP bunker when Brown was told to find someone to take the position of RTO. Taking the job seriously, Brown spent the entire day observing and talking casually with the new arrivals before making a decision. His choice was a soldier from the backwoods of North Carolina named George Scott Dawkins.

Scotty had been ecstatic about being chosen. To him, it was an honor to be the lieutenant's RTO. And why not? That was the most important RTO position. Right? Brown had an ulterior motive. The other veterans had flat out refused to be the lieutenant's gofer. So, the seldom times the lieutenant showed his face in the field, Brown had to do the job. But Brown wanted to be with either Sergeant Denning or Sergeant Yamane so he had to find someone who would put up with their always lazy platoon leader.

On the first evening in the CP bunker, Brown and Scotty had been left alone to pull guard. With the start of training, Brown spent a good part of the evening explaining the radio language and how to take care of the rifle. Then seeing that Scotty was feeling comfortable decided to move into the hard realities.

"Scotty, pointman is the deadliest of all positions."

Scotty stops cleaning his rifle and looks over wide eyed.

"The second deadliest position is the RTO."

The NFG takes a deep breath trying not to belie his feeling of terror.

"I don't know if you're a religious man . . . ." Brown considers himself very religious. A believer in God and heaven. But he didn't want to sound too soft, so never spoke to anyone about his innermost convictions.

"Oh, I go to church all the time."

"Okay, that's real good."

"Am I gonna die?" The question is so shockingly childish, Brown is left speechless. It reminds him of a little boy who turns to his mother just as he slips beneath the water and drowns.

"Well," he tries to sound positive. "I've been an RTO a long time and I'm still here." Brown tries to sound cheerful. "Still going strong."

He smiles bravely.

"Scotty, listen. To be afraid of dying is like . . . well it's like being afraid of living. Put your faith in God. That's what I've done."

"You'll help me though. Right?"

"Sure I will. We're buddies right?" This is becoming too emotional for Brown. He needs to get out of these slippery waters before Scotty starts crying or does something crazy like . . . like reaches out and wants a hug.

"Tell ya what. Tomorrow practice hittin' the ground. Practice all the time 'till it gets to where you hear anything . . . anything at all, you'll drop like a rock.

"Incoming!" Brown hollers so loud it hurts their ears. "Hit the dirt. No question." He pauses then adds caustically, "Cause there's theirs, then there's ours, but ain't none of it friendly."

They had talked for a while longer as Scotty attached two hand grenades to the pistol belt ammo pouches. Earlier Brown had explained that he shouldn't carry hand grenades on a road sweep because a piece of shrapnel could accidentally detonate it.

"Just in case we have to make a run for it." Scotty looks spooked, as he places the pistol belt securely on the bench.

Brown walks to the front of the bunker and looks out over the minefield with dusk fast approaching. The NFG bellies up next to him.

"Got a round in the chamber?" Brown asks casually knowing Scotty hasn't even inserted a magazine. Suddenly, Brown opens fire with a short burst, ejects the magazine and in a flash inserts another and is ready to fire.

Scotty in the meantime struggles with the ammo pouch straps trying to get to a magazine. Brown watches bemused as he finally gets one out, into the rifle and jacks back the charging handle to slam a round into the chamber.

"You're already dead. And you got everyone around you killed too."

"Shit!" He looks at Brown nervously.

"Who knows when a split second could mean the difference between life and death," Brown lectures. "Forget about the rules. Forget about everything. It's up to you to save your life and no one else."

"But the sign says 'Clear Your Weapons'," Scotty pleads in defense. "I just didn't know when I should load my rifle. And the lieutenant said . . . ."

"The lieutenant? What does he know? My weapon is always loaded with a magazine." Brown eyeballs him. "Always. You understand?"

"I think so," Scotty is obviously confused.

"Listen the lieutenant doesn't know jack shit," Brown finds

himself screaming. "You listen to him and you will die." Brown raises his rifle, "The M-16 and a full magazine is the best friend you got. Does that make it any simpler?"

"Yes." He lowers his eyes.

"How many magazines you got?"

"They gave me eight."

"Most of the men carry over thirty. As for me, on a road sweep, I usually only carry about fifteen magazines. Here," he extends a hand, "lemme see that magazine." Like Bull had done for him back during Tet Offensive, Brown now gives Scotty the low-down on the magazines.

"When we get back from road sweep, remind me, we'll pick you up some extra magazines and some tracer rounds. Okay."

"And a quick-loader?"

"That too, buddy," Brown smiles.

Brown walks out the back of the bunker for a smoke.

"You always do this?"

"How's that?"

"Stand out here to watch the sunset?"

"Well . . . yeah. Never thought about it until you mentioned it. But yeah. I always do."

They both calmly smoke as the sun sneaks behind blackening rain clouds. Sunlight flows through a cloud window making the sky glow like cathedral stained glass. Then follows an ever changing kaleidoscope of colors ranging from red, yellow, orange, green and blue. The rainbow light sweeps across the ground in an ever changing celestial display.

"You don't see this kind of sunsets in Chicago," Brown muses.

"On the farm . . . there's times. But nothing quite like this."

The red ball slides behind the distant grey mountain peaks. And with only the molten red crown of the sun still showing, Brown scans the minefield across the triple stacks of razor edged concertina wire and beyond to the freefire zone.

"Things can happen pretty fast around here," Brown says. "The nights belong to Charlie Cong." He looks over at Scotty. "Since there's only the two of us, we'll go two hours on, two hours off."

"The lieutenant said only one hour guards."

Brown pulse quickens with the word *lieutenant*. He decides to ignore it. "You wanna go first?"

"Sure. I'm really not that tired."

"Well, I am. And we got us an early morning mine sweep. So I'm gonna grab some shut-eye."

"Brown," Scotty says and pauses. "I heard we gotta walk right over live mines on those sweeps. Is that true?"

"Yeah, the sweep team is behind us. So really, the only way to protect them is to walk out in front. Right over the mines."

"God. I thought they were pullin' my leg."

"You'll get used to it." Arranging his sleeping gear on the wooden bench, Brown buttons his shirt cuffs, pulls on the cover, puts on his helmet as a pillow and lays a towel over his face. Minutes later he's fast asleep.

"Wake up, Brown!" comes a harsh whisper and touch on his shoulder. "I think something's wrong."

Springing off the bench, Brown grabs the rifle and quickly comes alongside him at the rifle slit.

A flare pops in the distance lighting the sky. It is followed by a few sporadic rifle bursts and explosions.

"Don't look at the flares," Brown warns. "It'll l ruin your night vision." Brown pulls the helmet rim low over his eyes.

"What's happening?"

"Apparently someone's made contact." Brown isn't concerned because it happens like this all the time. "That's pretty far away. Nothing to worry about."

A drizzling rain began just after one A.M. while Brown is on guard. Within a half hour it had increased into a full blown shower. Looking through the front rifle slit at the sheets of water, Brown decided there wouldn't be any attack so he takes off his helmet, draped the towel over his head and relaxed against the cool side of the bunker. Throughout the bunker there is the soft mesmerizing sound of water dripping through the roof and into water puddles.

It takes time to understand and become aware of the danger signs leading to falling asleep while on guard duty. Because always lurking in the background is the patient and ever so wily Mr. Sandman. The one who will sing sweet lullabies and whisper promises.

"Blink," Mr. Sandman would say. "Let your eyes rest for just a second. I'll make sure you won't fall asleep. Promise."

In the beginning Brown was prey to and believed he could take long blink. But found too often he'd wake with his heart in his throat, feverishly checking the field-of-fire to see if the enemy had gotten past.

"Close one eye at a time and count to ten," Mr. Sandman would suggest. "It'll help. I'll make sure you won't fall asleep. Promise."

In the meantime, Mr. Sandman would ravage his reserves and purge him of all rational thought. He would take control and lead him step by step closer to total, complete restful bliss.

"Go ahead," Mr. Sandman would urge, "close both of your eyes at once and count to ten. I'll keep my ears open to make sure nothing happens. Promise."

But way back in Brown's subconscious he knew it was unadulterated seduction. Knew they were empty promises, but found himself falling passionately within its spell. "Whisper more sweet lies." He didn't have the power to resist. His eyes would close, head would slump onto the rifle sill. Then the dreams, sweet dreams of home, of riding a bicycle in the summertime along the lake shore. Of a BBQ picnic out on the beach.

Brown had adopted several ways to beat Mr. Sandman. First line of defense was slapping his face and pouring water over his head. Second was drinking cool water or better yet munch on food. But his strongest ally was his inner mind. Brown also found that writing kept him attentive and alert. Under extreme situations while in a desperate fight with Mr. Sandman, he'd learned to take deep breaths, move around the foxhole or walk outside the bunker to increase blood circulation.

Since the battle of Lo Giang, he was pleased to find his body adapting well to the nights and seldom had trouble fighting off sleep while on guard duty. The key was in making a day one solid twenty-four-hour cycle. Every few hours he'd grab some rest or sleep if possible. Five minutes here—five minutes there. They all added up. For instance, Brown had discovered that he could be attentive for up to four hours at a time by using his around-the-clock cat-naps. Some of the others soldiers were beginning to catch on to the technique as well.

He'd seen times when during a long march, a soldier's eyes would glaze over into a trance though they were either still standing or even walking. If startled, they'd nearly fall over, but if a normal voice was used, "Let's move it out" or "Shake it up," they'd wake up and continue as usual.

An artillery round flies overhead. Which reminds him that he'd seen soldiers sleep right through an artillery fire mission but if so much as a twig broke, their weapons would be ready to fire.

"You're up Scotty," Brown wakes him "It's three A.M.."

With Scotty taking over guard, Brown rolls under his sleeping gear and within seconds is fast asleep.

"Shit!" Scotty shouts, the noise waking Brown.

He throws off the poncho, grabs his rifle, and leaps to peer into the black night. There was no sign of movement. He turns to a shocked Scotty with blood running through his fingers held tightly around his neck.

"I'm sorry, Brown," Scotty apologized, for what Brown doesn't know. "Well, anyway, it works," he says staring at his bloody hand.

"What?" Brown whispers. His eyes go to Scotty's rifle with affixed bayonet then back to his neck. "Did . . . ?"

"In training they told us to put the bayonet on the rifle and prop it under our chins when on guard. Then if we happen to fall asleep it'd stick us." He checks his neck to find it has stopped bleeding.

"A little dangerous especially with a round in the chamber."

Like anyone going into combat, there is a lot to learn. But Scotty was eager and willing to listen. Brown enjoys Scotty's down home ways . . . .

As Brown continues walking to the second squad bunker, the platoon leader pulls up in a jeep with a blond-haired passenger. The blonde soldier slides out of the jeep, a .38 Colt revolver strapped to his waist. He grabs a rucksack out of the back of the jeep with the style and strength of a healthy California surfer. After a moment of instruction the lieutenant points him in the direction of Yamane's bunker.

"Say, Yamane, there's a guy . . ," Brown shouts when within ear shot of the bunker where Bedford and Yamane sit drinking beer.

"He's here?" Yamane jumps excitedly twisting around.

"He's here!"

Both soldiers dash past Brown shouting, "Anderson."

"God, it's good to see ya man," Bedford says grabbing the soldier by the arm. They greet the GI who is grinning ear to ear, shaking hands and patting shoulders.

"We'd heard you got hit at Da Nang with Charlie Company," Bedford says to an old friend from Fort Hood, Texas.

"They can't kill us ol' guys." Anderson lifts the side of his shirt to show a bullet scar.

Anderson looks inside the bunker, deciding there was no room yet, he drops the rucksack outside the bunker. Unstrapping a pouch, he produces a fifth of Jack Daniels, several packs of Marlboro cigarettes and the February issue of Playboy. "Are we gonna party?"

"Alright." They slap hands.

"Holy shit, man. I haven't seen that much whiskey since LZ Gator."

"Let's do it, man!" Bedford beams.

"Hold it," Sergeant Yamane looks around guardedly. "Let's get inside the bunker." Everyone follows.

"W*alll*a*,*" Anderson says producing two shot glasses from a cargo pocket. "Stole it from the Officers Club."

"I know this might be a let-down, but we have a road sweep in the morning."

"So?"

"So," Yamane comes right back, the always diligent squad leader. "Let's get a few things outta the way first. Then we can party later. It's already gettin' late." They look around and realize Yamane is right. The sun is already dropping behind the distant mountain range.

Gathering four sticks, Yamane breaks them into different lengths, then holds them in his clenched fist. "Let's draw straws for guard. Smallest one goes first."

After checking their rifles and equipment in general, they relax on the benches. With everything squared away, the three old friends gather around a flickering candle and raise a bottle, a shot glass and a beer.

"Here's a toast. To us getting our asses back home in one piece." They click with the usual, "Cheers," salute.

". . . Did he die later?" ". . . From what I heard. ". . . did anyone find out what really happened?" ". . . You know the guy. What's his name. U*mmmmm.* He always wore that handkerchief around his neck . . . ."

Yamane and Anderson sit on benches while Bedford opted for a case of unopened rations. Brown rested on an upper bunk-board not wanting to interfere, basically tired anyway, and peers at the dirty faces of the three soldiers. They were intent an comparing notes on their fallen buddies and the going-ons of others in the warm cocoon of the bunker.

"... At least half of the guys shot-up in Da Nang, re-enlisted," Anderson claims.

"Re-enlisted?" Brown asks not being able to contain himself. "Why?"

"To get off front line infantry," Anderson explains. "That's why."

"No matter, you couldn't pay me enough to stay in this man's Army for three more years."

"I wouldn't mind the thirty-day leave they throw in when you re-enlist," Yamane enjoins.

"And don't forget the bonus money," Anderson adds.

"My sister said that she heard most of the guys in Vietnam are volunteers," Brown dares to re-enter the conversation.

"Well, that's probably true. But now we know why."

"Yeah. All the draftees get sent to the front lines and the only way out is reenlist. So walla. No more draftees." Anderson fills up the shot glass and everyone knocks one down. Then they all go for a Marlboro.

"I heard these cigarettes make you sterile," Bedford says smoking while glancing through the Playboy.

Continuing their reminiscing, Brown looks over the collarless fragmentation jacket he'd found in the mud a few days back. The label had printed on it:

ARMOR, VEST, M-1952A

This vest may save your life! When properly worn it will protect vital areas against shell and grenade fragments which cause most combat casualties.

It fit a lot better than the other one. After the morning's road sweep, he had started to draw the Brown's Fried Chicken Logo on the back with a black Magic Marker. Hours later, satisfied with his handiwork, Brown relaxes ready to sleep.

"... by our own chopper," Bedford explains.

"No shit. *Our* chopper. I heard he was killed when you guys got hit one night. But not by friendly fire. Damn, man," Anderson sounds shocked. "You ain't jerkin' me around, right?"

"No," Yamane shakes his head, "Swear to God it happened just like I said. . . ."

Brown fell asleep.

"Wake up Brown. Your guard," Bedford says tapping him on the shoulder. "Hurry up, man. I ain't got nowhere to sleep. I need your spot."

"Oh yeah, sorry," Brown says. Though still groggy, he slides off the wooden platform and moves to the bench at the front rifle slit. With pistol belt and helmet placed nearby, he props the rifle against the wall, exhales and peers out. While staring into the night across the field of fire, he drinks some refreshing water he'd gotten at the river. Still unable to reach full awareness, he pours the cool water over his head, with old sweat stinging his eyes and running into this mouth. He spits and shakes his head.

"Shit." He leans low and lights a cigarette. With Winston cupped in his hands, he looks up into the heavens with the brilliant stars and the ethereal full moon that looks like a China plate.

"Boooom!

Boom!

Boooom!" A salvo is fired from the howitzers.

"Shuuuu!

Shuuuu!

Shuuuu!" came the sounds of the rounds rushing overhead, sounding like a freight train, on a mission of destruction.

Leaning against the dilapidated sandbag wall Brown becomes aware of the distinctive odors of this combat line bunker. The strong scent of stale body odor, trampled vegetation, nicotine and alcohol that swirl together. Then the underlying smells of urine, feces, mildew, vomit and gunpowder. Beneath his feet the dirt floor sucks in cartridges, old smokes, C-ration cans and SP packs.

He remembers listening to the dog-tired veterans with joints dangling from their cracked lips, grumble about the food, Coke and beer rations, festering cuts, the weather, fighting conditions and the lousy leadership.

As the clawing fingers of dusk had progressed, the soldiers had all doused themselves with bug juice to stave off the malaria borne mosquitoes that swarm about them like vampire disciples. Then with deadpan eyes they had done the final inspection of their weapons, ammunition, grenades, and claymore mine detonators.

Brown knew that the raw pungent smells of this war torn bunker would stay with him forever, along with the fear-sweat and cold reality.

Brown's ears perk at the distant sound of a gicko lizard, which would call out its *FU* insult throughout the night. He welcomes the lizard's call knowing it will serve as a sentry and become quiet if an enemy approaches.

Brown gazes meditatively at the full moon and takes a deep breath of clean fresh mountain air. He feels strangely alert, strangely mellow. And in a strange way feels like he belongs here-and-now with these men of war. It is destiny that he should end up inside this bunker. He had never felt so fulfilled. Never felt so healthy, awake and alive as he did at this very moment. Never felt so completely at home with his surroundings and the situation.

Putting the cigarette out on the floor, he lets his eyes drift over these hard sweating, whisker stubbed grunts in their rotting fatigues sleeping on bayonet scarred benches. They were so completely authentic. Everyone in the bunker had a shared experience of groping along a vague path trying to sense danger with every foot drop. Of living twenty-four hours a day, seven days a week on the edge, surrounded by the enemy.

Brown and his fellow combatants, not so dissimilar to their hippy counterparts, could never be described as establishment. They too where skeptical of conventional principles and power. But unlike their counterparts who expect a handout from society, Brown and his ilk know all to well they would have to make it on their own.

Americans who possess courage, integrity and honor have always been the *real* back bone of America. They were the ones who would stand ready at the American Eagle's beck and call. With them it was automatically understood that the price of freedom doesn't come cheaply. That their freedom came from those loyal patriots who came before them.

These men possess a wisdom that helps them learn quickly through observation. A quick, precise understanding of what they see, hear and smell will ultimately decide their very survival. To fail a quiz in a combat zone is to die a slow death. War is life on fast forward.

"Crunch," the smallest of sound breaks into Brown's reverie. A rat stands on Yamane's stomach. Brown stares and the rat stares back with dark beady eyes. The rat sniffs for traces of food on Yamane's uniform, then scampers off to find an open C-ration can on the floor.

"I could use some company," Brown whispers softly to the rodent.

When the rat scurries away, Brown walks outside and around the bunker to listen and get a better view of their field of fire.

So beautiful. The stars in the black sky look so close it's like he could reach out and touch them. The fingers of a breeze wipe his brow. He takes another long deep aromatic breath and whispers.

"Yes. I admit it. I have a romance with the wind, the rain, the rice fields, the jungle. And yes, I have a romance with the war."

Dear Ma and Dad *2 March 1968*

You know the Chop, Chop you sent me. I make a scrumptious meal from them. I took the tomato paste and mixed it with spaghetti. Then I added the Chili Sauce. We added Beef Spice and sauce with it and a little onion, Tabasco Sauce, also garlic. Fabulous. We put it on crackers.

I got the pistol. It is just right. I carry it in my compass case. I am getting 'hollow points' from a friend. (These are bullets with holes drilled into the head). These kind will explode when they hit something. Deadly—very deadly.

I got the socks. I took a shower and put them on. New socks feel so good.

Sounds like Don is doing great in Florida. I got a letter from Roxanna and Lorraine. All at once they came from all of you. What a boost. I felt good all day.

Well we are going out tomorrow. I think we are going back to the Rice Bowl. B Company will come in. Every time I go out I feel more prepared. It isn't too bad going out in the field anymore.

I got paid! You will be getting more money. About $130.00. By the way did you send the bank draft? I heard that no one can leave Viet Nam. We are frozen here until it is lifted. It might be a rumor. I don't know.

R&R is so close I can hardly wait. I am going to bed right now and will write when I'm on guard.

Well, I was too tired to write on guard. It is now 10 A.M. I am on a road sweep.

I finished the road sweep and I just finished eating. I am going to be choppered out at two P.M. Well, I am a little short on time now. I got to clean my M-16, so I will say bye for now. I will write again soon.

Fred Leo

Dear Cousin Karen *3 March 1968*

Karen, I guess I didn't explain myself enough. When I leave Base Camp, which is LZ Baldy, I bury all the luxuries I have. Like my air mattress, also some trophies. If I turned them in to supply they would lose them. So I bury them so I only know where they are. You know X marks the spot.

I gave some of those balloons to the kids. They love them. I threw it at them and they hit it back. They went wild.

Wow! Those brownies were great. I ate them all in a day. I got so full I didn't even eat my C-rations. I gave one to everyone in my platoon. Next time I'll hide them away.

Wow! Summer is coming on real strong. The Monsoon has been over for a while. Now the heat is coming on strong. We had three guys nearly pass out yesterday. Another guy did pass out, so now we hold up in the middle of the day. We work in the morning and all evening.

Well, I'd better close so I can get this letter on the chopper. It will be the last one in for today.

Bye for now, Fred Leo

Dear Ma and Dad *4 March 1968*

Well, here I be. Sleeping near a bomb shelter. I also was near straw. I was in great shape last night. There was a last minute change of mission. We made a CA (Combat Assault) into an area where there supposed to have been a communication center. So far no contact, but we found some pieces to a switch board.

I am sitting down right now watching a bombing raid. It is about 5000 meters away. Guess what kind of planes are doing the job! Our Second World War Sky Raiders. I think that is their name. You have seen them on TV, one propeller jobs. I seen them open up with their machine guns.

Well, it is about three hours later. We killed two VC. We

found them in a *spider hole*. We threw a grenade in after them. It blew their feet off. We're not going to leave any alive so we put five .38.cal. bullets in his heart. The other one we found out would die. So we put a round through his head. They are confirmed VC because they are dead and because they had some literature.

When we moved from that location, some people walked over to see the bodies. When we saw them, we yelled for them to stop. We wanted to ask them questions seeing they wanted to see the two dead VC. Two of the people ran.

We yelled "Stop!" "Stop!"

They continued to run. We fired over their heads. They didn't stop. Blam, Blam, Blam. "Get those people!"

We hit two, or rather both of them. As we ran up to the two we found they were two ten-year old girls, just frightened to death. One looked like she would die. But the other one was in fair shape. We called for a chopper and they were lifted out to a hospital.

As I said earlier, we had to shoot the two VC. The guy who shot the VC in the head said "I hope this helps repay for my dead buddy. This is the third one I killed." He walked away with his head down, talking to himself. Probably remembering the battle at Da Nang.

Well, no one shot at us. It is nice (pun) to know we have made friends of the villagers. I guess now they are all VC. By the way we captured a VC suspect yesterday. We did treat him like the Geneva convention said we should.

It is 11:30 P.M. I am on guard till midnight. Then I go back on at three A.M.. I can't see to write it is so dark. Maybe I can see it good enough on my next guard to continue.

Well, it is morning. No one woke me for my second guard. I am glad because I wouldn't have been able to write.

Today I am on another village sweep. They are determined to find the two squads of VC in the area. Communication type VC. So around and around we go.

My rifle is in good shape, never jammed on me yet. I can see how easily it could jam. There is so much mud, sand and dirt everywhere. The weapon can get dirty so fast. Dirty enough to jam.

Well, we have continued our sweep through the area. We are walking through all kinds of creeks and muddy rice patties. It is monotonous walking in rice patties. I like going through villages. Well we are moving again.

Today the fifth of March.

True hassle! Hardly have time to write. I would have mailed this letter yesterday but I was too rushed.

Ma, if you send about fifteen of our Brown's Fried Chicken tags I will get a picture of my squad with them on their helmets. Okay?

Well, this morning I am located at a small village. We are going to take all their rice! They don't have much rice really but we were told to take it so here we are. I guess we are doing it because we found several completely buried. Well, I better start packaging the rice. Bye for a while.

Oh, before I forget, send Kool-Aid. Pre-sugared. Okay? Put one or two at least in each envelope. It gets so disgusting drinking straight water. Okay. Don't forget.

Well, I am going to clean my rifle.

Well, all we are doing is getting out of work. *Ha, Ha.* We tricked the Army. So I will close now, so I can mail this letter.

Bye for now, Fred Leo

Dear Ma and Dad *6 March 1968*

Well, that last letter was a hassle trying to get it out. Last night we had a sniper with an AK-47 shooting at our perimeter. When the AK-47 is on automatic it gives a *whining* sound.

The AK-47 is made in China. It has a bullet similar to the M-16. I haven't seen it yet but I have seen rounds and clips which are used in it.

We had a medevac last night. A guy got real sick. We brought the chopper into our position with two flash lights. That is hard. The chopper had no idea where we were.

This morning I am on a sweep! We are sweeping a grid coordinate on the map. A grid square is 1000 meters by 1000 meters. The reason we are checking the area is because one of our ambushes fired on some dinks. So we came back and we are going to try and track them down with the dog team that is with us.

Well, I will stop writing for a while. I will continue in a few hours with a new piece of paper.

I have a few more minutes so I will continue.

When you watch those old movies they always have these guys telling each other what they are going to do when they get back from the War. That is so true. We always talk about home, movies, girls, cars and what we are going to do when we get back from Nam.

You should see my boots. I have holes where the ankle is. The eyelets are almost all ripped out, the leather is white and ripped and cut. They are truly raunchy looking. But they feel so *good.*

I decided if I can't get to Germany via the Army, I will join the Merchant Marines. Then after the Merchant Marines I will go to college or maybe college first, then the Merchant Marines. Oh well, one way or another the world will pass before my eyes!

Remember the road sweeps I was on. Well, one man was killed and nine injured. It is a rough run to go on. So I am probably safer in the boonies than in the Base Camp. Well, got to move out. I will write on fresh paper now.

Today is the 7th of March.

We stayed at the same night logger last night that we stayed in when we saw the NVA about a month ago.

Well we are going through a routine search and destroy. We are about to search out a village. Time is going *Fast! Fast!* I will go on R&R the first of May. If you play your cards right it can last or rather keep you out of the field for a month. When I get back from R&R I will have six months left. "Real Fine."

Well, it is two hours later. I just finished washing up by a well. Did that feel good. I drink about five (quart) canteens of water a day. Some days even more. You can imagine how bad I needed to clean up. I just had a B-3 Unit. That is cookies, and hot chocolate. That was *good!*

I have been shamming all day. We are supposed to be looking for rice. Little do they suspect. This is the only way to go.

I guess you are wondering what the purple is on this paper. Well, I got some Kool-Aid from a friend and it spilled in my pocket. Every time I sweat it starts dissolving and presto!

Well, I will close this letter. Oh, before I go, remember the Life Saver discs you sent me in the can. It was fine. I eat one every night. They were the sour kind. You know what I mean, don't you? I give one to only my best buddies and then only once in a while. I feel good when I have one. I think of the U.S. and everything.

Well bye for now, Fred Leo

Well, Hi Ma and Dad *7 March 1968*

I just read your letter. My address changed! I am in "D" Company. Not "E" Company. Everything else is the same. Okay.

The snakes around here are not bad. There are not too many. I haven't come across one yet. But it only takes one to do the job.

Roxanna wrote me and said she was sick. Tell here to keep warm, eat good food. After all, she has better things to do than sleep and be sick. Right?

You said, "there is a light snow falling and you can see the lights of downtown. It's just about dusk." I can imagine how it looks. Right now I see what you described. I love light snow.

Well, the jungles are west of here closer to Cambodia. Where I am, the whole area is abandoned rice patties. It is unbelievable, how many there are. Then on the mountains, there are rocks. Nothing big grows on them, just tangled up vines and thorn bushes, cactus, pineapple.

The Monsoon is over! It gets hotter every day around here. I am half way between Tam Ky and Da Nang. I can see the lights of Hoi An or is it Da Nang from LZ Baldy.

I had spaghetti & beef. It is great. But we don't get many new

C-rations. The oldest rations we got were dated in the 1940s. The cigarettes were real dry.

Well, I don't have a foot locker up here. My foot locker is at Chu Lai. All the stuff I don't bring in the field with me, I bury in the ground.

Oh well, fox hole time. *Dig Dig Dig*

Today is the 8th of March.

I received your letter saying you are changing my address. Today I went with a squad. That is I am a roving RTO. I have no squad now. Well, anyway me and the squad I was with found 15,000 lbs. of rice. How is that. When we started putting the rice in bags, I found 1,200 lbs. in one place. I found boo coo rice.

I have it good now. I am the Platoon Sergeant's RTO, but he had to go to another platoon for a while. So I just roam around with no one telling me what to do except the Lieutenant. I take orders from no one. *I give orders*. I do what I want when I want. So my job is more interesting. I only worry about myself. I search any hooches I want without anyone telling me. It is Boss.

Right now I am relaxing. We walked a long way this morning. I feel like resting so here I be. Well, I better go look like I am working. I will write again.

Well, it is a few hours later. Oh, boy. I am guarding the rice we bagged today. I will be here until the ambush squad takes over.

Be sure to tell Lorraine to keep writing. I received her letters. I really like to hear about little Danny and the house.

Ma, could you send a balloon in each envelope. Also a little Kool Aid. Okay? Buy a BIG BOX OF KOOL-AID. Then send a little at a time Okay? The little kids love the balloons. I threw it at them and they caught it. Then I had them throw it back. Then I bounced it off their heads. You should have seen them grin. You don't see these people grin and laugh much when we are around them.

Oh, well, I better stop writing. I am getting carried away. See you on the other side.

I think I will start another letter tomorrow.

Bye until then, Fred Leo

Dear Uncle Ken, Maude and Karen *8 March 1968*

Oh, well, another day gone. The sun is beginning to go behind the mountains. I head a rooster crowing, I guess it is mixed up, I don't know. I am located right next to the mountains. They are big. I climbed them about a month ago. I will never forget it. We walked 12,000 meters up and down mountains. *Bla.* But that is in the past now.

I am in my foxhole. We carry ten sand bags each, so we can make good foxholes.

Well, we have a total of 28,000 lbs. of rice extracted from this area. Me and the squad I was attached to found 15,000 lbs. They give the rice to orphanages and refugees.

Well. How has the winter been, cold and harsh wind? Well, for that reason I don't mind being here.

I hear we are leaving the field in about a week. It is better to be in the field than at the LZ because we go on mine sweeps there. One sweep is twelve miles long! One man was killed and nine injured on it two days after we went into the field.

The knives I have are more than just useful. I try to make a hooch every night, so I chop down trees and cut rope. We go near a lot of sugar cane fields so I use it to open up the canes.

I am afraid I missed your package somehow. The mail gets messed up a lot. Everyone missed a package or two. How about sending more. I can always use more cookies. Scrumptious.

Well, I will be hustling tomorrow. Lots of rice to find. The radio I carry gets heavy. If I only walk five miles I am lucky. Oh well. *'Tis life.'* Be sure to remember I'm in "D" Company now.

Bye for now, Fred Leo

10 March 1968

Second Platoon arrived by Huey from the bush filthy dirty and exhausted late yesterday afternoon after ten days in the field. Landing at LZ Baldy, they climb off the chopper and move sluggishly away from the dust and debris of the blade wash.

Though casualties could often times be higher working in and around a firebase like LZ Baldy, to the grunts it is still considered a "safe haven from the storm." The field could take a toll on the soldiers in more ways than just getting hit by shrapnel, booby traps or bullets.

In the bush there were always the deadly viruses carried by a score of hosts including scorpions, flies, ticks, leaches, spiders and mosquitoes. There was nameless diseases and the infections that would rot the skin and boil the blood. There were poisonous Cobras, vipers and water moccasins. There were huge cockroaches, rats and flesh eating piranha. There were heat stroke, exposure, hyperthermia, river drowning and of course friendly fire. There was physical exertion that could ruin internal organs, tear out tendons and muscle. There were river drownings and of course tripping and breaking a bone. Ways to get killed or ruin a soldier's health for the rest of his life seems virtually endless when out in the boonies.

So anyone could see why the bunker line at a fire support base like LZ Baldy was like an oasis in a world of hurt. If nothing else, they didn't have to be constantly on guard, didn't have to carry the weight and could actually rest with their boots off. They could congregate without becoming a target. And sometimes just the little things would become the best things. Like they could get a beer, hot food, clean clothes, and a shower.

Though still energy sapped, at 6:30 A.M. the platoon forms up at North Gate for the road sweep up Highway 14 leading to LZ Ross. Feeling half dead, the soldiers start down the ten kilometer stretch of gravel road.

An hour out they come upon a stick driven into the middle of the road with a piece of paper attached. The sweep team comes over and informs Brown that it isn't booby trapped and he could pick it up. So he removes it and stuffs it into a pocket.

"Well, at least the monsoon is over and we aren't freezing anymore." Yamane wipes sweat from his brow and flicked it off his fingers.

"We ain't freezin' in the rain but we're still soakin' wet," Brown says noting the sweat-soaked fatigues.

Hours later they arrive at the river which is midway to LZ Ross. LZ Ross's road sweep team will arrive later in the day. After waiting for a half hour only a small M-37 truck arrives and there is only enough room for the Marine mine sweep team. Second platoon will have to turn around and walk the ten kilometers back to LZ Baldy.

On the way back, they veer off the main road and head across the arid, rocky and shrub covered terrain. At the top of a ridge they follow a well beaten trail into the dusty valley.

"What the hell?" pointman Shepard exclaims as he turns west heading down an amazingly level gravel road bed thirty feet wide. On either side of the road are deep drainage ditches. Brown looks back over his shoulder to find that the road seems to be going nowhere. He looks to his front and again the road seems to be going nowhere. The adjoining area suffers from erosion so severe that some ravines are sliced twenty feet deep and four feet wide.

"Holy shit!" Shepard again calls out from point and slows the pace. "Would ya look at that."

"Jesus Christ," Bedford is awestruck.

The platoon continues on the wide trail till they come in full view of a gigantic concrete and steel reenforced dam. The concrete wall stretches over six-hundred feet between two hills and is two hundred feet high. It appears that a long time ago, a huge blast had torn a hundred-foot gaping hole and opened a crack that stopped just short of the base.

Shepard, Bedford, and Okie were sent to check out the dam that had a cave leading from the upper concrete catwalk. The rest of the platoon continues along the wide road till they stand on a concrete bridge that crosses a river sized gorge.

"Yamane," Brown says, "that's the biggest dam I've ever seen. Its like . . . like it can't really exist, yet here it is. It's like," he looks around at the arid desert-like terrain, "we're some fifty years in the future and . . . ."

"You've just entered the Twilight Zone," Yamane finishes the sentence. "Do,do, do,do," he hums the introduction to the weekly television show.

"You got that right. It's dry as a bone out here with all the rice fields turning to dust. Then suddenly there's this Boulder Dam. And what's with the road?" Brown questions.

"According to the map, this is the famous Saigon to Paris Railroad."

"Railroad?" A stunned Brown looks up and down the gravel road bed. "Railroad?" It had never occurred to him that a railroad of any type had ever been in Vietnam.

"Check it out if you don't believe me," Yamane says pointing.

Brown follows his finger to a mass of twisted steel railroad tracks.

"What kinda tracks are those?" The tracks are made of all metal that includes both cross ties and rails.

"Don't ask me. Never seen anything like it myself. But this is definitely the railroad bed that comes through Hanoi, North Vietnam. At first I didn't see any sign of tracks. But then there they are."

"I thought you said this was the Paris to Saigon railroad?"

"Yeah, the French built it sometime in the early nineteen-twenties across India, China and stopping at Hanoi before moving on down to Saigon."

"Sounds like that would take a couple weeks of travel time."

"Well, back in that day the only other way would be around the Cape of Africa in a boat. And that might take two months."

Brown peers as far northeast as possible. It is probably the wind, but something makes the eerie sound of a steam engine whistle.

. . . . Rounding the corner is a steam engine with an apron of white smoke billowing around the wheels, and black smoke pumping out of the stack as it chugs pulling a string of wooden coach cars. Brown's mind goes inside a coach where both French and Europeans are seated on horse hair cushioned benches. The men wear tan boots, safari hats and khaki clothes. The women wear long, now extremely dusty dresses pulled to expose their shapely ankles. Their large brim, plum hats ripple in the breeze of the open windows.

A Frenchman turns to address his wife. Their antsy children having just spilled into the aisle from a sudden jolt of the passenger car.

"Notice the change of scenery in this rather arid area?" the man asks. He pointed out the low shrubs. "We will be passing a dam in a moment that holds the irrigation water." He gazes deeply into her big beautiful blue eyes saying, "You'll love my rubber plantation, dear. It's nothing like this. And Saigon, the Pearl of the Orient, is so much more civilized." She forces a smile as they settle back to admire the concrete mammoth . . . .

"Nothin', Sarge," Bedford reports, returning from the search of the dam and immediate area. "A few caves up there. Some newer C-ration cans—empty. The wood in a fire place couldn't be a day old but nothin' around."

Bedford turns to look at the monstrous structure. Then with a sweep of his arms adds, "There's a huge water basin that goes as far as the eye can see."

The dam, the railroad, dropped here by a civilization long since gone, seemed so out of place. Then Brown begins to imagine they are part of some bizarre movie. Their role is to walk out of this time-eroded valley and into . . . ? Into what?

They spread out and begin to move up the valley and Brown imagines the cameras pulling back and upwards to watch them disappear into an abyss. Then Rod Serling's voice come on:

"These common soldiers are about to find out 'things are not what they appear'. They have inadvertently walked through a portal—over a threshold to become permanent residents of a living trauma.

"File this episode under 'Dirty Laundry.' Or if you prefer 'Grim Business of War'. Next stop, The Twilight Zone."

Dear Ma and Dad *11 March 1968*

Well it has been a few days since I wrote last. I have been doing a lot of work.

Well, on the ninth what did I do? I dropped my radio and took off. I went over to a well and took a bath. I also washed my shirt. Me and the platoon sergeant poured water on each other for the bath. Did it feel good. We then took a little pan made from cement and put our shirts in it. Then started pounding it with a stick. The sides were rough enough to scour the shirts. How is that for an invention. But the platoon sergeant thought of it.

Well, after I did all that I sacked out for the rest of the day. I should have been working, but you know how it is. I would have written a letter but I was *TIRED!*

Yesterday was my 16,000 meter day. After that I was too tired to write. But guess where I was. Have you ever heard of that railroad that stretches from Saigon to Hanoi? Well, I walked on it. It was fabulous. The ground, mountains and the railroad ties, and bomb craters all told a fabulous story. We walked past blown bridge after bridge. We seen an old automobile. Then we came across a blown bridge with a gigantic dam. Of course, it was blown up too. Some of our men went up to it and checked it out. They said there was a dry river bed as far as you could see. The mountains rose all around.

Everything was concrete and built strong. Even rain troughs along the railroad were concrete. It was just like one you would see in the U.S. Just full of ghosts, you know.

I also could see an old French Fort about ten or fifteen miles away. It is huge. It has walls about two feet thick. They are built like old castles. I haven't seen this one up close. But I have seen small ones.

Well right now I am resting by a river. I just washed up and am resting. I also chowed down. Beans and Meat Balls. We don't feel like hustling so we are taking it cool. Third platoon just killed a guy. The lieutenant is on route to them right now.

Well, I will stop writing for now. See you on the other side.

In one of your last letters you asked what we did with the rice. Well, I asked my lieutenant. So he asked the captain. Then the captain asked the Brigade. It came down that it was given to the orphanages and refugees. The captain sent word to the whole company about the rice. You cause a lot of trouble (Ha, Ha) Guess how much rice we found to date. 34,000 lbs. That is a record for the Americal Division. How's that. Fabulous huh.

Well night is setting in. We just got finished killing another man. We went through the regular procedure of stopping them. But he wouldn't. We wounded him. He lost about a pint of blood. He didn't look scared at all. Not until one of the men walked behind him. *Blam Blam Blam Blam Blam*! Oh well, another VC another day. My weapon works every time.

Well, I am going to finish. Bye the way, that is two men we killed today.

The coins I found in houses, some are Indochina coins. That is what Viet Nam used to be called.

Well by for now, Fred Leo

P.S. Dad, you hope and feel like I do! I hope some day I will be home and the war behind me. Also I have built a beginning or a foundation for my whole life. You see, like father like son.

Dear Ma and Dad *13 March 1968*

Today we are making a routine sweep. We fired on three men but they all got away. It is hard to maintain a stable piece of mind. When we go into villages we help, that is medically, the people. But at the same time we are killing their father or their fathers son. It is so hard to be rough and mean and laugh off the man you see killed today. I don't know if I will ever get used to seeing men put out of their misery. So we just say they are in misery but they really are only wounded slightly.

Well, today is the 14th of March.

We have killed five VC since we were out. What a bring down. It is so disgusting. One G.I. fainted today. It is rough. But only a month and a half left to R&R.

Well, I will write again in a few hours.

A few hours have gone. I jumped in a river and washed up. That is the only way to go. I have a mustache and a small beard on my chin. I look weird. When I get to Japan in about a month and a half I will get a picture. They say you can call home from Japan. So it will not be long now. My hair is long but not as long as in civilian life. Well, we are going to chow.

By the way, send about twenty of those *Brown's Fried Chicken* patches. I will have a picture taken of all of us. Everyone wants a picture taken with the patches on it. I told them when they get home they can get a free dinner if they are in the picture. Okay.

For the last few days I have experienced what happens when a bullet flies by your head. You see movies of gunfighters and bullets flying at them. I can hardly talk myself into running and standing up to fire back.

I received your letter, Ma. I felt so messed up. So funny last night. I hope I can get used to it quick. Your letter just helps. What more can I say.

Could you send Kool-Aid. Okay. I sent a lot of Indochina coins. If you get them tell me. Be sure to tell me because I don't think it will get there.

Well, I think we are going back to LZ Baldy.

Today we are searching for rice again.

I got the letter from the store. I was glad to hear from them. I was going to write but I just don't have time. Could you tell them, Thank You? When I get time I will write. Tell them some friends from Nam will be dropping by. And tell them no one can bread chicken like me. But they can keep trying. Tell them to have a hot piece of chicken ready for me when I stop at the store when I come home.

> What do you say about an Army of a Foreign Country invading the USA. Massacring your people: Burning your home: Destroying your village and rice field? Repression, massacre, houses burning, women raping are not the Democratic American idea!

There is a lot of propaganda in this area. This is one just one. I sent the words to Roxanna too. We find it all around this area and it seems the whole of Viet Nam is hot! General Westmorland's idea of building up is a good idea because every so often the enemy builds up its forces and attacks. Maybe this attack was just a bigger gamble than they have been trying.

Well bye for now, Fred Leo

Dear Ma and Dad *15 March 1968*

I am patrolling around the area of our night loger. We are going to be a blocking force for another company this afternoon. So today I am going to keep cool. I should be in good shape by the time we go back to LZ Baldy.

I have another pair of boots on order. Not that I need them. Just joking.

Well a few hours just passed. I just shaved my chin. Oh well, I couldn't keep it forever. But my mustache is nice.

Well, resupply just came. I must get ready to move so I will get this letter mailed on the next chopper.

See you later, Fred Leo

16 March 1968

Everything becomes quiet. The confusion subsides. It all seems like a dream. Without realizing, Brown has on his rucksack and is mindlessly following the survivors of second platoon back down Hill 45. The column crosses a river on a makeshift wooden bridge. The remnants of second platoon is lost in thought as they move roboticly.

Rifle fire can be heard throughout the area as they enter a village with chickens roaming about.

"What's going on?" Brown asks, staring down at a bloody chicken.

An M-16 fires and he turns to see another chicken flopping on the ground. "Rat-t-t-t!" Feathers fly everywhere as the chicken virtually disintegrates under fire. "Kill the VC chickens."

Throughout the village, rifle fire continues. Anything living was being indiscriminately killed.

"There!"

Another chicken's body gets splattered into a bush.

Artillery begins firing in the distance and within seconds a round can be heard rustling through the air as it comes right for them.

"Incoming!" Everyone drops to the ground as the rounds impact. The earth erupts with dirt and shrapnel splattering throughout the village.

"What's goin' on?" Shepard looks around.

"This is the South Korean AO. Guess they don't know we're here," someone replies. Then the Howitzers begins firing once more.

"Take cover!" Everyone scrambles into a shallow irrigation ditch at the edge of the village. Curling as small as possible, the rounds explode closer and closer.

"They're walking the guns!" Green screams in terror.

"They're gonna end up on top of us!" Shepard yells as another artillery salvo is fired.

"Run! Get up and run!" Brown shouts. "Hurry up!" Brown yells. Yamane had been killed an hour earlier. Both Sergeant Denning and the lieutenant were wounded and medivaced out There is no one to command second platoon. Everyone instinctively follows Browns' orders.

"Incoming!" Brown yells when he hears the rounds sliding through the air. "Get down!"

The rounds hit next to the trenches they have just evacuated. Clods of dirt splash over them. When the last round lands, Brown jumps up and shouts. "Move it out. Get back over the river. Hurry it up."

Following Brown, they zig-zag through the area taking cover when the artillery lands. Coming to a bridge, they make a mad dash to safety hitting the ground just as the rounds hit short of the river.

"Ain't no Korean 'Rock' gonna put a hole through me," Shepard says his face still in the dirt.

"Holy shit!" Green reaches for a four inch piece of shrapnel. "Oww! Son of bitch, it's hot." They move off waiting for the next salvo which never comes.

"Just cleanin' the guns, that's all," Bedford speculates.

"Didn't scare me none," Shepard states. "Shit."

Leaderless second platoon joins with third platoon at a night logar at the base of Hill 45.

"RTO, you and two of your friends go on top of that hill. You're the outpost tonight," an officer orders.

"Yes, sir," Brown acknowledges the lieutenant who hands him a starlight scope. "Green, Okie, get your gear. We got OP."

While assembling the equipment, Brown begins to hum, doubtful at first as it wells from deep in his chest. It is as though he is showing his resolve. Taking heart he begins to hum and sing softly a boyhood Song Of The South. "Ohh, zipidi du da . . . zipidi a. My, oh my, what a wonderful day."

"Hey, I know that song," Okie says picking it up, "Plenty of sunshine headed my way. Zipidi du da zipidi a."

"Mr. Blue Bird's on my shoulder," Green sings and they laugh.

"Alright you guys let's go," Brown says.

"Now ain't this some shit," Green complains as he keeps losing his footing as they climb the steep grade. They stumble and crawl over loose rocks up to the crown. Brown leads them to an artillery crater, the same one where early that morning he had run for cover. He had been the only one left standing after the booby-trap artillery round had exploded nearly wiping out his platoon.

With twilight minutes away, Green and Okie snuggle into their poncho and liners and immediately fall asleep. The sun begins to play hide and go seek behind cumulus clouds, sending its hazy yellowish rays through pure white passage ways to give the impression there might be another world up there. Like a window into heaven, Brown thinks. Where angels live.

An earlier breeze subsides, leaving the air motionless.

Under the cover of darkness, he creeps from the crater and makes his way unerringly to the blood stained earth where Yamane's life had spilled.

Dropping to a dink squat, he scoops a handful of the crimson stained earth. In his clenched fist, he could smell Yamane, could feel his presence. He gazes at the blood laced earth in the waning light.

When the re-supply chopper came in yesterday afternoon, Yamane had received orders to report for R&R in Hawaii. However, he had opted to stay with the platoon through the morning of the 16th of March because the platoon was going into an enemy stronghold un-penetrated since 1964.

There had been a lot of excitement about the coming operation and some of the soldiers couldn't sleep. They stayed up talking through the night. During a conversation, Yamane had stated he was leaning toward atheism. But when Brown rolled over in his sleep, he distinctly heard Yamane say, "I believe in God. And if I die you know where I'll be . . . ."

"Ashes to ashes, dust to dust." Brown sends the dirt flying to watch it swirl in the air.

A simple truth: through his memory he could make Yamane live on. Brown had witnessed heroism from a mortal who did not die in battle but who was born in battle.

"I will not say good bye," he says steadfastly through misty eyes. "You are going to stay with me because . . . because I need you to watch over me." Tears now roll down his cheeks. "I need you to be my guardian angel."

YAMANE

Dawn's
early light
brings a
sky that
sparkles
sapphire blue. The sands
of time trickle as a baby is
created. The sun marches to zenith,
a sweet smell of jasmine in the air,
and the sand dances merrily about.
The child is appeasing destiny. A
raging ball of fire spews a horrible
blood red. And inside a blinding
sandstorm the peacekeeper lay
dying. Dawn explodes, sending
spirals of light cascading through
the wide eyes of a newborn.
Oh Lord Is it now this child's
turn to give his life away?

Dear Ma and Dad *17 March 1968*

Well it is four in the morning. Tomorrow I go into LZ Baldy.

Ma, God has been with me thru all. Your prayers have not gone unanswered, I assure you of this.

I imagine I will go in and get drunk. I don't know.

Tonight I am an OP (observation post) on Hill 45. I can see our night loger position below. We look through the Starlight Scope continuously.

When I go on R&R to Japan I wish so much to see you again, Ma, but I must see the War through. What I have seen and done would only make things hard to bear if I told you on R&R. So I can not let you come. If God and destiny will it, I will be home.

I am going to try to get a direct assignment to Germany. If it goes through I will have one month home and then I will have a thirteen month tour of duty in Germany. If I get it I want you to come over. There are real groovy things to see and do.

I received your letter from March 9th. Try and call Roxanna often because I try to find time to write to both of you but I can't. Sometimes I am lucky if I get one out every three days.

Well I feel great. Ain't that disgusting. I haven't been sick yet and I am in great physical shape. My legs give me a little trouble every once in a while but they are turning into two power houses. I get cramps when I don't carry my radio. The weight helps my legs. Of course, I mean when I drop my heavy gear.

A couple of days ago we moved to our night loger and a man fainted a couple hundred meters from our old loger. We didn't realize this till we were 1200 meters passed the man, so I, I mean me and a few other men, turned back. We picked him up and returned to the new loger site.

I was so hot that I was beginning to stagger. Well I happened to be right next to the captain and I flipped my radio off and dropped it on the ground. The captain jumped all over me for dropping it! A few days later we turned it in because it didn't work. Oh, well, I got another radio now.

I don't care because we are all going to get new, brand new radios from the States. Also the new M-16. The M-16 has a chrome chamber in it now. It helps stop the jamming problem. I don't have any trouble with my weapon because I brush it off at least twice a day. Oh well, my guard is just about up. The reason it went so fast is every once in a while I re-scan the area with the starlight scope. Well, I will write in the morning. Bye for now.

Well, it is morning. We went on a routine sweep. After the sweep we went into a blocking position. "A'" Company is going to sweep to us. Maybe we will get a couple VC. By the way we have killed at least three men in the last two days.

We aren't going in tomorrow. Maybe, I don't know. Four months are just about over. When I get back from R&R I will have six months. Half way mark.

Be sure to send those Brown's patches. I will get you a picture okay? It should be real wild.

Are you putting Kool-Aid in the envelopes yet. Be sure to get the kinds of different flavors. Cherry is groovy. Well, I better get this letter into an envelope.

Bye for now, Fred Leo

Dear Ma and Dad *18 March 1968*

We are going in to LZ Baldy tomorrow.

You really improved in Bowling, Ma. Your first scores were about one-hundred. It don't take long to get in the groove!

A couple of men are going back to Chu Lai. So I am going to have them make me up a magazine jacket. I hope when I get in you will have all those "Brown's Fried Chicken" tags. Man, I feel great. Our Platoon Sergeant is really fabulous. He gives me so much confidence. We are getting a new lieutenant for our platoon. None of us know him. He isn't around yet. I hope he is as good as our last.

Well, I will write when it gets light out. It is about four A.M. I can see fairly good.

I can see LZ Baldy from our night perimeter. We are going in. WOW! I sure do feel good.

How are my stocks coming along. Be sure to tell me how high they are now. Wow! I don't have much to write right now. I know I will have a *lot* to say tomorrow night. So I will write another letter.

Bye for now, Fred Leo

P.S. Did you receive those coins? I guess you didn't. I didn't put a stamp on it. So maybe it was lost.

Dear Ma and Dad *19 March 1968*

Ma, could you do something for me. Go to Whopper (*Burger King*) and buy a hamburger with everything on it to go. And a strawberry shake. Okay. Then tell me about it.

In a week I am getting the new chrome chambered M-16. Brand new radio too. How is that!

Well, we are going in to LZ Baldy. Two platoons are going in there at 6:15 A.M. They will make the road sweeps. Our platoon has the day free. The first thing we will do is get our laundry and go take a shower. Then we will pick up our packages and go to the bunkers. Then they are going to bring us beer and coke. How is that for a fabulous day.

I woke up for guard and I feel like today is Christmas. Man, I hope I have all kinds of goodies.

By the way someone stole my little knife. But I hid my Big Knife so no one could find it. I didn't bring it with me this last time. I will this time. You need a knife here.

Did I tell you I lost the Big Knife on a road sweep one day and the next day one of our men found it. How is that for luck.

Could you send me a five more $100 Bank Drafts? They say I can cash them at the Air Force Base in Japan. That is a lot of money but I want to buy a few things that I will be able to use for the rest of my life. I am going to get a beautiful $400 camera. It is worth about $800. Or wait. No, I will get it. If I go to Germany then I will have pictures that mean something.

I will buy a cheap camera also. I will carry it around during the rest of my tour.

I received the letter from Lorraine. Tell Lorraine it will not be long before Danny will tell her when he's hungry. Then she'll wish he couldn't. *Ha. Ha.*

I better finish tomorrow. Bye till Noon or so.

It's two days later.

Today is the 20th of March, Uncle Raymond's birthday!

I was just about to write when we had to leave the LZ to secure Highway One for a convoy. I didn't bring my pen. I was pooped so I didn't get time to continue.

Wow! I received two packages from you, Ma and one from Roxanna. I don't go to chow. I eat all the things you got me. Wow! I had a can of mandarins. I have been munching on prunes all day yesterday and today. That Orange Kool-Aid is wild. Try to send all different kinds of Kool-Aid. Okay. The reason I like Kool-Aid is because I get tired of the taste of water. If I get too much of the same type of Kool-Aid then I get tired of it. You understand! Some days I drink seven canteens (quarts) of water. Sometimes even more.

I am going to eat the Spanish Rice for dinner and the beans. Ma, they go great together.

It surprises me how much I look forward to the packages. A lot of little things make my whole life bearable over here. Like when I get thirsty I look forward to drinking Kool-Aid. What else can I look forward to? Things put me in trances and a letter just brings me back on my feet.

Today I took a shower and got new fatigues. You could imagine how much I needed them. The way we sweat. I just got new supplies for my M-16 cleaning kit.

Roxanna sent me some sausage and cheese. How is that straight from New York City's Greenwich Village! Bleeker Street!

I just finished putting new ammunition in my magazines. I also cleaned them and stretched the springs. We have some rats in our bunker. I am going to take out my .22 cal. pistol and zap a few. I am going to put those new socks on you gave me.

Oh well, time has come to eat my Spanish Rice and Beans.

Bye for now, Fred Leo

P.S. When I get those Brown's Fried Chicken patches I am going to buy a roll of color film and use my buddies camera. I will send the film to you. Okay.

Dear Sister Roxanna *22 March 1968*

What a day. HOT *Ugh!*

Well, I am coming up in the world. I am part of the CP. This is the position of the leaders. I am not sure what the abbreviation CP stands for but it is the controlling element of the Platoon. The Platoon sergeant asked me if I wanted to be his RTO officially. We get along real good. He is twenty-five years old. If anyone lives in the platoon he will. He know's his stuff. He will help me stay alive.

The colonel is going to promote me to Sp/4. He hears what I have been doing. Me and my buddy Okie are the only ones in our platoon to get one.

I am in for a couple of medals for valor. I will not know exactly what they are until I get them.

I got your goodie package. About half of your sausage is gone. I am going to *scal*e the rest of it tonight. It is hanging from the ceiling in my bunker. You know why? Those darn rats would get it otherwise. Oh, well.

The Platoon Sergeant said I could have tomorrow off. I haven't been off for about two or three months.

Roxy, I have your picture in the top of my helmet. Every time I take it off you say HI to me. *How silly.*

I heard you might go to Europe. Tell me if you do, okay? The platoon sergeant, Sgt. Denning, is trying to get assignment to Germany too. He has been there once. So he knows his way around. I have talked with a lot of people that know where Bleeker and Jones Streets are in New York.

Roxanna, now don't get married or give those boys a hard time. Okay. You can when I get back though.

Well, I am going to test fire my M-16.

Bye for a while, Fred Leo

P.S. Roxy, I want to say something. I say this in truth. Your prayers have saved me. Something happened this last time out. By all rights I shouldn't be writing this letter. I would be somewhere else.

Remember there ain't no way in Hell "Charlie" is going to get me because I got everyone at home pulling for me.

Love, Fred Leo

Dear Ma and Dad *23 March 1968*

Guess what. A certain frequency I turn on has a bull session. My call sign is Chicken Man. I asked for a man from Chicago. He said he knows of us. I told him we are the Best. He said we have no competition. I said, "Roger Livers & Gizzards." He said "I am a leg man myself."

He also said it's been two years since he was there.

The call signs are wild. Here are some, "Long Horn" "Big D" "Lake Charles"," Oklahoma Kid " " Bat Man" "Motown 2."

I got your picture. wow! I got it taped in my helmet.

Bye for now, Fred Leo

Dear Ma and Dad *24 March 1968*

What a day. We didn't have road sweep, but we had a ten-man detail. I was not on it!

Guess what we did on St. Patrick's Day. We wore all *green* clothes. Oh well, would you believe OD (olive drab).

Well, last night was the first time in Nam I got drunk. I still got a hangover. The way things turned out it helped. How wild it was. We all talked over what had happened since we were here. There are only a few old guys left. I guess if you lasted through four months of infantry you are old. We had three new men killed already. Well, 'tis life.

You know those Brown's Fried Chicken tags. Okay. All the guys wear them around. How goofy. If this keeps up the whole 1/6 Infantry will know about us. I got a roll of film from my buddy. I haven't finished it yet. I haven't taken pictures today. I took most of them yesterday. I got one real good picture. I am standing on this hill. In the background is that railroad I told you about. It winds through the mountains. It may sound better than it is. But it is in color. It was taken with Okie's $100 camera—State side price.

Send those money orders. Send the money different ways, so I know I can cash most of them. Send a lot of money. I am going to buy an Accutron watch. Tape recorder for college, and a beautiful camera. That is about $500 right there. I only have about $100 in cash right now.

I couldn't cash the check. They said you could cash it in Tokyo at the Air Force Base. If I don't need the money, I won't cash them.

How do you telegraph money, you know, by Western Union?

I don't know when we go out again. I really don't care. Two more days and another month. Where I am, I don't even touch my rifle. Does it look motley! I better fix it up. Well, we haven't received the *Delta* Package yet. I can hardly wait to get a new rifle and radio.

Could you send me a black magic marker. Okay. I need it to write on my camouflage cover and color in those "Chicken" tags.

Also I need a couple more pens. This Bic Pen is just about out of ink.

Have you heard any more on the 30-round magazine. Those things are valuable. Get as many as you can. I can always use them. Wow! I can't get R&R off my mind. I haven't any orders cut yet but I have seniority so I could get it okay. I will be glad when they give me a date.

I am on another road sweep. Found some propaganda. This is how it read.

American Officers and Men!

The Saigon government is the dictatorial despot vs imperialism's stooges. The South Vietnamese people are determined to overthrow it. Within six days from January 30, 1968 to February 4, 1968 the Patriot Armed Forces and people simultaneously attacked seven Big Cities, 47 provincial capitols, townships and hundreds of district capitols over South Vietnam.

Wiped out more than 50,000 enemy troops, (including 10,000 G.I,s. Completely destroyed seven Army Regiments, 47 Battalions, hundreds of companies. Shot down or damaged more than 1500 aircraft, destroyed more than 4000 military vehicles of all types. Captured a big quantity of weapons, disintegrated more than 200,000 puppet troops. Almost all enemy airfields, military depots from top to bottom were attacked. The Patriot Army Forces and its people had seized the control of many areas and are continuing with their offensive to drive U.S. and puppets to complete failure.

American Officers and Men

Do realize clearly about the South Vietnamese people 's present rising Revolutionary movement which no force can check? The U.S. and its Thieu Ky puppet clique of traitors will completely be defeated. Show your noncommittal attitude not to interfere in the South Vietnamese People's internal affairs in order to save your lives.

Demand your repatriation

The Central Trung

30 Nation Front for Liberation

well, so be it. Propaganda right.

By for now, Fred Leo

Dear Karen, Maude and Ken *25 March 1968*

Well, I received your letter Karen. You really, truly live a good fast life. The next letter I get from you, you probably will be in Hawaii. *Hope, hope.*

Be sure and tell me if you are getting married for sure. I will be home around Christmas. But then I guess this summer would be the best time.

Well, I am still at LZ Baldy. I hear we might stay here another month. Then we will go back to Chu Lai and be Brigade Reaction Force. In other words, if anyone gets in a tight spot we are called in. It is rough stuff. Our brigade is in all hot areas now. This is life. Oh well.

Guess what, R&R Tokyo, Japan here I come. One more month. I haven't got my orders yet but I have seniority over most of the men in the platoon.

My ma told me to look for a goody package. *Ha Ha!* I am ansious anxgcious (can't spell it right) to get it. I imagine the whole platoon will like it. It is hard to keep your goodie packages hidden. *Yum Yum.*

My fourth month is going by now. Eight more to go. But the next two months will go fast because R&R will be here.

Guess what my platoon lieutenant did? He told his sister to write me. *Ha!* I didn't even know about it. Oh well.

We are going to test fire weapons so I got to get some more oil on mine and clear the bore.

Bye for now, Fred Leo

Dear Ma and Dad *28 March 1968*

Dolores Young wrote me. Tell her I received it. I really liked hearing from her. Tell her if I get time I will write. See, I hardly am able to write one now. I am securing an LZ for a chopper. They are bringing in resupply. I am in charge, me and my platoon sergeant. The chopper will call us and we will pop smoke so they can find us.

I came out here the 26th. We are with the Armored Personnel Carriers. They carry our gear so we don't hump gear at all. But it wouldn't bother me to hump it because I don't carry a poncho any more. I just have a light weight *poncho liner*. I am the only one to do this. It will work because if it rains I have a big piece of plastic. Real thin. It weighs about *one pound.* The poncho weighs four or more plus it takes up a lot more room. The plastic I can put in my fatigue shirt pocket.

I am carrying a water bladder. It holds two quarts. It is plastic and weighs about as much as a canteen cover. It really helps on weight and room.

Guess what, SP/4 is on the way. My platoon sergeant said he seen them. We have a new lieutenant. He knows his way around. He has been in the field for three months. The lieutenants rotate to the rear after six months.

I have my First Sergeant working on getting me direct assignment to Germany. He should be able to get it for me.

I have your picture and Dads in the top of my helmet next to Roxanna's. I can see it right now.

I already scaled that Kool-Aid you sent me. Could you send maybe two packages of it in each letter. Put all kinds. Different brands. All Kinds. It makes life enjoyable. I drink *boo-coo* water.

A couple of days ago we chased a squad of VC. But they

spotted us before we seen them. So we didn't get them. They better run. We had the .50 caliber machine guns shooting at them.

Well, the APC just went across the LZ to help secure it.

I just got back from a well. I washed up. I always carry soap with me. It helps a lot to beat the heat. It opens the pores. Next time in I will get a hair cut.

I have two Cokes in my pack. I am going to *feast*.

Could you send me some *Fizzies*, you know. Okay. A package at a time. Man, I can't say how much those silly little things help.

By the way tell Aunt Maude I scaled all her Brownies. They were great. About everyone had one. But I had about ten. They were great.

By the way send Root Beer *Fizzies!* Do you Roger? Over.

Oh well, the chopper will be here in fifteen mike (radio language for fifteen minutes)

So bye for now, Fred Leo

Dear Ma *30 March 1968*

I Received a letter from you that asked what happened on the 16th of March and why I had a part censored. *Most of the guys believe you should abbreviate on your letters.* Well in my case I don't think it would apply. The men say you just scare the people at home when you tell them everything. You sounded like you would rather have it said then hid. I feel better when I do, but what I am about to say, when it happened, and how, was ghastly! For this reason I didn't tell you sooner.

Well, Sergeant Yamane was my squad leader. We called him *Same Same*. The reason was because he was Japanese and look similar to the Vietnamese. Same Same means the 'same as' in Vietnam. Well, I have known him since I have been in Nam. You could say he *weaned* me. You know. He was hard on me at first but then I set him straight. From there on we were the best of friends. He asked me to be his RTO. I treated him good. I kept water for him. Got his C-rations. Heated his coffee and helped him in general. That's part of a "good" RTO's job. He had other things to work on.

We bitched about things together and slept together you might say. He told me about his girl Sandi and I told him I didn't have one yet. That didn't matter, I know how he felt and that I wanted that some day.

Well, as time went on I got good. He put me in for promotion. I am now SP/4. But we started losing radios—they broke. Soon I had one of the only two radios. I was the *best* so I was the lieutenants RTO. Soon our Lieutenant left, see, after 6 months in the field they go to the rear. I guess they are better than us—but not really. I guess the army has its classification.

Finally the 15th of March rolled by. We were snipered at and one man was shot through the heart and killed. He just came over. I didn't know him personally. That night we talked over things. The next day we were going to be on a blocking force for "A" Company. They were going into an area that wasn't touched for three months. Yamane was going on R&R at 4 P.M. the next day. He should have gone on the 15th of March, but we needed him.

By the way Sgt. Denning wanted me for his RTO. I can't get along with lieutenants. They have to be babied. Sounds funny. I wish it was.

Well, the next morning came early.

"Wake UP!" It was 6:15 A.M. "Get up, get packed, then chow down."

I emptied the sand bags we had filled the night before and got my gear packed.

"Say Scott," I said to the lieutenant's new RTO, "you got any Kool-Aid?"

"Yeah," he said, "I got some Cherry."

"Thanks, I'm glad you got a lot of Kool-Aid. Say, how's everything going Scott?"

"Well, Brown, I am tired. And we got *boo-coo* humping in front of us."

"Say, how's your father, Scotty?"

"Well, Brown, he still don't like me being here you know. He's a conscientious objector."

"MOVE OUT."

We started up a hill, Hill 45. They are named after their height. My squad was in the lead. We started up the hill. Okie (his real name is Smith) and Green got tired and couldn't make it up the hill.

"Come on you guys, you're in the second squad," Sgt. Denning yelled because they were falling behind. "Smitty you stay here." "Come on, Brown."

We went to the top. I usually walked with my head down. That way I can't see when people run. So then I will not have to kill them.

I was third from the front. Okie and Green had been in front but were way behind now and Yamane was the pointman. Everyone was spread out. There was a four-man front.

Cablam!! The whole mountain shook.

"Oh, My God." I couldn't see him but Sergeant Denning was somewhere in front of me.

"Mortars!" someone screamed.

I turned and ran. I jumped into a shallow hole. I thought they were going to walk the mortars right over me.

"Medic! Medic!" The medic started toward the men. Then I threw my gear off and ran over to the men. I saw a dead man. I guess I can't help him.

Then I seen Yamane. First I looked at his body. His leg was dangling. There was no chance for his leg. Then I came to his face. Face to face with me. I don't know if he said my name.

"I can't breathe," when he said this all of a sudden I realized there was tear gas all around. Now I couldn't breathe. I had been holding my breath, but I couldn't hold it any longer. I then breathed the CS gas. My guts growled and began to rumble. I ran out. I almost fainted. My stomach *heaved* and I tumbled onto the ground. Then I turned around and went back in.

"Yamane! Yamane!" He didn't say anything. I think he was dead, but I couldn't admit it. I then tried taking the pack off his back. But then the gas played another round with me. I ran out and came back in and dragged him out of the gas. My sight was bad now from the gas. My face was watering. His leg didn't bleed much. I don't know why. So I opened his mouth and tried to give him mouth to mouth respiration. At first it didn't work.

"Someone, please help me, help me. I can't give him respiration. Help!!"

No one was around. They were helping everyone else. I tried and soon I got it working. My mind got weak and my body. I gave him respiration for about twenty minutes, then Okie took over. I stood up and Sgt. Denning grabbed me. I was faint. He said, "Take it easy Brown. Go sit down."

Then "Okay, get some poncho's over here. We got to put these men on the Chopper." I helped lift Yamane onto a poncho. I lifted him on the chopper.

"Bye Yamane."

I turned from the chopper and found out there were two men laying there dead. I also found out Scotty, the lieutenant's RTO was hurt. I helped him to the chopper. Also two other men were hurt. They were hurt bad enough so they would never return.

I also found out later that Yamane died. The Lieutenant's RTO, Scott, was hurt beyond repair. He is now paralyzed on one side and might die.

It was an artillery round that blew. Shrapnel hit a CS Grenade on Hick's belt. The man in front of me is dead now and Scott, the RTO was on the side of me. Everyone shielded me from the blast. That is why I am here to write these words.

Now, I know *sorrow*. Young teenagers think they know about sorrów but they don't.

One man, who was on his second tour said, "It was the worse thing he seen during his time in Nam." He said he couldn't help out because it was so ghastly.

Well, that is in the past. I am facing today and tomorrow now. I am one of the oldest men here. Most of the men have been killed or wounded. Well, an Explosive Team will be here soon. I must get this letter on the chopper.

Bye for now, Fred Leo

April 1968

1 April 1968

"Rat Patrol!" Third Squad Leader Muton, complains. "Not tonight Sarge. It's soup out there. Look." He motions to the dark cloud cover in the approaching twilight.

Their company commander had been with Delta Company in the field for over a week. To clear the area, the CO's strategy was to send first, second, and third platoons in a different direction and have them rendevous at a night logar position in evening. He had also started a competitive rivalry among them based upon body count. Brown's second platoon was still in the running, though they didn't know their official count. So there was added pressure to kill as many people as possible. Reputations meant a lot. And in all fairness, Delta Company had to show its mettle to the rest of the battalion.

To increase contact, the CO had instituted night time Rat Patrols. That's where, throughout the night, the ambush would rove. Four positions were the standard. It was very hard on an ambush since they would have to virtually march all night with little to no rest. Then show up at dawn to march along side the rest of the men during the entire day.

"Save it for the Chaplin," Sergeant Denning yells. "But I'll tell ya what, I won't make you go to all four sites. How's that?"

"Anything Sarge."

"Okay, just go to the first ambush site and the last."

Sergeant Muton gives an appreciative nod.

"Alright. Now, I want you to push out right after the Mad Minute. *Dee-dee* pronto."

After Muton leaves Brown comments, "I wouldn't want to do it, Sarge. Shit, it's gonna be black out there tonight." Brown lifts the last sandbag into position to finish their foxhole roof. "They'll be lucky to even find the last ambush."

"Well the Mad Minute will at least get 'em safely to the first ambush site."

"How long before the Miracle Minute?" Brown asks changing Mad to Miracle. Depending on their weapon, everyone in the perimeter will fire off a magazine of M-16, or two rounds of M-79, or a fifty round of machine gun ammo. In essence for one minute everyone would give it their all.

"The CO will fire his weapon for the signal."

"Rat-t-t-t-t!" roars the CO's rifle signal.

The entire perimeter erupts. Red tracer fire rockets, M-79 rounds explode and the M-60 machine guns thump out the rhythm. The most incredible display of fire power an infantryman could ever see except for a real firefight. Brown wonders how an aerial view of the Mad Minute might appear. It would definitely give the VC pause if they were planning an attack. For a long sixty seconds the sound reached an ear shattering height.

"Damn, man," Brown laughs from the adrenalin rush, his ears ringing. "If the VC lost track of us early, they'll have a pretty good idea where we are now." He watches as Muton's squad moves into the night.

Settling in for the night, Sergeant Denning taps his beer with a church key. Puncturing the rim, he cups his mouth around the foam that shoots out. "What came out on supply is all the beer and Coke we get."

Taking a sip of his beer, Brown looks over confused. They had given their platoon leader nearly two-hundred dollars to buy them two pallets of beer and Coke. Enough to last for a couple of weeks.

"The lieutenant said someone stole our money."

"He lost the money?" Brown questions in disbelief.

"The CO bought us this beer with money out of his pocket."

"I really like the CO."

"Best officer we've ever had."

"Sarge." Brown never did like their lieutenant but didn't want to talk too harshly because of protocol. "That's not a good idea to be stealin' a grunt's beer money. The lieutenant had better start watchin' his back."

Sergeant Denning drinks his warm beer. "So damn hot out here, you can't drink enough to get drunk," he sighs. "Here, catch." He tosses Brown another beer.

"Thanks Sarge. I'll save it for guard."

Around the bewitching hour, "*Crack! Crack!*" rifle fire is heard from the direction of Muton's Rat Patrol.

"Rat-t-t-t!" came the sound of an M-16 rifle in response.

Sergeant Denning grabs the radio handset and waits for a communication.

"Two-five. Two-five. This is two-three. Over," Muton calls.

"Two-three this is two-five. Over," Sergeant Denning replies anxiously.

"Got incomin'. No casualties. Out."

Rifle fire once again echoes followed closely by a hand grenade explosion. They listen with anticipation. What if they have to go out there and help? In preparation, Brown pulls on his pistol belt. Sergeant Denning buckles on his web gear. They stare in the direction of third squad rat patrol and wait. That horrible feeling of death fills Brown's mind and jabs at his heart.

"Two-five, this is two-three. We've scared 'em off. Over."

"Two-three, this is six," the CO breaks in. "Pursue and give coordinates. Do you copy? Over?"

"This is two-three. Wilco. Out," Muton signs off.

Brown smiles to himself knowing that the last thing Muton will do is try and follow the VC in the black of night. Most likely he'll sneak away and hide and, if need be, send back bogus reports.

In the wee hours of the morning, Brown sits on guard gazing over the dim landscape. The area beyond the perimeter has become alien and hostile. The huge hay stack, that during the day appeared far away, seems to be moving closer. Its ominous presence casting shadows.

Raising the rifle, he takes aims on a threatening shadow. It would be a good place from which a VC could shoot and harass. Working on a strategy, Brown decides he'd have to somehow get a hand grenade directly behind the hay pile to pick off the VC, but from his position that would be nearly impossible.

Howitzers commence firing from LZ Baldy. Brown takes a drink of beer and waits to hear where they will land. "Pumk! Pumk!" The sky is lit with illumination rounds. Another two rounds are fired. The air sizzles as one round slams into a bed of pine needles just short of him.

"Friendly fire?"

"It ain't," Sergeant Denning enjoins rolling over.

At dawn Brown receives a call from Muton.

"Everyone," Brown calls to the perimeter positions, "Hold your fire. The Rat Patrol is coming in."

Third squad emerges from the tree line, Muton, Billy and three other soldiers dragging themselves along. They walk like the living dead, slapping mosquitoes off with weak hands.

"Four klicks while you guys sit on your ass," Muton groans, as he literally collapses on the ground.

"Mosquitoes as big as helicopters out there," Billy complains, pointing to the welts on his neck.

Flecks of sunlight filter through the pine trees and begin warming the air. After a stimulating stretch, Brown grabs his rifle and steel pot to take a walk while Sergeant Denning debriefs Muton.

"Damn, I'm pooped out," Muton moans ten minutes later as he trudges past Brown toward his position. "Now the CO wants me to take 'im back to the ambush spot. Man, I've gotta get some shuteye. Shit!" He slouches away. "Wake me when the dog team gets here."

At eight A.M., Muton takes point, followed closely by the handler with a big German Shepherd pulling eagerly at the harness. Finding several expended rifle cartridge casings, the dog picks up a scent off the ground. A few feet away, they find a small piece of cloth dangling from the brush. The handler give the dog a few seconds to sniff the cloth before plucking it off and placing it inside a plastic bag.

The dog leads them through the trees and out into an open field. With the temperature rising, their pace slows as feet crunch on the dry crackling ground of a rice field. Heat waves roll throughout the area. The Shepherd leads them to a village, and by that time Brown has already used two canteens of water.

"Ratatat! Boom!" The point makes contact on entering the village. Everyone crouches, spreading out, but keeps moving.

"Over there!" Bedford yells pointing to a Vietnamese running out of range. With no more contact, fire-teams forms up and start a routine search-and-destroy. Meanwhile the dog team continues to follow the scent to the far side of the village.

Moments later the dog is pawing on the ground. A trap door is located and when opened, a young girl is found crouching inside.

This seems like a good opportunity to fill canteens, so Brown ambles over to the village well.

Next to the well is a nicely maintained hut, which Brown decides to search. Inside there is the usual altar set on a table with incense burning, dried flowers and a container of water. These the soldiers never touch. A picture of Jesus and a crucifix next to a candle makes him curious. Are they Catholic? Near the village, he now remembers seeing a crucifix in the graveyard.

Along the far wall is a stone fireplace framed by a solid dirt and straw wall. He wonders if there might be something stashed in the fireplace, like they did in those old war movie. Taking his bayonet, he begins tapping the stones to see if any are loose. Next, he kneels and runs a hand up along the inside of the chimney. His fingers clear out some loose stones to discover a cloth bag. Knocking off the dust, he opens the bag to find a handful of old coins. Chinese coins with square holes in the center are strung together. A few solid face coins had *Indonesia* imprinted on them.

The chopper meanwhile arrived with a Vietnamese interrogator. When Brown walks over to the clearing where the villagers are corralled, he sees the interrogator standing over a young girl—the one from the spider hole. She is pinned to the ground like an animal. Fresh marks in the earth showed where she had been dragged from the hole.

Sniffing through the villagers, the dog begins to paw and waggle its tail at two young boys. The ARVN interpreter pulls the three children ranging in ages from about eight to ten years old, to an irrigation ditch away from the rest of the villagers.

The interrogator begins to talk in a gentle voice. Getting no significant answers, he switches to yelling, shouting and threatening. Brown has seen these brutal interrogations before and doesn't care to watch.

"Sarge, what's the deal?" Brown asks.

"Well, the dog ID'd those three kids. They're our snipers. From what the ARVN tells us, the local VC honcho comes to the village every night and gives the villagers a loaded rifle and a few chincon hand grenades."

"Ah*hha!*" one little boy screams in pain.

"The oldest one, that girl," he points, "she's the ring leader." In his hand he carries her ID card.

"I thought if they got an ID card that meant they were on our side?"

"Apparently not," Sergeant Denning answers. "Anyway, the VC honcho comes back around in the morning, picking up the rifle and any extra Chicoms not needed for booby traps." Sergeant Denning takes a VC hand grenade off a wall and hands it to Brown.

"Looks like a Second World War Pineapple Grenade," Brown remarks, analyzing the grenades lumpy metal skin.

"I've heard they ship 'em empty and the VC have to fill 'em up themselves with explosives." Sergeant Denning is called away.

"So, what you got there?" the dog handler asks motioning to the grenade as he comes over to sit in the shade with the German Shepherd. "This hot weather plays havoc with these dogs, they're just not made for it." He puts the canteen up to the dog's mouth and lets it drink.

"Chicom grenade," Brown answers. When the dog finishes drinking, the handler puts the canteen away and curiously takes the grenade.

The Shepherd is a lean animal of average size, black across the back and sides. The belly and legs are mostly white. "Stay. Lay," the trainer commands. He unsnaps the lead from the leather harness. "Good boy. Good boy, Radar." The trainer pats the dog on the head as it rests on the cool ground. The Shepherd pants, it's tongue dripping with saliva, the sides of it's mouth foamy.

"Hello there, Radar," Brown says rubbing him behind the ears. He ruffles and pats the black fur. As the handler busies himself, Brown opens a can of Ham and Eggs and spoons out a morsel for the dog.

"No!" The handler kicks the food away and smacks Radar's face. "No," he repeats in a calm voice. Then he looks angrily at Brown. "Sorry, man but that'll get 'im sick. These dogs are on special diets, can't just eat anything. That's my job. I keep him fit and healthy."

He must have seen the amazement on Brown's face, because he adds, "C-rations don't have the nutritional needs. I even give Radar supplemental vitamins." He gruffly rubs the German Shepherd's head and leans over saying, "Don't I, Radar. Good dog."

"Really," Brown says, astonished that the food they ate wasn't fit for a dog. "And vitamins."

"Yeah, we gotta take special care of these dogs. One day on the job and they get one day off. If we go into the field for say three straight days we get two off. Like that. They don't want to burn the dog out." While the trainer talks he pours water into a canteen cup for Radar.

The handler reaches into his rucksack and pulls out an old battery operated radio. "Here," he offers. "Sniffed it out of that haystack in front of your perimeter."

"No kidding! Wow! Thanks!" Appreciatively Brown accepts the battered gift. "You know, there's one thing I've been wondering about," Brown says while checking out the radio. "Why are all the scout dogs German Shepherds?"

"Well, we have different breeds but like my friend would say, 'In a pinch, they taste better.'"

"No?" They laugh.

Station VNSRS comes over the radio, "*Yeah! Yeah! Yeahhhh! It's like a ball and chain.*"

"Wow. Reception is great." Continuing the conversation, "So how long is a dog's tour of duty?"

"A life sentence with no parole, my friend," the handler says, with saddened eyes. "My buddy tried gettin' his dog out at DEROS'd, but no way, man."

"Why not."

"Too many diseases and things they could pick up. Things we don't even know about. So all in all it's probably for the best."

"So every year Radar here will get a new handler?" Brown pats the dog on the head.

"Pretty much. And when they get old, they're turned over to the Vietnamese. But dinks don't appreciate their worth. It's probably cause their own dogs are so stupid and sickly from all the garbage they eat. To the Vietnamese, a good dog just makes their mouths water. They love good dog meat."

"For chrissakes! You weren't kiddin' about saying Shepherds 'taste better' were you?

"Nope." They laugh at the serious comedy. "And if you really want to see something funny, you ought to get a load of the face the ARVNs give when they're told they need to take a course on 'Speaking English to American Dogs'." The handler smiles.

"Back at base, this guy managed to get a pregnant dog. A couple of weeks later it gave birth to six healthy black puppies which the guy's hootch maid pampered like babies. Fed them milk, gave them vitamins, washed them all the time. A couple days back, I noticed two pups were gone." His brown eyes squint mischievously, as he asks, "Know which two?"

"I dunno. The biggest ones?"

"Right! My buddy bawled up a storm after telling me the hootch maids were raving the entire next day about the feast they'd had. "Numba one chop chop. So good."

"Oh my God. They didn't." They were both nearly hysterical with laughter. "Numba one chop chop. Ah*hhhh.*"

"Then it started making sense to my buddy why she took such good care of the puppies. When all the time she was plumping them up for the stew. What an idiot!"

"Well, I wouldn't have known that either."

"I've heard the Vietnamese have a special place in their stomach for black dogs, especially young plump ones."

While talking, the handler takes off his boonie hat and places it on Radar's head to shade him from a ray of sunlight shooting past the shade tree.

"That Vietnamese interrogator is pretty rough on the kids," Brown notices.

"Pretty tame to some of the stuff I've seen." They turn away when they hear the little girl scream again.

"Did you hear about the two dog handlers who went outside the perimeter to do some training?" the handler begins. "Well, one of 'em gets bit by a cobra on the dick." He winks and smiles. "So his buddy tells him not to panic and takes off running back to base camp to find the medic. The medic tells him to cut an X across the puncture holes and suck out the poison. So the guy runs back." He pumps his arms and breaths like he is running frantically. "His panicking friend sees him comin' and screams, 'Well, what did they say?' The guy runs over and says, "They said you're gonna die!"

They break up laughing as they visualize the handler holding his snake bitten penis. Meanwhile the handler is absentmindedly toying with the chicon grenade.

"Tick."

Their eyes jump to his hands. The handler has accidentally pulled the pin and detonated the primer. Frightened senseless, he drops the chicom into Brown's hand. Like a hot potato, Brown flings it down the well and they drop.

After a heart throbbing minute they realize it didn't explose. Slowly they stand and brush themselves off, pretending nothing has happened.

"Get the dog over here!" Denning yells. "Chopper is inbound!"

"Shit, Sarge," Muton swears, his anger boiling over. "You know as well as I do, those kids relatives will pay some money and they'll be back in business in a matter of days. We outta just kill 'em right here right now while we got the chance. Shit," he looks around at everyone angrily, " you're just as dead from a bullet fired by a ten-year-old as from anyone else."

"Muton, I ain't no dink lover either," Sergeant Denning rebukes him. "But the reality is the VC will drop off those rifles again tonight. Now either this village goes out and fires on us, or the VC kill a villager. Maybe we're just lucky those kids couldn't hit the broad side of a barn."

"I think we have better odds with her behind the trigger," Brown says putting in his two-cents-worth.

Sergeant Denning turns. "Alright. Saddle-up. We're movin' out."

The air temperature steadily rises until it cooks in excess of 115 degrees. The soldiers march dreamily through the arid terrain, mesmerized by the dancing heat waves that twirl gracefully about them. It doesn't take long for the heat to start taking its toll.

Brown's body tries to keep up but the internal organs start to strain and grind from overuse. His lungs become so dry they squeak with each breath. His heart swells from pumping such hot blood. Brown begins a slow panic because he knows he cannot keep the pace much longer in this Death Valley. The ground rises and falls beneath his feet and he realizes that he must keep a certain pace or else the soles of his feet will burn from contact with the ground.

Soldiers all around waver and float disjointed, their equilibrium questioned with each step. He takes another raspy breath the scorching air burning the hairs in his lungs.

The whole afternoon is filled with a mixture of soldiers stumbling in the dust and fighting for breath. Canteens are emptying quickly. Topping a rise of thirsty earth, the heat waves crash into them like a tidal waves nearly throwing them out of their bodies.

The sandlike ground reflects a cruel glaring sun into their beet red faces. And the once light blue sky has become heavy and hazy its throbbing white eye lusting for their juices. Squinting through the glare, Brown watches as the distorted figure of Doc Holliday is surrounded by swirling heat rivulets, vicious ghosts that lash and pounce on him. Overcome, he swoons, knees turning to rubber and collapses flat on the ground.

Doc struggles over, removes Doc Holliday's steel pot and splashes his face with water. Sweeping back the rucksack shoulder straps, he opens Doc Holliday's shirt and splashes more water over the chest. Whispering waves of heat continue to roll over them bringing the entire column to complete stop. The ground heat is so enormous, Brown begins marching in place, lifting one weighted foot then the other. He weaves. With strength waning, he unsnaps his canteen, lifts it out, unscrews the cap, pulls back the cap, and finally brings it to his parched lips and takes a swallow.

He reaches to remove the steel pot. "Ouch!" Brown shrieks finding his steel helmet too hot to handle. He opts to push it back enough so he can dowse water over his forehead to let it dribble down his face and onto his chest. The water quickly joins the sweat that is already dripping off the fatigues.

Washing salt from his eyes, he looks around to see four other soldiers have collapsed from heat exhaustion.

"Move to the trees!" Sergeant Denning yells spotting shade. "Grab hold of those men. Come on. Hurry it up."

The knoll is covered with staggering, hunched soldiers dragging themselves and other heat victims across the inferno. They teeter onward resembling survivors from an ill fated wagon train.

"Let's get the hell outta here, Doc," Brown says in a raspy voice. They both reach over and lift Doc Holliday to his feet.

Dear Linda *2 April 1968*

So how is it going? Hey, what is all this, "Do I miss you" stuff. Silly. Hey, listen you said these pictures were enough to satisfy me. I'll tell you what. These pictures look like some silly girl I had the misfortune to meet. *Now*, send a *color* picture of you. Tell my ma I want her to take one, okay.

Wow! I would have loved to see *Brigadoon*. I bet it was a lot of fun. You met a lot of new friends in the play I bet.

Don't mind how dirty and messed up this paper is, it is in better shape than me. This pen I'm using, I got from a village we *cleared* yesterday. It doesn't write so good.

Well, here I sit. I can see Hill 45 from here. My best friend was killed up there two weeks ago.

We just killed an old man, wounded a woman and shot a kid's leg off. We also captured three VC.

Linda you asked me if I changed my mind about kids. Yesterday one of our *rat patrols* was hit. We found one of the people who did it. He is under ten-years-old. Also a ten-year-old girl threw a hand grenade.

See, the young kids around here are just as dangerous as the grown ups.

Well, are you going to work in a convalescent home? I also believe money isn't everything. *Do what you must*. That is all we can ever want or hope to do.

Well, we are searching another village. I found a radio but it is too big. So we will listen to it till we leave.

How are you doing in school? You are doing real good aren't you?

My doctor or medic is setting here with us. He is pulling out all his stuff. We all need something he has.

So you're now sixteen and have a license to drive. Do you ever go to Argon Laboratories? You know the white deer are out there. Go by yourself. The same night you receive this letter. Go there for me.

Ha, Linda, let me say this once and for all. Don't ever tell me again you wish you were here with me. *You ain't!* Your job is at home. Now don't tell me ever again, okay. My job is here, not yours, okay!

Well about two hours have passed. I am at our night logar. We work all morning, hold up during the day and send out rat patrols at night.

I have it made for the time being. I don't go on rat patrols. So all I do is hump all morning. I have the rest of the day off. If you would call it that.

Well, for a week the armored personal carriers have been hanging around us. They are going to leave now. They haven't done much.

Right now I am listening to a three band radio we found in a hay stack. Mary Ann Faithful is singing her song.

Listen, tell everyone in the family, *Hi*. Benny, Muts, Betsy and Betty.

Well keep cool, Fred Leo

P.S. Don't drag race with the kids in the car!

Dear Ma and Dad *2 April 1968*

Wow! I got your package with the Little Teddy Bear. Silly! How did you know I needed a watch? Did I say I needed it? No one has a watch anymore. It has been over two months since I have been at a PX. I can't say how much I needed this watch. I am going to put the Teddy Bear in my ruck sack.

I already scaled your Kool-Aid. I ate all the fruit. I have one can of stew left.

Well, here be today the second of April. It is exactly 7:45 P.M.

We just got finished firing artillery and had our *Mad Minute*. See we have been snipered at three days in a row. Last night, at dusk they popped some rounds in. But we still had to push out our ambushes, or rather, Rat Patrol. So to do this every one in the perimeter fires eighteen rounds of M-16, fifty rounds of machine gun ammunition and two M-79 rounds. The whole perimeter goes absolutely nuts.

We are set up alongside "A" Company's perimeter. It has taken us three days to build our bunker. It is strong, real strong.

Well, I have sounds every night now. We found a radio in a hay stack. It is a three-band radio. We get good music from Da Nang.

Well, today is the third of April.

Right now I am sitting down. The squads are searching a village. *"Can Cook"* that means ID card. Everyone is supposed to have one. If he doesn't, he is either VC or NVA, because only the South Vietnamese Loyalist are supposed to get them. When you kill someone with an ID you burn the card. Otherwise there is a big stink about it. We are overlooking a place that looks like a market place. There are a couple shade hooches. Just sort of a lean to.

It is set up on an open area, flat and fairly large. There is a bomb crater next to it. It was made by a 500 lb. bomb. The market place is surrounded by rice patties. I pulled a little stem off the plant. It is in this letter. This rice is ripe and ready to pick.

We are taking it easy today. The reason will be evident as soon as you read the next few sentences.

We left Base Camp about 8 A.M. The temperature rose to about a hundred degrees. We wear our *flak* jackets over our shirts. We walked for about four miles. Our platoon had three men suffer from heat fatigue. First platoon had a dust off and one man passed out. It was rough. We sweat so bad that water dripped from our shirts. I felt at times I was under a shower. The water just streamed down.

We are all still messed up. Also we were snipered at. No fatalities. Those VC are lousy shots. It's been a couple of weeks since anyone was wounded or killed by hostile fire or otherwise. That is alright.

I hear the children crying when we come around. They automatically cry - no tears - just noise. Oh well, let them do what they wish.

Well, I am back at the company perimeter. They are trying to let us have the middle of the day off. So we work all morning, send a patrol out after chow and then send out a rat patrol at night. This is *wild*. I don't go on patrols or ambushes. So I work every morning and have the rest of the day off. The longer we do this the happier I am.

A couple of days ago, we passed a grave with a Cross! I never saw one. Then we went into a village and in a real nice house, compared to the rest, there was a Christian Cross, a picture of Jesus and candles. Wow! The first one I have ever seen over here. It made me feel *groovy*. None of the people were around. I wish I could have talked to them.

See, every house in Viet Nam has a religious corner, or area. It is all set up just like you would see in a church but on a small scale. I have seen houses completely demolished but on a stool there is the religious set up. The people are very religious.

When we go into villages we usually break and tear the place apart, but we do not touch their religious set ups.

I got your gifts. They were just out of this world. Those *Easter Eggs* are gone!

I still don't believe I have a watch!

Hey, Dad I took a glance at my helmet. I see you. Ma, one of the straps cover you up. I am going to fix it.

We just had a little jelly and peanut butter.

Oh, by the way, they told me I don't have to worry about income tax until next year.

I am looking from my bunker. I see an old *'gook'* looking over his rice field. He has on white clothes. The Japanese type of fit. They wear a lot of white clothes. Also a lot of *silk* black clothes. None fit tight. The people are so skinny.

I think I am getting *Fat!* Well not really, but the CP group gets all the extra C-rations. They way I figure it, it doesn't matter how much you eat. I feel good!

I am glad you got me the leather watch band. It allows air on the wrist. Have you ever heard of Shake-A-Pudding? Could you see if they have any you could send me? Also how about a couple of Bic pens. Oh, ya, could you get me a Black Magic marker? Okay.

That is a good picture of you and Dad, Ma. On all my gear I have the Chicken. But my pen ink keeps on wearing off. So this is why I could use a Magic Marker.

I was talking to a guy on the APC (Armored Personnel Carrier). He said he knows about us. He looked surprised when I asked him if he knew us. He is from Chi Town (Chicago) He thought everyone knew about us.

The whole company knows our stores. Soon the whole 1/6 Infantry Brigade will know.

Well, by for now . . . or wait. I am not going to be lazy. I am sitting away from my paper. Wait a minute, okay?

Wow! I forgot to tell you I got a ring ordered. C.O.D. I will use my next check from the Army. The ring is so groovy. My brigade patch will be on it and the C.I.B. also a diamond. It costs $89. I imagine I will not have any money saved from my tour. I will have more things than just money. It will be worth three times as much the way I am using it. At least to *me*.

Well, chow just came in. So I am going to eat. I guess I will get this letter on the next chopper.

Hi, Uncle Raymond. Received your letter. Save some of those garden fruits and vegetables for me. Okay? How is the Rambler's Ram Charger Six, still going good?

Bye, see you soon, Fred Leo

P.S. I have the best radio in the platoon. How's that!

5 April 1968

Waking from the commotion Brown sees Sergeant Denning in the early morning light. "Get some extra shut eye, Brown. Charlie Company is gonna pick up the road sweep."

He pulls on the pistol belt, dons the helmet and grabs the rifle. "But stay close-by. We're the reactionary force today," Sergeant Denning tells Brown as he walks out of the bunker headed for breakfast.

Rolling over, Brown pulls the poncho back on and starts falling back asleep.

"Oh, Brown," Sergeant Denning sticks his head back in, "After lunch we got formation up by the LZ."

"Formation?" He looks over. "For what?"

"The Chaplain's gonna do a memorial service for all the guys killed."

"Roger," Brown mumbles and falls back to sleep.

While at the infirmary picking up rash cream for his back, Brown picks up an Official Army Report. Walking over to a sandbag wall, he climbs on top to relax and sun himself. And reads:

WHAT THE ENEMY BELIEVES

"As for my wife and child, I have not seen them for 17 months because US troops are stationed in front of my house...." One hundred and thirty people at "Lower Ha Nong" Hamlet were killed during the third month of occupation by US troops at Binh Long. Most of these people are old women, children, and pregnant women.

The enemy used many savage policies in order to change this area into a white zone. Now only about 1/10 of the population is living in the Village and most of them are cadre and guerrillas. Faced with fierce attacks conducted by US Troops, our people were determined to fight the enemy down to their last breath. One women said, "Although dead, I have decided to stay here. Nobody can make me leave!"

The more the US troops defeat us, the more cruel they become. They have slaughtered 191 people living in Thuy Bo and La Thoh Hamlets. Some families were all killed so there is often no relative to pray for those poor dead. They killed new born children by hitting their heads against walls. To destroy the corpses, they put them in a well, then throw in a mine which blew the bodies into pieces. Sometimes they burned the bodies of the people they had just killed. They raped the pregnant women and with sharp stick, pierced the women's stomach until the baby fell out. Sometimes the children sit near the body of their mother for many days. These sights that cut out the heart are so numerous that I cannot tell you all of them.

The Americans are the wildest people in the world. There is no place to hide their crimes and the whole sea will not erase their behavior. The more American crimes increase, the deeper our people hate them. With bayonets, weapons and spike pits, our people are forcing them to pay for their crimes. Recently, they killed 37 of our people in Trung and Chau Lauh Hamlets and Dien the Village. The hate grows higher and higher in the hearts of everyone.

"Mrs So living in Chau Lau, said when she was alive, 'Until the end of time, I will never leave the Revolution."

An old man living in La Tho said, "I have 100 ang (1 ang = 6 kilos) of rice I can contribute. 70 ang of rice to the Revolution for fighting the enemy and avenging our people."

At present, cadre's mothers and sisters do not dare give them food secretly at night. The children do not dare alert the cadre when the enemy comes. The Americans have prevented all these things.

Our ancestors' graves were dug up and crushed by the enemy's tanks. The village is deserted and poor. The immense and fertile ricefields which were filled with ears of corn are now burned grass meadows with plenty of buffalo dung. There are deserted areas where we do not even hear cocks crowing or birds singing. Living in such areas, the guerillas and cadre are in a difficult situation. But their determination in fighting the enemy is higher than ever because there is nothing more valuable than INDEPENDENCE and FREEDOM which we have fought for without being afraid of sacrifice.

In the middle of the eulogy, Sergeant Denning hollers, "Okay! Listen up! The Chaplain's trying to talk here! I know it's hot but just hang on, will ya," he scolds. Everyone becomes quiet and Denning nods to the Chaplain. "You can continue, Chaplin."

"As I was saying," the chaplain clears his throat. "God wants to hear from you when you don't have a prayer in the world." He stops for a moment of silence.

"*Of making it through this shit*," Okie mutters, irreverently finishing the sentence.

"I lifted a child into the air," the Chaplain continues in his holiness and raises his arms into the air. "And in this act of assertion between us, there arises values where before there was a non-existent understanding. While spinning the child around there was a little whirlwind of communication from his universe to mine. There is a commitment to life, that, we do not want to turn BITTER AGAINST LIFE. Through this WAR OF DEATH, a sparse mercy persists, but in that mercy there is a hope whose time has not yet come, but is no less innocent than the child I held in my arms."

"*I love these guys*," Greens whispers to anyone, "*You never know what in hell they're talkin' about.*"

"*Praise the Lord*," Shepard rejoins.

"*Halleluya brother*," Green mumbles under his breath.

"There was this young boy who got lost in the jungle," the Chaplain continues. "By and by that little boy came face to face with a big, hungry tiger. The beast begins to drool as it contemplates it's next meal. The boy knows there is no escape, so he slowly drops to his knees and begins to pray. The 'King of the Jungle' observing the boy, drops to it's knees as well. Then as soon as the prayers were over the tiger leaps to EAT THE BOY!"

A chorus of mumbles washes through the platoon at the unexpected twist in the story. The Chaplain breaks in loudly, "See the tiger was sayin', 'Thank-you oh Lord for this gift I'm about to receive'. The boy's prayers, on the other hand, weren't so timely. But, that doesn't mean the prayer will go unanswered!

"Which brings me to why we are here. Gary Hicks, the NFG, known as a hard working 'turkey' with a speech impediment," the Chaplin continues the eulogy trying to sound like one-of-the-boys. "The men gave him the nickname 'Beanie Wienie' because his favorite meal was Beans and Wieners.

"Benji Yamane, who you fondly called 'Same Same' because he looked so much like the Vietnamese. Everyone knew Yamane the best. Of the men who died in the last few weeks, he'd been here the longest. He was a teacher of humility. He cared and put his fellow man's needs first, like all great men. Although scheduled for R&R, he feared for the safety of his squad and platoon. So he stayed one more day and gave the ultimate gift. He gave his life so we might have a tomorrow."

The Chaplain's takes a few seconds to straighten the wind ruffled religious scarf with embroidered cross. He names off the other soldiers who had died within the last few weeks.

"With the passing of these courageous men there is a peace in the air. For to escape into death is to be born again. GOD forms a bond with us. Those who have survived are given a gift, not the burden of guilt. Ask, 'Oh Lord why have I been spared'?

"We here live in a growing experience. Let GOD's love take root. We have seen pain and brokeness in our short lives. We have bloodless wounds, let them heal. Do not let pain and sorrow keep you from others. We have become vulnerable, let GOD in and we shall become one. Let the spirit of our fallen brothers exist in us. John says 'Tend my sheep'.

"LET US PRAY." The Chaplain places his hands together lowering his head and everyone follows. "Dear Lord. God bless these soldiers and give them strength for they are going into the Valley of the Shadow of Death," the Chaplain speaks solemnly. "Give them the strength to know right from wrong. Let their sword find and route out all evil."

He raises both arms. "May the Lord be with you." Settling back on his heels he asks, "Anyone wishing Holy Communion, feel free to come forward."

"What's he offering?"

"The Last Rites."

Not exactly sure what Holy Communion is, Brown nevertheless lines up with the others. The Chaplin places a piece of bread in his mouth and is offered a sip of wine.

The CO meanwhile walks to the front and prepares to speak. Although their CO has seldom spoken to them, he is one of the few officers the soldiers categorically respect.

"Listen up troops," the company commander begins. "We've got a big job ahead of us. And I wish I could say, I'll see all of you on the other side of Operation Burlington Trails. But that's just not realistic." He seemed to have run out of things to say, so he lowers his voice and simply says, "Good luck, men. And good shootin'."

As the CO walks away the Chaplain moves back to the podium. "Always remember in times of trouble that GOD IS ON OUR SIDE! The service is over. You may now go in peace."

Okie walks over to the Chaplain and after a short conversation hands him a camera.

"Men," the Chaplin hollers over the noise, "we've got a picture to take!" He directs everyone to gather around a bunker. "Hold it! Go-ood, now say Cheee-rations."

Walking down the hill toward the bunker line, a battery of 155 Howitzers opens fire with a salvo. *"Boom! Boom! Boom!"* Listening to the explosions in the distance, Brown feels unsettled. A holy man in the midst of all this destruction has said GOD IS ON OUR SIDE. He kicks a rock clear across the road and off the edge of the hill. Taking out a cigarette, he turns to shield the match from the wind.

"Brown, did ya hear?" Bedford questions.

"Hear what?"

"The truck carrying the sweep team hit this huge land mine."

"How bad?"

"Truck rolled right over the top of 'em. At least one is dead."

Dear Ma and Dad *5 April 1968*

Well, here I am at LZ Baldy. We all got the today off. So I went on *Sick Call*. I had a heat rash so I just went for the fun of it.

I heard we are going to be here till the ninth of April. So I have a couple of days to sack out.

Oh, by the way we had a change of mission. Remember me saying we were at a company perimeter. Well, they decided bring us in, so we tore it all down. What a bring down. We worked for three days straight on it.

Man, my hair is long. I got to get it cut off. Wow! We haven't been in a day and I have had two showers already. I got clean clothes on. Do they feel fabulous.

I wrote to my Platoon Sergeant's wife for him. He was too far gone to write. Drunk or *tipsy!* We made a whole night of it last night. We scaled a box of C-rations. A whole lot of beer. You know what he said, "I am not going to drink anymore while we are in." I don't know if I should believe him.

Wow! My watch is ticking right along. The crystal doesn't look too shiny *now*. Oh well, at least it isn't cracked.

That Teddy Bear is my mascot. I am going to carry it with me. I have it inside the bunker now.

By the way, I got new boots. I wore these in fast. The first pair I had, I had a hard time breaking them in. These boots were easier. My feet stay in good shape now. They don't get wet too often. Every night, well almost every night, I take my boots and socks off. It feels so good.

I told Sgt. Denning (Platoon Sergeant) I didn't want to be a squad leader. I wanted to stay his RTO. If I was put in as a squad leader I couldn't do half the things I do now. I keep watching Sgt. Denning to see how he operates. He has a knack. If I was squad leader I would be in a position of leadership. I wouldn't be around Sarge so I couldn't learn anymore about how he works.

Everyone analyzes the squad leader. The squad leader must have a formulated way of doing this and a way to act. I am still working on this so I told Sarge I am not ready so count me out as squad leader. I think he was going to make me an acting sergeant, then Hard E/5.

Wow! I am getting drowsy. I think I will dig up my air mattress and see if I can get some shut eye. We might have to go out today for some reason. So I am going to rest. I will write when I get up. Bye.

Well, I got up and went to chow and test fired my M-16. I put two magazines through it. It only jammed once. A grain of sand got on the face of the bolt. So the round didn't seat right.

Wow! I still can't hear anything. My ears are still ringing

from the range.

I fired my .25 cal. pistol. Two other guys in the platoon have .25 cal. now.

I am listening to my favorite song "Living in the Love of the Common People." It is so fine.

My M-16 has been worn in good *now*. The bolt is real loose.

I have been receiving letters from you, Ma, most every day. Man, it's wild. When I get letters I don't realize where I am. I probably would go mad if I would sit down and think about where I am and what I am doing. Sometimes I do get a little funny. But not too often.

By the way. You don't have to send any more balloons. Okay? I don't like making these kids happy because then it gets harder to pull the *trigger*. So I must keep a rough composure. When we go through villages I kick and break things. I don't hit women and kids but I don't play games. You can't break the composure. The balloons do this. Do you understand? It makes me two-faced, shooting the old man on one hand and baby sitting the children on the other.

I got enough "Brown's Fried Chicken" tags for now. But be sure to send that Black Magic Marker. By the way I got back all the parts to my radio. I have a certain radio, handset and antenna that I consider mine. When the radio was fixed I got a radio on loan. So then when mine was fixed I got it back. Also Third Platoon had my antenna and hand set. I got them back just lately.

I fixed my rifle again. Even better than before. I drilled a hole in the hand guard just big enough to slide in my ram rod. Now it is out of the way but easy to get if my rifle jams. It has taken me four months to come up with the idea. No on has ever done it that way before. Some close, but I have never seen one exactly like mine.

Well first platoon is going to CA out of here. It just came on the radio. I hope we don't go. I feel like taking it easy for a few days.

I was just going to write and tell you to keep sending me paper and envelopes. I got low at one time, but then I received the letter from Raymond and you, all at once. Then today you said you went to New York to see Roxanna. I guess you are home now. Tell me what you did. Okay?

We sure needed those combs you sent. I gave them out. Some

times our hair gets long because it is hard to get a hair cut.

I heard about Martin Luther King. *Too Bad!* Maybe something good will happen out of it. "Hope. Hope."

You see now that it was a good idea to join the Army because everyone is being drafted. If I was in college, I would probably have ended up scared of this place. I only have eight months to go. Then I will be *up tight outta sight*.

About the old lieutenant. They rotate out of the field after six months. That is why we have a different one every once in a while.

I got your letter. It had stamped on it 'ten cents due". One of Roxanna's said 'two cents due.' I guess they deliver them anyway.

Well, bye for now. Here are a few coins. We were on a Search and Destroy mission and I started breaking down a bomb shelter and these coins were stuck in between the beams.

Well see you soon, Fred Leo

Dear Ma and Dad *6 April 1968*

Well I am on a sweep. We are about a third of the way finished. We are held up because they are going to shoot *Red_Leg* (artillery) about 2000 meters from us. The sweep team is new. They act like they know-it-all. A few Vietnamese had some grass mats that they use for doors and stuff. Well, they stopped them for an I.D. One guy threw a match on the mats. Soon the whole thing was engulfed in flames. The cart didn't burn though.

Well, we moved out and it is now ten hours later. It is about 5:30 P.M. here. Gee! Does time fly. It is now 7:45 P.M. What a way to go. Something is always coming up.

Well, things are happening to me. I could apply to become a chopper gunner but I just don't like the killing. Plus, I would have to extend here for six months. And another thing, I think it would kill my whole insides. Your nerves begin getting funny. See, you have a twenty-four hour a day job. You are under danger at every second. If I extended I would never make it. I would come home more of a nervous wreck than I will otherwise.

I don't know if my letters say what my mind is going through. I have been shot at and been close to death. It is no more an exciting experience. At first it seemed so *cool!* Exciting. But *now* it is different.

I will not hide things from you like I attempted to do at one point. I must tell you. I get so closed up inside if I don't.

A few days ago I felt good. We had been snipered at three days in a row. But no one was hit. Then at midnight our own men put artillery on us. It was a mistake. They were shooting 105 rounds. They shot two into the perimeter. I didn't know that they had shot three rounds into the perimeter till the next morning. A dud 105 round hit twenty feet from me. I don't have to say what it would have done. There are not too many dud rounds. What a bring down. I hear artillery and firefights going on around me most everyday.

Wow! I received your package. I ate all the nuts.

Wait a *minute*. I am thirsty. Okay.

Everything is so vivid now. I can see the agonies and trials of people. Now maybe I can live a life uncluttered and I know or rather I can imagine what you mean!

Well, here it is—the latest scoop. I am going to CA (Combat Assault) out of here to a place near Tam Ky. The mission is to set up a new Fire Support Base. We will be the forward element. The engineers and marines will come in later. The 101st Airborne tried the same thing in November. They were pushed out. A Division of NVA works the area. It will be the hottest area you could go into, except maybe *Khe Sanh*. Oh, well, I will soon find out how bad.

I just got finished putting brand new ammunition in my weapons. I change the ammunition as often as possible. You would be surprised to see what happens to the old ammunition after it has been in there a while. It is bent and seared. This is one reason your weapon jams.

Well, I guess you can tell I quit writing. I can't stay on the lines. I am writing at 2:15 A.M. in the morning.

It is the seventh of April.

Well, I ate those mandarin oranges already. All I have left is the tomato rice soup. I am going to get some milk and fix it up right.

Wow! I can mark another day off my Short Timers Calendar. Wait, I will get out my other calendar and tell you how many days left. 227 days!! But I am counting off a week. I will finish all the fighting and work here on the 20th of November. They give you a week to get ready to go back home.

Well, here is a bit of good news. We will stay at that new Fire Support Base for maybe two months. Then, I will go to Brigade and pull bunker guard at Chu Lai. *Hope Hope*. But then you never know.

I haven't heard word on R&R. I am trying to stall it off until August or September because I don't think I would be able to go back to the field. I might break a bone coming off R&R. So I can get a few more months. I got to hang tight, then I will break a leg. There's these guys you can pay to do it for you. Accidentally of course.

I have been hearing all about Dr. King. I don't know what I believe. He seems to cause more trouble than anything else. But what do I know.

It makes me mad. They were going to be peace talks, but home is so messed up the President has to fight his own country too. If peace talks do come through and work, the President will have blood on his hands. I hate so much to hear about home. It makes you wonder if a man can leave Vietnam behind. I don't think you can. A man must continue his fighting elsewhere, but for more personal gains.

Well it is 2:35 A.M. It is real dark out. The moon is short now.

You can open up the box and take a look at my ring when it comes, but leave it home. Don't send it to me. I would ruin it. If I ever put it on, it will mean much, much more than anything I have ever had.

By the way I need, really need, those 30-round magazines for my M-16. Could you try again to get them. Give them a hard luck story. Okay.

Could you send some .25 cal rounds - 50 of them. Okay? I got to break in my weapon. It is stiff. I will have to bring all my souvenirs with me this trip because I don't think I will ever see LZ Baldy again.

A flare just went off. I took a look outside. Nothing to see.

Well, the last time I was in, I took pictures. I sent them to Kodak. They will develop them and send them to you. But don't get your hopes up. The guy who took the last picture thought he knew how to run a camera. He exposed the film. It may still come out a little. But he messed it all up. I had *beautiful* pictures.

I tried to get some pictures home. But I guess it didn't work. I have such a hard time finding time to write that I never get time to snap a picture or buy a roll of film. I wish so much to get a few pictures.

Well it is three A.M. I have to call in a situation report. Wait a few minutes and I will start writing again.

Well, I just turned it in. I have a half hour left of guard. Wow! The news is on. I hope nothing happens. I heard about three-hundred people injured in Chicago, two people killed. Listen, I am serious. Get a pistol or rifle. Get a .38 cal pistol. Okay? Use it if they get out of hand. But be sure nothing happens to you, okay.

I hope they call out some of the Viet Nam returnees. Those people rioting will know who is boss, I guarantee it. Those NG (National Guards) fellows are nothing. They can't help themselves, let alone a city.

Take care. Be Cool. Don't even go around those places that are not under control.

Dr. King was good. But the people behind him were, and are deaf. They do not see principle. They only look for reasons to hassle and cause trouble. Will these people ever come out of the dark!

Well, it is now 3:30 A.M. Sergeant Denning just came staggering in. He asked me to write his wife for him. He was mad at himself for not writing her.

I am going to include in this letter some addresses. I want to keep them. I might lose them if I don't send a copy home.

Well, I imagine I will cover for Sarge. He needs the sleep. So I will be staying up another hour and a half.

But I'd better close now. It will be maybe a few days before I get another letter out.

So bye until then, Fred Leo

Dear Ma and Dad *8 April 1968*

Well, I am on my first leg of my trip to Hill 218. Our mission is to *search and clear.* There is an air strip up on this hill. We are going to build a Fire Support Base up there. This hill was captured by the 101st Airborne, but they were overrun. The hill overlooks a valley called *Dragon Valley*. Our mission is co-signed *Blue Dragon.* Our secondary mission is to re-open a road to an Artillery Base. We must clear an area two or three miles on either side of the road. The Arvans have been by the hill. They say there are no NVA. But the 101st Airborne was pushed out on Halloween day.

They are going to *prep* the hill. This means they are going to hit the hill with everything they have. They will put Artillery on it for two hours. They will put Napalm on it and air strikes. Also they will call gun ships in and around the hill. Immediately after that our platoon, thirty men and a mortar squad, will be CA to the hill. We will secure it and then the next day, the tenth, they will bring up the whole 1/6 Light Infantry.

We will leave tomorrow, the morning of the ninth of April.

Believe it or not, this place where I am is a privately owned air field. I am enclosing a commercial ticket form. These private planes land here all day long. To the left of me is a big *DC-10*, the old big commercial propeller planes like at Midway airport. It is setting over there with no wing. It crashed here a long time ago when the French were here.

This airport was hit by a human wave about a year ago. The 101st was here. Then they had a body count of over two-hundred. They shot Bee Hive 105 rounds into them.

Right in front of me is an ARVAN camp. It is located on Hill 118. They have two 155 Artillery guns. I am located right next to Tam Ky now, on this air strip. I am bringing in a Chinook right now. I pop the smoke. They land by the smoke.

Wow! You should see the heat coming off the ground. I got to stop writing until I get under some shade.

Sitting under a lean-to poncho. They want me to bring in another Chinook. You should have seen this one guy get off. He had so much weight I just stood there looking. Here's what he was carrying inside and out of the rucksack, and wrapped around his body:

* Five days of C-rations (cans of Ham and Mothers, and Choke and Puck for those desperate moments), a bread-can stove, and heating tablets supplemented with C-4 explosive scavenged from a claymore mine..
* Six packages of Kool-Aid (received from the World)
* Two pairs of extra socks (also received from the World)
* Towel, poncho and liner
* Map, climber's ring, pocket knife, mosquito repellent, foot fungus powder
* Cigarettes with matches, shaving kit, mirror, comb, sewing kit, soap
* Letters from home along with writing paper and pen
* Wallet filled with MPC money and pictures of his girlfriend
* Ten empty sandbags
* Pick handle only (someone else carries the metal pick head)
* Gas mask
* Fragmentation vest
* Pistol belt with two ammo pouches, compass, bayonet with sharpening stone, first-aid field bandage
* One riot (CS) grenade
* One smoke grenade
* One flare
* Six quarts of water and iodine purification tablets
* Flashlight with colored lenses
* Steel helmet, cover and liner
* Salt tablets, malaria pills (the daily-daily and weekly ones)
* Four hand grenades and booby trap wire
* Two 100-round belts of M-60 machine-gun ammunition
* M-16 rifle, extra firing pin, cleaning supplies and sling
* 800 rounds of M-16 ammunition dispersed between magazines, and bandoleer of clips with quick loader
* Claymore mine and detonator
* Wrist watch

I bet it weighs over—way over, one-hundred pounds. Plan on do some heavy "commie killing."

Well, I am on guard.

It is one A.M. the ninth of April.

By the way, there is an artillery battery, engineers and a mortar platoon being attached to our company when we go up there.

We will move out of here at nine A.M. All we have to do is dig like mad. We must get overhead cover by night.

Wow! I heard all about the Chicago riot. Did any of our stores get hit or burned? It was bad wasn't it? I hope everyone is okay. I imagine you didn't want to go out on the streets, Ma. Tell me if everything is okay. I have begun to worry. Well, wait a minute I have to turn in a *sitrap!* (situation report). Wow! How unusual, no one answered. *Ha Ha*

Be sure you try and get word to me as fast as possible if I haven't already had word sent. It makes me hot to hear about my hometown being messed up. What shall a man return to? It is disgusting. It doesn't look like I will put my weapon up, even after the war.

I was talking to a guy who has twenty some days left. That is so far away for me. If I make it through this Blue Dragon mission, well, I will be a lot closer because they think we might go back to Chu Lai. Also my R&R should be coming up soon.

Right now I have everything I own except my foot locker in Chu Lai. But I haven't seen it for two months. I have the jacket you sent me. I am going to have it made up on R&R. I can hardly walk with everything, but when we go into the field I will leave it all behind.

By the way, our forward resupply is Hill 54. I don't know if you ever heard of it.

I just seen something go by my position. I guess it was a dog. Wow! It looked weird. Probably not much worse off than us.

Tell me if you can figure out where I am. I am right next to Tam Ky on an airstrip. It might be harder to find me when I am on Hill 218.

Wow! Just got my hair cut. The sides are about 1/8 to 1/4 inch long. The top is maybe 1 to 1-1/2 inches long. While they cut my hair, this guy was walking across the landing field. He was trying to look *hard,* but he was definitely an NFG. It's so easy to tell the old grunts from the NFGs.

I think some of the guys are jealous because of the job I have and the other RTO. So you know we have it nicer. We work harder in a lot of ways. But we don't do the little details. We get out of a lot of day to day harassment. Also, it is better to be hanging around the top, in-charge people. I think I told you this, but I told Sarge I didn't want squad leader. We will go all the way *together*. As soon as he leaves the field I am going to play around. I ain't going to stay out here. He goes home the last of October. So I will only have a month left.

Wow! I don't see how I write such long letters. Before I get this one mailed it will be long. Maybe I will put it in two envelopes. You know I do a lot of Jibber, Jabber.

Well, I will continue when I get time.

Bye, Fred Leo

Hi Freddie *7 April 1968*

Sorry I was so long in answering your last letter. I wrote my first one in a month yesterday. I suppose you have been hearing about C Troop. We lost one track to a mine and one tank to a recoilless 75. It went right through it and set off all the ammo inside. Everyone came out of it. The driver jumped out of the tank without a scratch and then a PC ran over his legs. Last week we were on Seagore Island. I loved it out there. Cool all day. We rode the track along the beach in the water. That's okay when the big waves hit the front of the track and splash all over everyone. Going across the dunes, we just go like hell.

My track is about the slowest one, but I kept it floored all the way and once I got going I was okay. We went swimming one afternoon. The water was beautiful, but salty. The only thing is I can't swim. I went in anyway. We got mortared a few times but this great mortar crew that I drive around took care of that. We had our first round out before they had their third one in. And we were right on target. Well enough about the Cav. How's everything with you? I have been hearing a little about the 1/6th but not enough.

Hey, ya know the only money I have spent all month was on laundry, hair cuts, a few beer and sodas, etc. And a few dinky dows. I think that is the least I have spent since I started making my own money. Well, we have worked with the 196th Bde. The ARVNs. Maybe we will work with the 198th 1/6 next. Hey why don't ya put in a 1049 for the 1/1 Cav. C Troop. Ya may get it in May after your first six months are up.

Well I guess that's all for now. We are west of Tam Ky and it is a little hotter than on the coast. So, I'll see ya later and hope to hear from ya soon. Ha, I have a new A.P.O. number 96325

An old leg buddy, Ernie Brown

Stars and Stripes-Army Times 10 April 1968

Americal kills 129

CHU LAI, Vietnam — Americal Division cavalrymen recently topped one of their most successful weeks of fighting with a lopsided victory in a daylong battle with North Vietnamese regulars near Tam Ky. Ground forces of the division's lst Sqdn, 1st Cav combined with the air support of a 17th Cav troop and an infantry unit from the 196th Inf bde to kill 129 NVA soldiers in 12 hours of fighting. The action closed out a six-day period in which the cavalrymen killed a total of 293 enemy soldiers. Friendly casualties in the near continuous action were listed as light.

To: Fred Brown

Fred could you answer this we have written a letter to his parents but they want one from one of Scott's friends.

Dear Sir *March 31, 1968*

We are PFC George S. Dawkins mother and father. George was wounded on March 16. As of now they tell us it was a gunshot wound to the head and neck. He has been evacuated from Vietnam to Japan. We hope and pray he lives. George told us in a letter 15 March, they were up around Tam Ky. Gary Hicks of N.C. was a friend of George, he got killed, also George had a friend Fred Brown, from Chicago in Company D 198th Inf. Bde. Could you have Fred write us. We don't know his US Army number.

Sir, were you with George when he got hurt? If so, write us and tell us all about where at, and just how it happened. Was it from a sniper or one of our boys. George liked you very much. So if you know of any of the boys that was with George on this day or night of the 16th March, please have them write us of some of the things they did, up till George got hurt and how. We know he was a radio and an RTO he wrote us about a friend Smith. But Fred Brown and Gary Hicks were very good friends.

May we have all George's things pictures and bill fold. He also had a radio back at Chu Lai.

Thank you,
Mr and Mrs Clyde C. Dawkins
Biscoe, N.C.

Dear Ma *10 April 1968*

Well, it is 12:15 A.M. I just got situation reports from the elements. Tonight I am on Radio watch for the whole company. I take *sit raps* from first, second, and third platoons and call battalion. I will call battalion in about ten minutes.

Wow! Did I tell you I got my hair cut? I had most of it cut right off. My hair was really long.

Well, tonight I am sitting on Hill 218. We Ca'ed in and have had no contact. "A" Company only had five rounds by a sniper.

Wow! I have been receiving mail most everyday. I got the two checks. Wow. Kool-Aid tonight! I think I can drink more water if it has Kool-Aid in it. That is the best thing to do. Drink. as much water as possible. You will not believe how hot it was today. One of the mortar men said it was 125 degrees. It didn't seem that hot. But I know it was over a hundred. You know the bumper sticker you gave me? Our old platoon lieutenant is going to put it on his Jeep. Ain't that great.

It sounds like your visit with Roxanna in New York was in the groove. You got home just in time. King got zapped a few days later. It is so good to hear you say you go places now. Always take time for yourself.

Today I was on battalion *push*. I was answering the radio for majors and captains. Wow! In one day we took this whole area over. We have everyone on this hill. I can see the road and Dragon Valley from here. They had air strikes and gun ships beat it all day. *Time fly.*

My pack was heavier today than it has ever been. I could not even pick it up off the ground. I had to sit down and get into the harness. I carried everything with me, that is why it was so heavy. I will get rid of it when we move out. My pack will be real light then.

By the way, all this talk about no air strikes north of the DMZ is not true. We are bombing sixty-five miles North of the DMZ. Nothing has been affected. We are still hanging in there. Bombs away.

Well, I will try to get this letter out tomorrow. Everything is a hassle right now. Well, everything is okay now. So, I will continue tomorrow. I am going to mail this letter, so bye for now.

Fred Leo

Mist oozes from the dark midnight sky as clouds churn, alternately allowing the bluish gray moonlight to lap over the almost complete Fire Support Base. For three days and nights they had hacked, dug and fought back the jungle to make this desolate Hill 288 mountaintop fortification into LZ Bowman.

While on guard duty on top of the bunker, Brown looks out over the base and has a vision. The vision is that he's actually perched on the eyelid of a monstrous dragon. The wide rolling saddle between the knolls is actually its reptilian body and the mortar pits next to the LZ with their three-foot high C-shaped walls of sandbags give the illusion of swivel thigh joints. The small snaking mounds of sandbags on the other knoll that led to the communication connex make up the tail.

To his right are two 105 howitzer pits. On their completion, they will give the monster nostrils and a mouth from which to belch the fires of hell. The 198th Light Infantry is about to release the Blue Dragon from its shackles. The Anti-life quest is about to begin.

His reverie is broken by noise coming from a tent encampment next to the chopper pad. It is situated across from the other two bunkers of second platoon constructed in the saddle. Short walls of sandbags had been hurriedly built around the tents to accommodate Charlie Company which had just been choppered out of the field after three horrific days in the valley.

That evening, Sergeant Denning had left Brown in charge and walked down into the saddle to play cards with some friends from Fort Hood, Texas. And from the sounds of it, they were having a jolly old time. Just before leaving, he had filled everyone in on the news about Charlie Company's firefights with NVA and how the pointman had been killed in an ambush yesterday.

"Well," Doc had said in response, "looks like we got three ways to go. First, starvation. Second, by working any harder in this 100 degree temperature. And third but not least, by taking a direct hit by a mortar."

"Right now," Brown rejoined, "I think working ourselves to death is the most likely."

Denning had laughed, and consequently they dropped their shovels, deciding a single layer of sandbags on the rear half of the bunker would be sufficient until morning.

"I'll tell ya what. This Dragon Valley is one hot mother," Sergeant Denning said. With twilight fast approaching, everyone pulls out their rations.

"Alpha Company swears they heard treads squeaking from NVA tanks the first day in the valley," Sergeant Denning had continued with the news. "Then next day they found a cache of weapons. Oh yeah, and I talked with my buddy in the rear. He promised to save one of those 21,000 AK-47's they'd found. With that many, there's gotta be a few left after the brass gets their fill of souvenirs. They said they were still hearing secondary explosions hours after they blew the ammo in the cave."

Then he had told them about the two GI's who had been killed in a firefight. Definitely NVA attach tactics verses VC run and hide tactics.

The sound of rifle fire echoing through the valley is becoming familiar. Since their arrival, there had been continuous contact in the valley. The soldiers in the field were getting mortared more and more often. Besides five battalion KIAs, the battalion has also suffered twelve WIA. And Brown's turn in the valley was coming up real soon.

Muffled blasts immediately jerk him to full alert. He listens and scans the dark valley, trying to decide from where the sounds had come. On a ridge to the north, he spots light flashes reflecting off the underside of the clouds.

"Boom! Boom! Boom!" An instant later the flashes became continuous and with their increased intensity comes a low ominous rumbling-like thunder. There is an eerie vibration and then their mountain starts to tremble as shock waves from the explosions surge through the earth and air. This is the first B-52 bombing he'd ever witnessed. Mesmerized, Brown continues to watch while fires gradually replace the flashes.

Then in another part of the valley streams of fire begin pouring out of the sky, followed seconds later by a the heavy chatter and whine of electric machine guns from Puff the Magic Dragon. It is said that Puff has the fire power to cover every square inch of a football field in under a minute. The valley is alive with dying.

It suddenly becomes so quiet that he thinks he can hear the cracking of the ever expanding fire from the Rolling Thunder bombing raid. Carefully he scans his field of fire.

Though tired beyond reason, Sergeant Denning had forced Okie and Green to roll out a single roll of concertina wire. Later, with what little strength remaining, they set out claymore mines, trip flares and booby trap grenades.

"Heard they found elephant tracks down there," Doc had said as they relaxed after stopping work on the bunker. "They say the NVA use 'em to haul supplies over the mountains from the Ho Chi Minh

Trail."

By this time Sergeant Denning had joined his friends and the sun had drop behind the mountains of Laos. "Sack time," Brown had said sprawling on a C-ration cardboard box atop the bunker. "Wake me when it's my guard."

It is now one A.M. as Brown wearily slides off the bunker and over to the sandbag bunker wall where Doc sleeps on an air mattress.

"You're up, Doc." Brown touches his shoulder. Doc's eyes shoot open and he stares around. "Guard duty. Sorry buddy, but Sarge never came back. There's only the two of us."

"Ah, wah," Doc mumbles still half asleep. Brown waits until he works himself into a sitting position before stretching out on the bunker roof.

Minutes later . . . . "Phoof! Phoof! Phoof!"

Brown's eyes shoot open on hearing the distant sounds. "Doc! Did you hear it?" He detects the sizzle of an enemy mortar round. "Incoming! Incoming!"

"Szzz-boom! Szzz-boom! Szzz-boom!" Mortars erupt slamming into the saddle, smoke billows from the explosion and a tent roof collapses in the Charlie Company area where Sergeant Denning had gone earlier.

"Incoming! Incoming!" The call echoes through the fire base.

Brown grabs his pistol belt, helmet and rifle then rolls off the bunker top and dives through the spider hole size entrance. His face crashes into the earth sending his steel pot rolling across the dirt floor, his rifle ending up in a pile of dirt.

"Phoof! Phoof! Phoof!" More mortars are fired and Brown scrambles to the front of the bunker, props his muzzle on the rifle slit and prepares for the assault.

"Szzz-boom! Szzz-boom!" The mortar rounds are being walked up the saddle and heading directly for his position.

"Shit!" Doc yells diving into the rear entrance along with three engineers.

"Szzz-boom!! Szzz-boom!!!" No one makes a sound as they crouch inside listening to the explosions coming nearer and nearer. Crashing louder and louder. Then Brown detects that unmistakable sizzle of a round that has you in its kill zone.

"Ca-blamm-blam-blam!!!" The roof of the bunker lifts and collapses filling the bunker with dust. The stars now show through where the single layer of sandbags had been.

"I'm hit! I'm hit!" an engineer closest to the blast screams. In a moment of silence, Brown can hear the moans and cries for help throughout the fire base. With the rear entrance choked with debris, Brown peers through the rifle slit knowing that if attacked there is no easy escape. Then comes another mortar barrage.

Mortars now begin exploding more at random than in any particular pattern. This would signal the attack and Brown is the only one with a rifle and unwounded. He scans back and forth across the field of fire knowing a good sapper could easily get through the wire and over the minefield.

Doc busies himself with the wounded, while Brown prepares for the assault by pulling the claymore mine detonators close and putting a few hand grenades in easy reach.

"Son of a bitch! Son of a bitch!" Sergeant Denning blurts as he comes flying through the front rifle slit tumbling over Brown. "Goddamn! Son of a bitch!" he continues cursing while crawling off to settle against the wall where he could watch the field of fire. Shaking like a leaf, he looks around at the wounded.

"Had a good hand," he says about the card game. "Damn it to hell!" Then he looks at the blood on his shirt sleeve. His voice is quaking as he says, "Direct hit, man. They all got it. All of 'em. Pieces splattered all over the place." Just then he notices a large bloody gob on the front of his shirt and quickly brushes if off like you would a big ugly spider. "Shit!"

Several more rounds crash into the LZ near the communications connexs. Then everything is quiet. They wait for a continuation. Doc finishes bandaging everyone's shrapnel wounds.

"Sarge, let me get past. I've gotta get outta here," Doc demands, working his way through the front rifle slit.

"Okay, if you can, let's move out these sandbags and put the bunker back together. We could still be attacked at anytime," Brown orders, realizing that for the moment Sergeant Denning is in shock.

Everyone waits for someone else to move. Brown scrambles out the front and hurries over to start clearing the rear entrance.

"I knew we should've built a bunker first thing," one of the wounded engineers laments, handing out sandbags.

Where's Sarge? Looking anxiously around Brown spots him through the drizzle and faint moonlight helping collect the wounded and helping to lay out the lifeless bodies of his friends. Brown wipes the stinging sweat off his forehead and finds his hand full of blood.

Dear Ma *13 April 1968*

It is now two A.M. Well, it looks like we are going to have to put another layer of sandbags all around. One of the companies found rockets, mortars and T&T, an even Russian machine guns. The NVA have a lot of stuff. The thing is we have them on the run. Because we have air strikes, artillery and gun ships pounding the whole area.

Well, it looks like we will be here for another week. I have 219 days left. Soon now I will have been here six months.

I am enclosing some of the material I had sent with the package from the newspaper people.

Well, I think me and Sgt. Denning are the first ones on this new Fire Base to take a shower. We got it up off the side of our bunker. Wow! It was cold. It has been cool for the last few days. The reason is because it has been raining. We didn't take the shower till after the sun was dipping down. But it really felt good.

All the companies have South Vietnamese Special Forces working for them. We were given a Kit Carson. He was an NVA who surrendered and came to our side. These people are cool. They take everything in stride.

Before I forget. Be sure to send a couple Bic pens. Okay? Also I could use a radio. Not a small one. Maybe a 8" X 12" or 4" x 6." Make it a real good one so it will pick up stations good. It can take a little beating. I need a small one, but most small ones aren't good enough. We need good tone on the radio. Also could you pick some extra batteries. The same as those used in a regular flash light. You know what I mean. The reason is because I cannot find these flash light batteries easy. Okay?

Make the radio as small as possible without skimping on the dependability and quality of the sound. See, we get music from *Da Nang*. It is so nice to listen to music while you work on a foxhole. Our other radio was hit by a mortar round, as well as my ruck sack, canteens, and my sleeping gear.

Well, everything is okay. I don't know when I am going to get R&R, but it shouldn't be but a month or two. I got your checks. I will try and get some cashed if I need it.

Bye for now. I haven't had much time to write for a few days. We have been working like mad on our bunker.

Bye for now, Fred Leo

Dear Ma and Dad *14 April 1968*

It is 3:30 AM. I am on guard duty. I am supposed to have guard for two hours. But the guy before me didn't look at the watch right. So, I will have only one hour of guard. How is that!

Well, we have our bunker in good shape now. Oh, by the way, let me describe a bunker. When I am in the field, every night we dig in. Every man carries fifteen sand bags. So we build a wall up. It is considered a *foxhole*. Just big enough for the amount of people at the position.

Now, when you put a roof over this foxhole, it is a bunker. You have all around protection and over head cover.

You take these sandbags and stack them on top of each other. The sandbags are about 1-1/2 feet by two feet.

For best protection you put two rows of sandbags. Looking from the top.

There is a lot of extra things you do to build a bunker. But you can see the general idea. When I say *Bunker*, I will mean a roof over my head. When I say foxhole I mean no roof. By the way, a foxhole you dig at least waist deep. A bunker at least high enough to stand in. Okay.

I haven't been clear enough in my last letters. But the foxholes I make are better than foxholes, but not as good as bunkers.

Well I have been building my bunker for the last three days. We have been working like mad. I got a package, guess from who:

Mr. & Mrs. Edward Vondrak *Southwest News Herald*
5045 South Kedzie Ave., Chicago, Ill.

Wow! They had books, candy, checker games, and just all kinds of things I have been trying to find time to read the magazines, but I don't have much. I guess they didn't quite know what I do. Today War – Books tomorrow. Could you send them some money and have them for dinner, or give them a free

Brown's Chicken dinner? It was just so nice for them. I will try to write to them tomorrow.

Well, I will finish this letter. By the way, my bunker had a direct hit from a mortar round. At the time we had only one layer of sandbags. I was sleeping on the roof. So all my sleeping gear was turned to shreds. By the way, the colonel said this was the first time he seen one layer of sandbags stop an 82mm mortar. Well, the *fin* to the mortar we found laying at the bottom of our bunker. Believe it or not none of us were hurt. I hope I keep this edge on death that I have. Since we have been out five men didn't.

Oh well, I am still in great shape. So will continue to march.

Bye for now, Fred Leo

Dear Mr. & Mrs. Edward Vondrak *16 April 1968*

When I first saw the package you sent I couldn't place your name. Then when I saw it was from the Southwest News-Herald I remembered the newspaper. I have read it before and I think is a real good paper.

Everyone in my platoon now has a book and is reading it. Hardly any of us had seen a book for about three months. That is how long it has been since we have been at the PX (Post exchange). Right now I am reading *Lilies of the Field* which is a wonderful book.

We have the balloons hanging up in our bunker. The chewing gum was really groovy, and we chewed on piece after another until it was gone. I took the thread out of the sewing kit you had in the package and sewed on my Sp/4 patches. That tooth brush and the toothpaste holder was great. I really needed something like this because my toothpaste would always break open in my combat pack.

I guess everybody in the whole battalion has been passing around the comic books, but I made sure I looked at them myself before I let them get out of my hands.

Right now some of the guys also have a card game going with the playing cards you gave me. We haven't had cards around here in a long time.

Everyone in the whole platoon has asked me to say thank-you very much for your package, and also extend out thanks along to everyone else who donated something to your cause.

I personally wish I could do something in return to help your project. It just makes me feel so good to know there are people at home who would give something and expect nothing in return except for us to come back.

Now I can tell all the guys that my home town of Chicago is really for us guys out there. I think I am the only one in this outfit who was so lucky to ever get something like this.

I'll be leaving here in seven months, and someday I hope to stop by and say thank-you in person.

Sp/4 Fred Leo Brown

17 April 1968

By afternoon Brown has finished rebuilding and reenforcing the bunker. As a precaution, he has added a third overlapping layer of sandbags to the roof. Climbing on top triumphantly, he strips off his shirt and stretches out on the poncho liner to let the cool breeze brush his naked skin.

"I'm done," he trumpets. With arms stretched overhead, he wiggles his spine to help stretch out the sore muscles. While relaxing on his back, he watches the clouds float through the clear blue sky. When his heart rates slows, he rises into a sitting position. "Finished." Spotting Sergeant Denning, he shouts, "Sarge, are the Donut Dollies still on the way?"

"Last I heard is they're comin' out along with the hot chow," Sergeant Denning answers. "I stole back our shower bucket!" Sergeant Denning proudly raises it.

Looking at the rivulets of sweat trailing down his chest, Brown raises an arm and takes an exaggerated whiff. "Oh yeah. Smell's gettin' so bad I have trouble sleeping with myself."

"Brownie, you look like somethin' dangling from the end of a fishin' hook." Okie is suddenly standing next to him. He checks his watch. "Yep, we got two hours before the Pastry Pigs grace this LZ."

"Tell ya what," Sergeant Denning breaks in. He is standing on a mound of dirt holding a construction stake. "Grab that big rock," he points, "over there and club it in. We'll hang the bucket from it. That way you short guys won't have any trouble pouring in the water for me."

"Yaaa, though I walk through the Valley of the Shadow of Death, I fear no evil, for I'm the baddest mother there!" Billy recites as he wanders over. Then he starts singing an AIT cadence song:

"Give me your left! Left!
Give me your right! Right!
Left, Right! Left!

I wanna be an Airborne Ranger
I wanna go to Vietnam,
I wanna be an Airborne Ranger
I wanna kill the Viet Cong!"

Everyone joins in with the well know marching cadence.

"With a knife or with a gun
Either way will be great fun.

But if I die in a Combat Zone
Box me up and send me home.
Tell my parents not to cry
And tell my girl I did my best

Right on, one, two
Right on, three, four
Bring it on down,
One, two, three, four
One, two three four."

Finishing, Billy flashes a self-gratifying grin showing a row of rotting yellow teeth. " If I were you, I wouldn't eat that crap they're gonna bring out they call hot *food,*" he warns. "Unless, you want Ho Chi Minh's revenge."

"They'll probably bring something edible today, now that the Donut Dollies are coming," Brown says hopefully. Some of the guys ended up with worms in their intestines from eating the food prepared in the rear. Often times it would arrive cold and smelling rancid. And the water they shipped from the rear had also made a lot of guys sick.

"Yeah, when the Biscuit Bitches show up, I gotta be ready for some ac*tion,*" Billy says. "Cleaned my rubber lady and have my poncho liner pulled over her tight."

"How tight?" Doc asks smiling with expectation about the visit.

"Real tight. Tight like . . . ."

"Billy, you're funny until you get gross," Brown scolds. "After all they volunteer to come over here."

"Well then, I should volunteer to do something special for them."

"And what might that be, Billy?" Okie questions.

"Anyone got some cologne?" Doc gazes around.

"Shee-it, Doc. After being insulted by everyone now you want me to give up my special stock. But even Old Spice won't make a turd like you into a swashbuckler like me."

Doc bumps into Billy with fists raised. "Them there's fightin' words."

"Anytime," Billy feints to the right then left. "You got a five finger sandwich comin' buddy."

"Billy what do you need a Donut Dolly for. We all know those pin-ups in the bunker keep you busy," Okie snitches on his bunker mate. Straightening his back in a masculine pose, he struts and says, "Now, when they see a Bushmaster like me in livin' flesh, they'll be reduced to begging!"

"Okie, I hope you got a bodyguard," Brown laughs. "Don't want 'em gettin' sloppy with the merchandise."

"Don't you worry none," Okie croons.

"Am I walkin' around like an animal in heat?" Brown says, strutting around with arms wide. "No, I ain't. But keep on talkin' dirty, it's beginning to sound good."

"Hey!" Sergeant Denning yells, showing up with a bucket of water in each hand. "Stop the bullshit and give me a hand." Okie grabs the buckets and bring them around to the shower.

"Alright, listen up. The battalion commander wants you guys actin' like you're civilized and smellin' like a rose. No horseplay. No walking around pawing at the treats." Then he fixes his attention on Billy who is clowning, tongue hanging out, a dumb look on his face.

"Shirts on," Sarge continues. "Brush your teeth if you got any left. Shave and get your smelly asses in the shower!"

"It'd help if we had some clean clothes," Doc says.

"Shower? Sarge, you ain't talkin' to me?" Billy protests. "Besides, a certain amount of dirt gives my delicate skin a protective coating. Tell me, why should I trade this dirt when it already works?" Turning, he makes his escape down the hill. "No sweat GI. It's Nam time."

An hour later. "Holy shit, that water's cold! Gimme a towel. Quick," Brown yells, his bare feet hurting from the rocks. But no one helps as he hobbles to the bunker roof to grab his dirty old towel.

"Smile!" Okie says, causing Brown to look over his shoulder. "You're on candid camera," he snaps a picture.

"You better get your ass in gear, buddy." Brown points to the yellow smoke billowing from the LZ. "Chopper is inbound."

With eyes bright as a child on Christmas Day, Brown rubs the towel quickly over his body. He slips on his sweaty combat pants, pulls on socks with holes in them and shoves his feet into the worn boots. Without lacing them, he grabs his dirty shirt and shuffles over for a better view.

With an escort, two bubbly Red Cross girls jump from the chopper. With one hand holding their hair the other holding down their white skirts, they hurry out of the blades wash. Infantry soldiers hurry over and unload the food and supplies. Off the platform on the other side jump two combat photographers, one short and one tall.

Brown watches as the engineer and communication groups cluster around. The girl's escort is a tall soldier who stands rigidly in starched fatigues, his hand resting menacingly on the grip of a holstered Colt .45.

"GI Joe," Doc declares. "I hate 'im already." GI Joe is tall, dark and handsome with broad shoulders. This dreamy male specimen is their all mighty protector, leader, stud and war hero all rolled up in one.

As for the *real* GI Joe . . . . He sleeps in dirt, mud and water. He sweats like a pig, humps through muck and mountains. He carries out dead or bleeding buddies, and can kill without conscience. Then after long days of cursing and nursing cuts, he collapses with dirt under his fingernails and smells to high heaven. No lingering smell of Old Spice anywhere near a real GI Joe.

Then along comes theater GI Joe who most definitely looks the part, acts the part, and probably has a voice that sounds—most definitely—the part. So therefore he must be the baddest grunt in Vietnam. Though an impersonator, these girls view him as a know-it-all. And they will certainly follow his instructions to the letter because if they don't, "You are going to die." At least according to the impersonator. They probably even took notes on his safety lecture. But all his tips are garden variety because survival in a real freefire zone is far more demanding than learning where to get your uniforms starched and pressed, or how to load and clean a pistol.

But what the hell, he has that devil-may-care bearing and the road to Hue over his shoulder. Brown tries to straighten his shoulders like GI Joe but feels ridiculous. Some have it and some don't. He at least straightens his collar and runs his hands over his cropped hair.

The Red Cross girls setup while every grunt on the fire base call the play-by-play skirt movements. Then the coveted question, "Would you like some hot coffee and a chocolate donut?"

"Oh *yaaaaaa,"* echos through the saddle.

An F-4 Phantom Jet, having finished a bombing mission, upon seeing the girls has swung around. It's sleek fuselage shimmered in the afternoon sun as it did a low fly-by through the saddle. Then there is the ear splitting, brain busting, bone shaking rumble from the engine as the jet screamed back into the atmosphere reaching for the height of high noon with flashes of fire spewing behind.

"Did you see those two combat photographers?" Doc says standing next to Brown.

"Yeah, I did."

"That was Dana Stone and Sean Flynn. You know the son of Errol Flynn. The star of that movie Captain Blood. They don't come out unless there was something goin' on."

"They should take a picture of those two." Brown points to Billy and Okie who stand in the entrance of their bunker appearing forlorn, showing no signs they are about to join the festivities.

"I thought they'd be coming up here and talk to us?"

"From the looks of it, GI Joe there is trying to keep us away."

"Why don't they just go," Brown angrily remarks. He had always imagined a beautiful woman as someone like his sister Roxanna. Right now, he'd have given anything to be talking to someone that reminded him of her. Anything. His eyes began to mist as she enters his thoughts.

Just then the thundering Phantom reappears over the far knoll and swoops hazardously low into the saddle. So low in fact that Brown is actually looking at the top of the aircraft. A split second later its black nose lifts like the tip of a spear and he finds himself staring straight into the black oxygen mask of the pilot with an afterburner's smile.

"Shit!" Doc and Brown drop to the ground.

The sound of its supersonic jet wash blasts as it passes within inches of their heads. Standing, they brush themselves off the dirt. Looking back into the saddle, Brown realizes he and Doc are the brunt of the joke. The Donut Dollies begin cheering and laughing while others point and laugh.

"What's so goddamn funny?" Brown's temper boils over as he screams. "You got no business being out here!"

Dear Ma and Dad *17 April 1968*

I have been receiving all your letters. I haven't written for a few days because I have been writing like mad to everyone . I haven't written some people in over three months, so I am just about straight.

Well, I am on guard. It is 3:20 A.M. I have guard till four A.M. I have been in this new Fire Base since we were on this operation. So nothing has happened lately.

Some of those Red Cross Girls were here today. We call them Donut Dollies. I didn't even waste my time to go down to get donuts and coffee. I took a pair of binoculars and saw them. *Thrilling.* Oh, well.

Today one of those big jets was snipered at. So he came in for a strafe run. After the run he swept up the hill right toward me. I didn't see him coming, but all of a sudden there he was. He was about five feet over my head, I was actually looking at his oxygen masked face, and he was flying at about seven to eight -hundred miles an hour. I ducked down as he went over. When the plane was past there was a big *Boom!* I guess it was something to do with the sound barrier. Wow! Chilling. He was showing off for those Donut Dollies. Oh, well, men will be men, even in War. Or should I say boys will be boys.

Tomorrow we are going into Sniper's Alley on our west side. It is hairy. It is a bring down. This will be our first time off the hill.

So, I will write while on the day-long mission. They just fired off a mortar. I jumped. It was outgoing, no sweat. I hope it really is a day long mission. I am almost sure it is.

Ma, could you be sure to send enough paper and envelopes. Okay. I have been doing a lot of writing these last few days and I have almost finished my supply in my helmet.

Guess what! Roxanna sent me a package. It got here before her letter. They get here fast now. I guess because everything has been moved out since Christmas. She sent me a Chocolate Easter Egg. I ate it faster then it took me to open it up. *Wow!*

You know I have been noticing this so much. The day before is so far away. I think I wrote you a couple of days ago. But I can't say for sure. The next morning after the mortar round hit my bunker, I had almost forgot about it. It seemed like it happened a week ago. Like I was at LZ Baldy only ten days ago. It seems close to a month already. This bunker is like a home. The third day with it and it was real home. It even seems like an old lost friend. I get letters from you, but if the next one comes two or maybe three days later I can't remember the last letter. I remember because I carry the last letter in my shirt pocket. It is truly weird.

Oh, well, I will start again in a few hours. It will be about ten A.M. in a few hours. Bye for now. I got to call for *sit raps* from the bunker line and then call it in. It is now 3:45 A.M. I knock off at 4:20 A.M. See you on the other side.

Well, it is nine A.M. We walked or rather climbed down the Hill 218. There's one thing for sure, this is the jungle. I have been in jungle like this only one other time. That was when we were in Que Son Valley.

Wow! I am slipping. I got two letters from you yesterday. I read one and for some reason I forgot to read the other one. The one I didn't read was about the film I took. *Wow!* I thought the film was ruined. Am I glad they came out a little at least. I wanted to get home at least a couple of pictures of me and the country before I left.

By the way, all those pictures were taken on the mine sweep between LZ Baldy and LZ Ross. I have an article enclosed talking about the sweep.

You asked about the four of us. The tall one is Sgt. Denning. The guy with something on the front of his helmet is Bedford. He has been here for seven months. By the way the patch on his helmet is the 198th patch. The other one is our Medic, Doc La Barbara. He is from Chicago. The background is the railroad I told you about. Look at the picture and you can see the gravel, the railroad's old bed.

Could you get duplicates sent of the pictures. When you send them put them in plastic. Okay. Our mail gets wet a lot of times. If you want, you can number the pictures. Then I can tell you what each picture is about okay?

Then I will tell you all about the picture and you will know which one I am talking about. I will say, "Picture number one is a picture of the railroad." You understand, don't you.

Be expecting the ring in a couple of weeks. Okay? Take it out and look at it. It is real cool.

Well, at this moment we are waiting for first platoon to blow a tunnel they found. It had a Cobra snake in it. The VC or NVA always put those snakes in the tunnels. Well, I will continue in a while.

Wow! This heat is *bad*. Man, am I sweating. This jungle is nasty. We found a whole mess of hutches, caves and little stuff. They could ambush us so easily. We stay off the dikes when we come into the open. Those patties are murder. The mud is gooey. Wow! Now we are going to go into a village. I am going to get some candles.

There is one thing for sure, that mountain is over 218 meters high. Maybe three-hundred or more. Oh well, we got to move out in a few minutes so I will stop writing for now.

Well, guess what. I am on guard. It is 3:30 A.M. When I came in guess what was waiting for me. A letter from the Sinku's. Wow! It brought back old memories. They still think I will get married before Roxanna. I don't think so. They said there are two young girls living at our old house at the farm. I guess I will have to stop in and say Hi.

I got your package. Everything was great, but the apple wasn't edible. *Squished.* Oh well. Ma could you send Pork & Beans. They taste so good after eating C-rations beans.

Well, today we came across some new graves. "Dig them up." We dug up two before they said, "Forget it." They were buried for a few months. They were VC killed during the Tet Offensive. There was a sign over the graves in Vietnamese that said, "You will not be forgotten." So be it.

They decapitated a head and put it on a stick. I went over to look at the grave to see what it did to me. I guess I just laughed. It smelled bad. I think if you let the War do it to you, you will become a *sadist*. I don't like killing but I am developing some minor sadistic ways so it doesn't bother me. So is War.

See you soon, Fred Leo

19 April 1968

Following mail call, Sergeant Denning is suddenly in a far different mood. Tormented, he sits on the bunker next to Brown, the new letter clenched tightly in a fist. Finishing the last swallow of beer, he crushes the can.

"I feel so . . . so useless," he says despondently, tossing the empty can into the garbage pile. "I just got married before I came to Nam." Choked with emotion, he finds it hard to speak. Brown had never seen him so emotional.

Sniffling, he continues. "I tell everyone I've slept with my RTO more times than with my wife." Sergeant Denning tries an unsuccessful smile. Brown listens with no idea where this conversation is heading.

"I don't wanna leave ya," he says avoiding eye contact, "any of you. But I gotta wife." In the depths of his blood shot eyes, Brown can see the horrors of having too many of his friends dying around him. The thin skin under his left eye begins to twitch, and his cracked bleeding lips tremble as he looks guardedly around, anywhere but at Brown.

Brown shivers when he realizes the platoon leader he once knew is gone. That the whole story of what has happened is right there in his eyes.

"I know a lot of guys," Sergeant Denning says. "I could've gotten outta this shit hole a long time ago. Maybe . . . ." His voice turns infinitely sad. A pregnant silence follows. "Maybe I should have."

Smoothing out the letter, he begins reading to himself. "I can't even sleep. Just look at me," he pleads. "When I close my eyes . . . . It's just always there!" Tears finally flush his eyes. "Even when it's not—it's always there.

"She wants me, she needs me, and I promised her I'd come home. Shit, man! I never promised you!" He rolls his eyes skyward to stop the tears. "You don't got no one waitin'!"

Dear Ma and Dad *20 April 1968*

Tomorrow we are going into *Snipers Row*. I plan to walk out of there. No sweat. A man was killed a few days ago there. It is thick, thick jungle.

There are a few things that *No One*, no one will criticize me about. They will never tell me how to take care of myself. Say anything about my weapon. If anything, I know how to take care of myself. If anyone says anything against what I do I jump all over them.

The new lieutenant. Lieutenant? God help me! Thought he could make a comment about me. I jump on him all the time. He criticized me having a round in my chamber. I jumped on him. I don't care who he is. *No One* will say a thing. Slowly, very slowly I am getting tough mentally. I was hoping the War would do so. In a few months I might decide to go for squad leader, but that is talk. I have a long way to go. I think I am going in the right direction, but who knows.

We saw some Catholic Vietnamese today. They had a cross. They are the second people I have seen that are Catholic.

Ma, my mustache isn't black. It is sort of brown, light brown. I was surprised you could see it in the pictures. I know the guys would like a picture to send home to their people. So maybe make up four copies. Okay? Maybe the guy from Chicago will have his parents see you okay? Just for a change of pace. Well, we will see.

The watch, no trouble, works like a clock! Oh, well. I don't have to wind it, although every once in a while I wind it just a turn or two.

I was talking to an ARVN Special Forces Translator. He said when he gets out of the army he is going to college. He gets close to two-hundred dollars a month. A lot for him to get. A second lieutenant gets $60 a month, and $90 when he becomes a first lieutenant.

You know if you make a candle right it will not drip or need a place for liquid wax. The candle will burn all the wax and have no residue. I know this because I got this candle from the village. It doesn't drip.

About the radio. Make it sort of small but be sure it can pick up stuff far away because the real small ones don't have a big enough antenna. Usually the radios with a couple of bands are better. FM & Short Wave and AM.

Believe it or not the candles melted in my pocket. I had to break them apart. True Hassle! I better mail this. I will start a new letter this afternoon.

Bye till then, Fred Leo

Dear Ma and Dad *20 April 1968*

I have been here almost five months. That is a long time, but I have even longer to go. Bla! Well, I am on guard. It is 1:15 A.M. I have guard until two A.M.

I have enclosed a letter sent to Lt. Wade. Lt. Wade was our Platoon Leader at Da Nang. Ours was on R&R during the Tet Offensive. The letter is from the parents of one of the guys hit by the claymore. His name is Scott. That is the boy I mentioned in my *Yamane* letter. Scott's first name was George. His parents use George in their letter. I wrote to them today. I didn't tell them that it was a booby trap because these people are conscientious objectors – don't believe in war, and the truth might conflict with the official report. These people didn't understand their son. It is too bad. It hurt him so much. This is the reason I am so glad I have parents that understand.

Scott's parents didn't see why he came over here. His father wrote bad letters to the Captain and to Scott. It saddened him so much. They thought Scott sinned by coming here. I don't think they have Faith.

I don't know if I told you where these coins were *lifted!* The people were rich at one time. You could look at the house and tell this. They were Catholic. They also had some Buddhist religious articles. The coins were tied together, a piece of twine was put through the holes. The reason these people had coins was because at one time the French had a road going by there, bridges and all. It is now deteriorating. I always feel funny when I walk along something that was a sign of an advanced civilization.

At one time three days ago I came across a French steel helmet. It was the kind with the double *brim.* I think only the *Brass* wore them. There is only one way the people could get a hold of a helmet like that and you know how! We also found a barrel to an old French bolt action rifle.

Well, guess what. We are going to move again. Remember the last time I was at Que Son Valley in January? The place was LZ Center. I am almost sure we will go there again. If not there, we will go to LZ Ross. These are areas that have had platoons wiped out since the New Year. It is hotter than this place.

By the way we went into a valley next to this mountain we are on. We had contact. One man in my platoon was hit. He will live and be normal in about a half year. The bullets came zinging over my head, but again I was in a pretty good place of cover, so they didn't hit me.

We called in the jets. They had 500 lb. bombs. They dropped them 200 - 300 meters from us. If you want to feel the earth shake and the sound so loud it makes your ears ring, this was the time. The trees leaves were dropping like rain. We then called in gun ships. They racked the whole area, killing three men for sure. I know more were killed then that.

Well, because of this contact we didn't get started back to the LZ in time. But we did finally make it at 8:30 P.M..

That mountain was something else at night with no path. During the worst part of the way up, I had to take *Point* with my radio. No one else knew what they were doing. The lieutenant was right behind me. We went through elephant grass over our heads. That elephant grass cuts you bad. You should see my hands and arms. I hope it doesn't scar me. My arms are something else.

Today on re-supply they brought out another radio. It works better than the one I have. So it's now mine. Also they brought out a new long antenna. I have it too. I have the best RTO setup in the platoon and the company.

Well, wait a minute. I have to ask for *sitraps* and call a sitrap in to the company.

Did I tell you I got your goodies. I have to fight everyone for the Spanish Rice. Could you send some Pork & Beans. I love them. Okay? You know I think I already told you I got your packages. Also those sesame seeds were good. The sesame seeds with honey.

Like a fool I lost the pen you gave me. The brush we went through must have knocked it out of my pocket. One of the guys lost a roll of film and salt tablets. Could you send me another pen. In care of 'butter fingers.'

Ma, I will not be able to go to Germany until after this tour. Too bad. But I got to finish this tour of duty first.

Ma, I am in the field so often I always eat at my bunker. Sometimes we go in and we have a mess *tent*.

I ride a lot in helicopters. The scenery is beautiful, but the only time we ride in a Huey is when we are on a CA. The Huey is the only chopper I have ridden in where I could see good. But usually I am shaking so it ruins most of the beauty in my eyes. I fly a lot in the Chinook. But I can't see much out of them.

I carry all the money orders in my wallet. That is the best place. We haven't got the new M-16's yet – or the new radios. I have a suspicion the Delta Package is going to be distributed throughout the battalion. Oh, well, it was too good to be true.

You asked how did I learn to operate the Radio? Easy. I learned a few basics. From there it was hard. They never say anything outright. They use the phonetic alphabet. You have to know what the letter stands for. "Send two echo mike and your sierra lima to my location." This means send two enlisted men and your squad leader to my location.

"The Alpha Charlie will leave my location." Alpha Charlie is armored convoy. Other phrases: "Send a foxtrot tango plus two echo mike from the 2-3 element to 6 location near the romeo by the blue line" *Foxtrot tango* is Fire Team. *Echo Mike* is Enlisted men. 2-3 is Second Platoon, 3rd Squad. 6 mean the CO. *Romeo Romeo* is Railroad. *Blue Line* is the river. *Red Ball* is Road.

See, these phrases go on indefinitely. You have to be around a long time before you know your job.

"Charlie, Charlie identify smoke nine 0'clock your location. Chopper, Chopper what color do you see?" I say that when I'm trying to bring in a chopper.

It takes time and a lot of situations to become a good RTO.

We have gotten new replacements. We are twenty-nine men with eight on sick call or hospital.

Well, guard is just about over. So, I will mail this letter and hope I get a letter from someone tomorrow.

Bye for now, Fred Leo

22 April 1968

In the evening Delta Company finds itself hacking with machete through thick jungle. They had finally broken contact with the snipers. While in the valley, they had quickly learned it would be a cat and mouse game with the persistent NVA.

A few days back, they had marched westward off Hill 218 in the pre-dawn hours. Reaching the valley, the sun was still blocked by the mountain peaks and the rays were muted by a thin layer of gray clouds. Then two things happened simultaneously. They had walked past the mountain's shadow and the sun had shoved past the clouds. A warm yellowish beam then bathed the trail making it appear like, "the yellow brick road to OZ."

The jungle then gave way to open space where Brown half expected to see the poppy fields that lay before the fabled Emerald

City.

Unfolding in front of him is a breathtaking view. He finds himself overlooking a river of lime green rice sprouts, fed by terrace upon terrace of rice waterfalls, flowing out of sight. This stunning view could change forever someone's perception of beauty.

On the first night out, the NVA had gathered a herd of local water buffalo and stampeded them toward Brown's night perimeter. That was the night they learned how hard it is to kill a frightened water buffalo.

Then last evening they logared on a hillside plateau that was a dry rice bed. After digging for hours, with the black of night closing around them, the CO gave the order to move-out. What the hell? was the question on the minds of the weary soldiers as they snuck quietly off the plateau and back into the jungle.

Fifteen minutes later while strung out along the mountain trail, their question was answered. They heard the sounds of enemy mortar tubes firing. Then from his vantage point, Brown saw mortars pummel the old night logar and watched as his foxhole took a direct hit. They continued to move through the night only stopping occasionally for rest.

They were having a steady diet of mortars all night, snipers all day and little rest in between.

Nearing complete exhaustion, they try to slip away by swinging toward the rice field valley and skirting the edge, searching for a night logar.

The cattle grazing corner adjacent to the rice fields is deemed suitable for a fighting perimeter. To their south and west unbroken paddies stretch for over a kilometer. The back two sides are bordered by an impenetrable vine covered jungle.

Since Sergeant Denning's departure, Brown had become the acting Platoon Sergeant and so is still attached to the CP. After giving the lieutenant his recommendations for a defensive perimeter, he surveys the area and decides to dig into the side of a two foot plateau. The plateau would serve the protective back wall. This way he would only need to pile sandbags across the front and on the two short sides.

Doc loosens the straps on his rucksack and pulls out his fifteen sandbags and shovel.

The lieutenant inadvertently flops on the very spot Brown has chosen. Without asking him to move, Brown begins digging and filling sandbags around his feet hoping he might offer to help. Instead, the lieutenant decides to follow Doc around the perimeter as he checks the men and dispenses salt and malaria pills.

After filling and stacking ten sandbags, Brown stops to catch his breath, and have a drink. That's when he questions the CO's decision about night logaring before dark. Is there a plan? Are they going to pack up and move out like before? His gut feeling tells him they're gonna stay put. But if they do, his gut feeling also tells him they're gonna get mortared.

"Ohh*hhh*." Brown straightens up with stars running through his vision. It feels like his insides are ripping loose and are about to bubble up into his throat. Good judgment or not on the CO's part, Brown knows his strength wouldn't have held up another hour on the trail.

Returning with Doc, Okie says, "Brownie, you couldn't be tired already!" Okie has a deep infected cut on his forearm and Doc washes it with peroxide before he wraps it with gauze.

"Did you hear all that blastin' at the rear of the column?" Okie asks. Brown nods but doesn't know the details.

"Well, a dink comes walkin' over pretty as you please, just as we moved out." Okie always delights in telling stories. "The dink starts kickin' around the empty cans lookin' for food. Then we spot each other at exactly the same time. We open up with everything we got. You should've seen that dink *jitter bug* then dive off the terrace! Guys ran after him, but the dink got away. Not a trace of blood."

"Bunch of sharpshooters." They laugh. Unstrapping the lieutenant's fifteen sandbags, Brown flings them over to Doc.

"Doc, now that you're finished the Purple Heart victim, maybe you could give me a hand. The platoon leader sure in hell ain't."

"Just look at 'em," Okie says holding his arm steady as Doc tapes off the gauze. He nods toward third platoon. "You'd think they'd have learned something by now." He refers to their lackadaisical way of setting up defensive positions.

"Just sitting around bullshittin'." Brown shakes his head watching them carry on conversations while smoking and eating. "Dig first. Then clean your weapon. And if you got time . . . oh well."

"Like my daddy used to say, 'You can lead a horse to water but you can't make 'em drink.'"

"Guess they'll have to learn the hard way." With strength returning, Brown stretches. "Say Okie, I sure could use that machete you got."

"And?"

"Could you get it for me? Pretty please. With sugar on top."

"Well, since you asked so politely."

With machete, Brown fells a three-inch diameter tree. After whacking off the limbs, he cut the trunk in half.

Meanwhile, Doc diligently fills sandbags. Completing the three walls, Brown places the logs longways across the roof and covers them with the last ten sandbags. Finished, he places his gear on top of the half-roof.

"How about some hot chocolate, Doc?" Brown says taking out the bread-can stove.

"Love it, Brown." He stands back to scrutinize their foxhole. "Nice work."

While the water heats, Brown cleans and checks the action of his rifle. Then by instinct, both he and Doc stop what they are doing to witness the glorious color display as the last rays of the sunlight disappear behind the mountain peaks that stretch all the way to Laos.

"Those guys." Brown again leers at third platoon in the darkness. "They're gonna get themselves killed and everyone around 'em too if they don't get their act together."

"They must think this is a backyard party. Like nothin' is gonna happen."

"Wait!" Brown raises an index finger. "Sh*hhhhhh*." He looks at Doc then screams, "Mortars! Mortars! *Incoming!*"

Everyone scrambles for cover. Both Brown and Doc jump into their foxhole. Brown starts to reach for his helmet and rifle just as the lieutenant jumps in right on top of them.

Five mortar rounds explode on the southern end of the perimeter. Then he hears more mortars being fired.

Though pushed tight against the wall, Brown tries to reach over the roof for his steel pot and rifle. At that instant, a soldier comes running over yelling, "I don't got a hole, man. Let me in!" He takes a flying leap across all three of them just as the another volley of mortars explode.

Listening, Brown realizes that indeed the last mortars had landed closer. That means the NVA are walking them across the perimeter and directly for him.

The next volley lands so close that Brown could actually hear them sizzling through the air just before impact. The ground trembles knocking dirt off the sandbags.

In the lull, Brown hears the mortar tubes go *thump thump thump thump* as more are fired in rapid succession.

"Come on, man. Let me in!" comes a panic stricken voice from yet another soldier. "Oh, shit, man! Come on! I can't find a hole!" The panicky soldier drops to the ground just outside the foxhole. With four soldiers already smashed inside the foxhole, there is obviously no room but he continues to plead, "You gotta let me in."

"Szzzz-blam! Szzzz-blam! Szzzz-blam!!"

Four volleys, five mortars in each, have already hit the perimeter and there is no end in sight as they come nearer and nearer.

"Oh man! Oh man! Oh dear God, I'm gonna die! I'm gonna die! Oh my God, don't let this happen to me!"

Cramps make their way along Brown's legs, but he can't move because they are packed like sardines. Wedging himself, he finally gets his butt onto the ground. Taking a deep breath, he tries to calm down. Sitting tight in a corner, he feels relatively safe. Now he starts working out the options.

Say they take a direct hit. Between the sandbags and the guy laying over him, he'd probably make it. But all the blood, guts and body parts would spill over him. Okay, I can handle that.

The ground shakes with rounds exploding within seconds of each other and getting closer.

So, he thinks, the NVA start the attack. Brown and the others would have to shove this guy off. Then hope they have time enough to grab their rifles. First things first. This guy laying on top of them will have to go.

"Oh my, God! I'm gonna die. I'm gonna die!" The soldier repeats over and over and over as the rounds encircle them. The explosions reach a deafening pitch as the ground rumbles and dust and smoke envelopes them.

Then Brown hears them coming right in on top of them. "Szzzzz! Szzzzz!!" The ground rocks sending dust and debris breaking from the sandbags, as mortar after mortar pounds within mere inches, feet, yards of their foxhole.

"Aaah! Aaah! I'm hit! I'm hit! Oh, God! Oh, God! Oh, God! I'm dying! Oh please someone, help me. Help please dear God, I'm bleeding to death!" the soldier's voice outside the bunker shrills as another volley of mortars again explode randomly throughout the perimeter.

The smoke from the bombardment is so dense that it stings Brown's eyes, so he closes them. Then it dawns on him that he isn't breathing. Why?! Panic shoots through him and in a claustrophobic frenzy, he tries to push out of the foxhole. But from his scrunched position, finds it impossible. His only alternative is to calm himself. "Lord give me strength."

As a child he would see how long he could hold his breath under the bath tub water. He learned that if at first you took several deep breaths, you could saturate your lungs and last for at least forty-five seconds. As he reaches the count of thirty the dying soldier's voice turns to whimpers as mortars continue to crash.

At sixty seconds and still counting, dizziness begins to overwhelm him. He struggles for a little air. It chokes his lungs but it helps. He goes back to number one and starts counting again.

Dear Ma and Dad *24 April 1968*

I am Okay.

I don't have time to write !

Everything is touch and go

I'll write as soon as I get time.

Bye, Fred Leo

Dear Ma and Dad *28 April 1968*

Guess what I am using to write this letter! The Bic pen you sent me. Man, it writes nice. Well I am on guard. It is like the monsoon. It has rained for four days now. But I have been able to keep my blanket fairly dry. I have the people in the rear checking on my R&R. I hope to get it soon.

I got your letter with the sugar sweetened Kool-Aid. I about drank the whole canteen full. I made up the Shake-A-Pudding. I felt like a little kid. But was it good! Send some strawberry next time. The chocolate was good, but I heard they have strawberry too. I wonder how it tastes.

Wow! Everything is a hassle. I have a lot of work. Our lieutenant is lazy so I end up with most of the work. We have men that are eager to Live & Learn. So we will see if I can keep them straight. You can see how bad off we are if—I, a nineteen year old guy takes over a platoon. I have only been in for ten months. That is, in the Army.

Well, we haven't had any weapons fired at us. We have killed one VC and have fired on many more. We found another radio. This was a three-band radio also. This one has dead batteries so I don't know when the guys will get it working. Do you have my radio on the *way?* I can hardly wait. Could you tell Roxanna I have been receiving her letters. I just don't have time no more. When I get on R&R it will be different. Well, I got to wake the perimeter up. By for now. It is 5:45 A.M. See you later.

When I was on Hill 218 I couldn't see the South China Sea. It was a long, long ways off.

You wondered where I get my water. I get it from rice patties, abandoned wells, rivers, and anything where the water looks clear. Also they bring water to us on choppers.

Ma, you talked about Mrs. Wallgreen going to college. There sure is hope for you, like you said. Maybe we could go to school together. Sounds funny! Oh, well.

You know the cartoons, well we have them in the Army Times. It is a paper completely dedicated to the whole Army. Well, I am going on a mission right now. Hang on. We are going after some "Dinks" we seen.

Ma, I still have a foot locker. I don't know where it is. I haven't seen it for three months. I still have my jacket. I haven't had time to make it up yet.

You asked, "Do they grow anything else in Nam besides rice?" Yes, corn, hot peppers, juka, potatoes, onions, tomatoes. They can grow anything we can. A lot of their land is good rich black dirt.

Some nights are cold in Nam. It got down to probably 60

degrees last night. But that is because of the rain. Even when it is real hot, the nights are fairly sleepable.

Ma, you said you thought I drank big gulps all day. About a quart each gulp. I can't believe how much I drink.

Well, today is the 29th of April.

I have 205 days left. Wait! I just pulled a leech off my back. Well, tonight we are night logering on the edge of Dragon Valley. By the way, I have my radio back. The other RTO had to go in, so we are short one. So I have it again. I don't think I will ever stop being an RTO.

I can hardly wait till I get the pictures. I don't know how we look. It will be wild.

What a bring down. Today I can hump my gear better than yesterday. What a bring down! I could hardly walk yesterday. I didn't get much sleep and here I am feeling better.

We always have jokes. One is "You could hurt yourself if you tried." The old guys are so rugged that they never give out, break a bone, strain ankles or anything. Well, I got to move out.

I just got re-supply broken down. I have been in charge of the chopper pad for the last two days. I got to go now. A chopper will be here in a few minutes.

Ma, I will get a direct assignment to Germany, so you can come over there. Okay?

We have been traveling on a road "A" Company was hit on two days ago. There are a few blood stains on it and expended cartridges. There is a blown up bunker made by NVA or VC.

I have been getting your letters all the time. I feel good now. I was messed up for the first few days out because of Sergeant Denning leaving.

Bye, Fred Leo

P.S. You asked, "Are there any dragons in Dragon Valley?" Really now.

May 1968

Letter From Father

Dear Fred *1 May 1968*

Your letter since the loss of your superior and your own promotion, points out the fact that there is nothing permanent in this world except change. Your view that the stress is becoming almost unbearable is certainly one that we arm chair strategists here at home are certainly not qualified to pass judgement upon. Who know what we would do if we were in your position to give good sound advice, even though I'm so much older than you. However the changes which have put you where you are will continue to operate and it would be closing one's mind to logic to allow one's self to believe one is at the bottom of a pit from which there are no exits to better things. It has been said that 'time cures all things' or words to that effect.

Repeatedly you have mentioned in your letters that you are beginning to see things more clearly, getting a better understanding of what life is all about. Perhaps life there is a sort of baptismal fire which will enable you to see across a span of many, many years in the relatively short span of two years.

I realize this can be of small solace to you as you struggle to survive under harsh battlefield conditions. But you do have within you remarkable powers for perceiving truths, for insights into things which lie beneath the surface. Within yourself I'm also sure you have qualities for leadership for coming back home and helping to make our country a better place in which to live, but even more important making our country a nation of which we can all be proud.

This is the extent of which I might be able to help you, though only just a little bit, to master your harsh trials and come out a proud winner as far as mastery of yourself and your environment are concerned. Perhaps I can help just a little bit in helping you define some worth while goals up ahead. They say that the world makes way for the man who knows where he's going. You are not only fighting for our country, you are fighting to become a better and wiser person. A wise persons is just that. WISE! He's neither always kind, always cruel, always sentimental, always hash. A wise person is one who uses the right tool to get the right job done. He is only wise if he realizes he must not hesitate to use whatever the tool necessary to get a worthy job done. He is wise only in so far as he has the ability to see clearly in his mind what jobs should be done. Perhaps lastly he must be wise enough to realize that there are jobs he may only just be able to get started, but also wise enough to understand that there will be others to carry on where he has to leave off. Even others to carry on if only the way is pointed out to them.. I've a feeling that you are going to win over all the obstacles from which you've suffered mentally and physically.

Again I want you to know that I realize we here at home can't begin to understand all that you've gone through and are going through. But I've believed for a long, long time that you've inherited the ingredients for becoming a very, very wise person.

Your father

Dear Ma and Dad *2 May 1968*

Well, It is night. I can hardly see to write.

I received your package of fruit, Spanish rice, chili, and beef stew and the writing paper. I received it on this hill. I humped up here. I was beat and had no C-rations. I opened the package up and *glub, glub!* I didn't have water either.

Well, everything has been a bring down. We have been mortared three times since we were out. One night they laid it hard on us. We had thirteen 82mm mortar rounds land on our section of the perimeter. Needless to say, I thought it was all over!

I have a new weapon now. There was a guy laying outside of our hole who could not get in. He was wounded. So, since my weapon was hit by shrapnel—I took his.

Wow! Dust offs are hairy. We took this man that was hit and brought him into the rice patties. NVA had small arms weapons so they could have picked us off. The chopper turned on it's belly light and we were lit up like daylight. We ran to the chopper and ran back to the trench. Wow! I think I lost a few years of my life. I went to bed shaking. Then they started mortaring us again. *UGH!*

You wouldn't believe how much we have humped. I don't. This area is hot. I have been shot at *boo coo* times. One night they mortared us and then they threw grenades at us for three hours. While they there doing this, I was running around from foxhole to foxhole giving out stuff and information.

Bye for now, Fred Leo

2 May 1968

"You're one lucky dog, Okie," Brown claims. They have just heard that his bunker on Hill 218 had been overrun the previous night. One occupant was killed and two wounded. "Now ain't ya glad you're in the bush?"

"Shit! I never wanna go through another week like this again. I'll take my chances on a bunker line. At least you get food, water and on occasion . . . rest."

Smoke from a purple grenade billows as the resupply chopper descends at daybreak.

Doc sends a soldier on sick call with a leach lodged up his penis. The soldier, who was on night ambush, had received a morphine shot to help with the pain but is still barely able to walk.

The re-supply soldier jumps off the helicopter towing the mail bag. Coming up behind is their new platoon sergeant Robin Hood.

Okie and Brown run under the blades covering their faces from flying debris and begin tossing out cases of C-rations. Still in charge of the platoon, Brown grabs the platoon's requisition bag and quickly checks the contents.

"Hey, man." Brown looks angrily at the re-supply soldier. "I don't see any fatigues in here!"

"Couldn't find any."

"Couldn't find any? Why the hell not!" Brown shouts over the noise of the helicopter engine.

"Hey, man. When I get my supplies, you'll get yours."

"This is Leach Valley, if you didn't know." Brown has moved to within three feet of the re-supply soldier. "And I have men with ripped pants out here. Have you ever had a leach crawl up your dick?"

The re-supply soldier turns, intent on ignoring Brown.

"Where are the pants?"

Their new Platoon Sergeant Robin Hood watches from a distance, not interfering.

"Hey, REMF!" Bedford shouts, joining in. "Where's our supplies!" He moves shoulder to shoulder with Brown. "While you're in the rear with the gear we're out here fighting a war!"

"Or didn't you know there was a war goin' on out here," Brown badgers.

"Hey, I'm only doing my job," the re-supply soldier hollers back sassy. "If it were up to me," he snickers, "hell no problem. Now, if you guys wouldn't tear them up so quick, maybe I'd have some to bring out."

Okie, walks over with his pants ripped from crotch to ankle. "Did I get any?"

"No. This guy's trying to shake us down for money," Brown glares.

"I didn't say that."

"Drop your pants." Brown stands menacingly with his rifle.

The supply soldier half smiles thinking it a joke. The chopper door gunner starts waving frantically for him to re-board, but Bedford steps over to block his escape.

Brown motions for Okie to take off his pants, which he does. Noticing a leach, he quickly squirts it with bug juice. It breaks loose with a little stream of blood running down Okie's leg.

With the rifle, Brown motions the re-supply soldier to drop his pants.

"No way, man," the re-supply soldier says not so sure of himself anymore.

"Now."

"Okay, okay." Quickly, he pulls off his boots. Hopping around on one foot, he pulls off the pants and throws them on the ground.

Brown scoops up both pairs off the ground. He tosses the good ones to Okie. Then he throws the ripped pants into the re-supply soldier's face.

"When I order something, you better get it next time," Brown warns.

The soldier stands in boxer shorts seething with anger.

"Do you understand me!" Noticing a leach on the ground, Brown picks it up and moves to within inches of the soldier. The soldier stares back and blinks. Brown drops the leach on the soldier's neck.

Bedford moves out of the way and the re-supply soldier bolts for the chopper while frantically grabbing for the leach.

"I hope you get wasted grunt," he swears, now safely on board the helicopter.

"Brown!" Robin Hood calls. Brown walks over. "Pass out the equipment then tell the men to get ready to move out." He looks at Brown. "I'm taking over now. Any questions."

"No."

"Good. You're not an RTO anymore either. I want you as a rifleman. You'll be second squad with Sergeant Grauer."

"Jelly Belly, right," Brown replies, using the Grauer's nickname.

Forty-five minutes later. "Saddle up. We're movin' out!" Robin Hood commands.

Despondent and feeling like he'd been demoted, Brown follows his squad and reminisces about the good old days with his friends, Yamane and Denning. "God only knows, how I miss them."

They move off the hill, the incline growing with each step. Not long into the march, Doc Holliday stumbles on a hole covered by the knee high field grass.

"Uhh!" He hits the ground hard, the weight of the heavy rucksack pinning him. Brown walks over and extends a helping hand.

"I'm not doing too good," Doc Holliday says as he tries to rise but loses his grasp and plops once more on the ground. Brown calls for soldiers to pass the word that Doc Holliday is down. When the word reaches Robin Hood, he turns and signals for Brown to carry him.

Giving Doc Holliday a drink, he pours some over his head. Everyone continues past without offering assistance and then the last soldier lumbers by.

"Hey! Come on, give me a hand," Brown pleads with the GI. "Take his pack will ya. He can't carry it." The soldier stares blankly. Picking up the rucksack, he moves on.

Brown slings the rifle across Doc Holliday's back, then working together, gets him into a standing position. Brown wraps his right arm around Doc Holliday's waist. His other hand secures Doc Holliday's arm that is draped over his shoulders.

"I feel dizzy."

"I know. But we gotta get goin'. So hang on." Moving slowly down the hill, Doc Holliday begins dragging his feet.

"Come on, man. It can't be that bad. Shit, why didn't you say something before? We could've gotten ya on the re-supply chopper. Shit."

"I don't know. It just came over me," Doc Holliday slurs.

"Well, I can't do this alone. Alright? Help out."

Reaching the tree line, they find the platoon is nowhere in sight. Needing to rest, Brown props Holliday against a tree, but he slides along the trunk until he's resting on the ground. Brown scans the area for any signs of danger. Then he checks the ground and terrain to decide in which direction the platoon has traveled. Resettling his heavy rucksack, Brown bends over, wraps his arm around Holliday's waist and gets a good grip on the pistol belt.

"Up you go."

"Brown, I . . . ."

With no definite path, Brown follows faint foot prints, broken branches and damaged leaves. Reaching an open field, he looks around for any signs of danger. The incline has increased, so that helps. Taking a few deep breaths, he tightens up his hold around Doc Holliday.

"Alright, this clearing looks a little dangerous. We're gonna try and hurry across. Ready?"

Doc Holliday mumbles.

"Let's go." With all his strength, Brown double-times it out into the open. Sweat pours over his face, blurring his vision, but he can't stop because this would make a perfect target for a sniper. He sucks in the sweat as it reaches his mouth hoping to wet his parched mouth.

While his body strains under the over two-hundred pounds of added weight, Holliday's rifle barrels keeps bumping his steel pot. His heart pumps like a rabbit, and just before the next tree line Brown loses his grip and they tumble to the ground.

Still in the open, Doc Holliday rolls onto his back panting. Brown struggles to his knees holding the rifle at the ready. They haven't been spotted . . . yet. Still needing to regroup his strength, Brown pulls out a canteen and takes a mouthful between breaths. Getting Doc Holliday into a sitting position, he hands him the canteen.

"Drink Holliday. It'll help." He slobbers down the water while Brown takes another canteen and pours it over his and Holliday's head.

"Come on, you ready."

"Ready," Doc Holliday mumbles as he hands back the canteen.

Brown hoists him off the ground. "Okay, let's go."

A half hour later, Brown's strength is waning alarmingly. Coming to a decision, inside a tree line Brown let's Doc Holliday down next to a tree and puts the rifle in easy reach.

"Listen Holliday, I don't got the strength. I gotta go for some help."

"Brown you're the best buddy a guy ever had," he blubbers with caked spit around his mouth. Brown pats him on the shoulder and gives him the canteen. Like a little baby, water oozes from his lips and his dark brown trusting eyes stare at Brown.

"You gonna be okay?"

He reaches for his rifle and pulls it onto his lap. With a rubber neck he checks to make sure it is on automatic. The he stares at Brown with the saddest face imaginable.

"Damn you Doc Holliday." He grabs him around the waist. "This kinda shit is gonna get me killed yet."

Yamane and Sergeant Denning were the ones always there to help out. "Only the Good die young," is the saying that reminded him most of Yamane. Since their departure Brown had taken it upon himself to walk in the shadow of death. Today being no exception. The first day out being another example.

Not long after reaching the *Yellow Brick Road to Oz* , they had been caught by snipers in the middle of a flooded rice field. It appeared that everyone had scrambled to safety but when he looked back, he saw three NFGs frozen in their tracks. As acting-platoon sergeant, he was responsible. Shucking the heavy rucksack, he rushed back into the open rice field.

By yelling and waving his arms around wildly, he got their attention and got them moving for cover. But seconds later they were again dazed and disorientated. He hurried further into the flooded rice field realizing he'd have to get beyond them. With sniper bullets creating water-jets nearby, he continued to herd them to safety.

Minutes later, the three NFGs were galloping up the incline to safety with him close behind. Then out of the corner of his eye, he spots one more NFG in the rice field crouched behind a boulder. The snipers were closing in quickly. Brown had dashed over, grabbed the frightened soldier by the arm and pulled him to safety. He had accomplished this with only one man wounded . . . .

Continuing to follow foot prints and broken twigs markers, they near the bottom on the hill. That's when Brown's body begins to shake from exhaustion. With still no one in sight, he simply lowers Doc Holliday, and walks off for help.

Twenty minutes later Doc Holliday is safely on board a Medivac.

"We're movin' out," the GI calls back to Brown who takes-up the rear of the column. Standing, he find himself so physically spent he has trouble keeping his eyes in focus. Wobbling, he turns by habit and slurs, "Wee . . .movv. . .oww."

Today's mission is to rendevous with some local ARVNs so he isn't alarmed to realize Vietnamese soldiers are now resting on the path behind him. They look up puzzled. Maybe they don't understand English, he thinks. So he waves them on. Brown puts on his steel pot and grabs his M-16 rifle, and they do the same. Except they put on NVA helmets and pick up communist AK-47 rifles!

For a pregnant second they stare. Then, without anymore hesitation, the NVA turn and jog off into the underbrush.

With no strength for a reaction, Brown simply turns and starts walking.

At first his pace is nearly normal as he catches up to the rear of the column, but gradually his muscles tire until he moves at a totter and loses sight of the platoon. Ten minutes later, he finds the platoon resting alongside the trail. But he can't rest for fear of being left behind. So exhausted as he might be, he keeps moving. By the time he reaches the middle of the platoon, they are ordered to move out.

This see-saw continues throughout the morning. Whenever the platoon rests, Brown keeps moving because that is his only chance of staying up.

While wading across a shallow stream that overflows the road, he dunks his empty canteen. Once again the rear of the platoon begins passing as he lifts the full canteen. Screwing the lid on, he slides it back into the pouch. That's when he feels something funny on his hand like . . . .

"Oh-h sheeet!" He tries restraining the horror of seeing a huge buffalo leach stretched across his entire palm waving around as it sucks at an open wound on the inside of his thumb. Rushing from the water, he flicks frantically at the leach. "Ahhh," he flicks faster and faster and by the time he reaches the edge of the water, the leach dangles and falls away.

The column comes to a halt on the trail within a shady area. With a soft breeze blowing through the trees, the scene is now very picturesque. Miraculously, Brown had been gaining strength and at the last rest stop he found himself in the middle of the column. But still this is no time to rest, so he keeps moving.

Nearing the head of the column, he sees the lieutenant talking with a squad of ARVNs. They stand overlooking the river's edge. Fifty yards further along the trail and to the left is an old stone bridge that had been dynamited years earlier. To their immediate right is a dilapidated guard house with its sandbags returning their insides to the earth.

Second platoon pulls cover as the ARVAN's begin to negotiate the stream on a makeshift log jam bridge. Crossing, the Vietnamese poke fun at each others balancing act or if they slip and slid. Are they just showing off with their nonchalant ways, Brown wonders, or is this laughter a part of their personality?

Second platoon's Kit Carson, Coa, decides to cross behind the ARVAN's. Arriving safely on the opposite bank, he gives the lieutenant the all-clear sign. The Vietnamese, paying little attention to security, sit and watch as the Americans begin their crossing.

Because of the heavy rucksacks, the Americans cross clumsily. They try to hold their balance on the slippery logs, now wet from the previous crossing, but keep slipping off into the shallow water.

With sticks in hand, the ARVAN's point and have a good laugh. Reaching their fill of entertainment, they hurl the sticks into the river and enter the village joking and laughing all the way.

While the platoon secures the village, Brown disappears around a hut and meanders until he come upon a garden. It has full grown stalks of corn, potatoes, onions, vine ripe tomatoes, cucumbers and juka. On the far side the ARVANs and Kit Carson Coa sit around a smoking campfire. Some ARVNs forage through the garden and one brave sole is attempting to collect honey from the village bee hives. Brown moves within a few yards of them, sits and begins to eat lunch from cans. For their lunch the ARVNs are sharing a vegetable salad along with rice and dried fish.

"Eat, GI?" Coa calls Brown after conferring with his new friends. "Numba one chop chop," he points and smiles. "You like." Accepting the invitation, Brown moves politely to sit near the fire.

The Vietnamese dip their food in a putrid smelling sauce. They smile, offering Brown this delicacy. Brown smiling back uncertainly then takes the offered cucumber and daringly dips it into the sauce.

"Nuoc mam. Numba one, GI. You like," one of the Vietnamese says.

Exhaling, he stuffs the entire slice of cucumber in his mouth and chews—possibly the bravest thing he's ever done. To his surprise, after getting past the smell, the nuoc mam tastes salty and rather good.

Taking another slice of cucumber Brown eats it along with his rations. Meanwhile an ARVN jabs Cao making him drop his food in the dirt.

Here these men are in a freefire zone goofing off and having fun. Somehow their attitude toward the war seems totally different than the Americans. Watching, Brown realizes there is an artistry to the way they handle themselves. These ARVNs didn't enlist in the military, *they were the military.*

"GI, elephant." Coa points making reference to Brown's massive rucksack. They all rear back laughing. One ARVN stands and plods around the campfire pretending to be a hunched over American infantryman.

In contrast to the American equipment, they have little fanny packs, only a few magazines of M-16 ammunition, but plenty of hand grenades.

Brown remembers how he would join-in whenever there was a

cutting conversation about the ARVNs. Those cutting remarks were highly unjustified based on what he is seeing in these seasoned warriors, the real masters of the jungle.

Brown finishes a ripe tomato along with honey on his ration bread. Refreshed, Brown stands and bows slightly to the ARVNs. "Numba One, chop chop. Thank you. Thank you very much."

Dear Ma *3 May 1968*

It is in the middle of the day. We didn't get mortared last night so we will stay at the same night loger.

We have some ARVNS who were living in this area when the NVA took over. Now they are going to work with us and try to take over the area again.

We walked off the hill and hit a village. The first thing the Arvan's did was check the immediate area out and then chow down. They got all kinds of stuff. They got honey from the bees, we fried fish, ate pineapple, cucumbers. Wow! It was fabulous having good food.

By the way my poncho liner got blown up. So now I caught a *cold*. It gets real cold at nights.

Well, we are moving again. I have no time. I can't even get this letter out.

By the way you know those pictures of the guys. Half of them are out of the company. I don't have anyone to give the pictures to. Oh, well.

Did I tell you we killed an NVA a couple of days ago. He had an AK-47 and web gear. I was shooting at him. I don't know if I got him or who did.

Well, we got an E-6 for a Platoon Sergeant. So I will break him in, then I don't know what I will do.

I hope I get R&R soon! I am turning into one big mess. I was right. I think these last few weeks have made a big change in me. I thought it would. One more month and I think I will be straight. If I go too far, I might get going in the wrong direction. I might get to enjoy killing and this stuff. Then I will never settle down.

Well, they are on me again. So I got to go, Bye.

I am sorry I can't write more. But this will last only for a month or so, I hope. Okay? Just hang on. Tell everyone *Hi.* I can't write. Okay.

Bye for now, Fred Leo

Dear Ma and Dad *5 May 1968*

Well, finally a break. We were CA'd out of Dragon Valley. We are now on Hill 488, known as LZ East. As was Hill 218 the 101st was pushed off this hill, too.

There is only desolation on this hill. We always end up in the old *deserted* Base Camp. It is another *Death Mountain*. The clouds are below us. The fog started rolling in this morning. Under us the sun made the sky a blood red, and the old abandoned bunkers were silhouetted against this scene. There are no blood stains, just burnt, torn clothes, boots which are charred. Whose they were, will never be known.

I am setting up in an old bunker. I must rebuild it fast. LZ Center was mortared last night. I look at the timbers and it looks like a man was practicing with his bayonet. Did this man have dreams and hopes like I do? Where is he now. Is he home or does he have a flag over his grave.

We now have a Platoon Sergeant. So I will go back to second squad, I imagine. Soon, I will end up as squad leader.

Ma, could you send me some more fishing line—10 lb. test. Okay. I can use it as trip wire.

I don't know what I have told you about these last few days, so don't mind me if I say something I already said. I have a new weapon and poncho liner. My rucksack and frame has shrapnel holes in it. My helmet has a shrapnel hole it and last but not least —a package of *Kool-Aid* was hit!

We will stay on this mountain for three days, then we will go after a regiment of NVA that are supposed to be in this area.

Yesterday as I waited for re-supply, thunder and lightning broke from the sky. I didn't move out of the rain because I was drenched from sweat, so it didn't make any difference.

I turned to my right as I sat there with the rain streaming off my helmet. I saw a man standing. He is a team leader, and has been here for three months. He had a small leaf fixed in his helmet which stood straight forward. We use camouflage in our helmets, but I think he put this leaf just so. The man lit a cigarette and the leaf protected it from the rain. He didn't take the lit cigarette out of his mouth for fear it would get wet and this little pleasure would be ruined. His shoulders were slightly slumped and his head slightly bent, but his legs were strong and straight. He was turned to the side against a patty dike and the jungle. How lonely he must have felt.

My weapon is in bad shape. I will continue soon.

I just finished working on my new weapon for over one hour. Still have a little to go, but I am tired of working on it.

Last night we were probed. We caught some NVA who tripped a trip flare. They shot an RPG Rocket at us, but they missed. They had another rocket unfired, also twenty grenades. But we caught them. *Ha, Ha.*

LZ Center was mortared this morning again. We expect something tonight, but we don't know what.

Here's part of an article I found:

Hill 488: A Fight to Remember. This is a story of a barren, rock strewn hill twenty miles northwest of Chu Lai, South Vietnam, and of the 18-man reconnaissance platoon of Charlie Company, First Reconnaissance Battalion, First Marine Division. These men were no elite force. They were an average lot who had undergone the seemingly magical training process which produces Marines, and this was their great strength, that long and terrible night when they fought one of the truly great final stands in all of history—they were Marines . . . .

The story goes on about how those Marines survived on this *very* hill! No wonder it looks so ripped up. And there is a sketch of a large rock that appears to be the one near our helicopter pad. Here's some more.

. . . Together these eighteen men of Charlie Company comprised for its size the most highly decorated unit in the 193 years of

American military history. As one Marine officer said, studying the action report, "This was an Alamo-with survivors!"

I have to go. Bye for now, Fred Leo

Dear Ma and Dad *6 May 1968*

Wow! I try to make time fly. *Wow!* It is a real hassle. I sacked out today for about four hours. *Man!* did I need the sleep.

The radio you sent has great reception but ten pounds? That is a lot of weight. I think I can carry it. It is the type of radio you need here.

Well, this whole area is hotter than anything. The tracks-APCs with .50 cal. machine guns are blasting continuously in the valley surrounding me. There are continuous air strikes and gun ships strafing the area. We have our mortars with us and we shoot them all night long. We have *mad minutes* often. I got off guard at two A.M. and we had the 'mad minute' at 2:15 A.M. I sleep good after these 'mad minutes.' If anyone was coming after us, either we killed him or put his head down.

Well, this LZ East is safe. We haven't been mortared or probed after the first time.

You should see my bunker. It is all underground. It is about the best one I have made.

I got new boots. I had holes in the sides of my old ones. Wow! They hurt, but they will wear in soon.

Hey ma! I am *not a Specialist 5*. I am a Sergeant Hard 5. I am a little higher than Spec. 5. Okay? Spec. 5 is an insult. Okay. I work hard, real hard. Men die and are wounded here. We are not Specialist, we are *Hard*. I don't mind you doing this once. Please - *Sgt. Fred L. Brown*. I am proud of it - *real proud*. Okay?

Well another day and a couple more friends *dead*. When we came to this hill "E" Company was securing it. Well, we took over so they were to CA to LZ Center. Well, they were 1000 meters away and an NVA .51 cal. enemy machine gun opened fire. The chopper burst into flames and fell 2000 meters to the ground.

A gun ship went over to help, but was hit too. He made it back to LZ Center. And then they got a LRRP team to try and go over and help. A few minutes later another chopper was hit. The engine died but the blades kept moving, even though the engine was dead. It went straight down but the men lived in this gunship.

A few hours later "B" Company 1/6 Infantry CA'd in to secure the area. So they blew the choppers and took all the ammunition and guns back. My friends were *burned alive!* Found his lighter though. Well, that is life.

The night before all this happened LZ Center killed 35 NVA in the wire, and six in the perimeter. They all had AK-47 rifles and Chicon hand grenades. I heard we had no casualties.

The NVA are real brave. They do everything in daylight. You only do this when you have men, a lot of men, and they do. They are shooting RPG rockets onto the chopper pad. The range of these rockets is three-hundred or so meters.

Well, I am leaving this mountain. Me and my platoon are going to LZ West. I don't know how bad it is there but it is closer to LZ Center than LZ East and I can see Center from here.

Ma, don't worry. Okay? One of the reasons I don't write is because I spend so much time improving my bunker and getting the little edge on things that mean life and death. I still haven't got orders for R&R. But in a few days I will check on it again.

Well, night is slowly closing in. Nights are bad now. Things are rough. Every night you wait for that *Poof!*. Then whoever heard it yells, *"Incoming!" Y*ou know mortars are coming.

I don't like writing because everything is ghastly. Nothing is fun or relaxing. I sleep with my steel pot and flak jacket on and rifle across my chest. I sleep listening to every sound. I am not losing my nerve, it is just that there are less and less relaxing times. I must relax to write. I can't anymore.

Right now I feel an urge to turn my head and look into the setting sun and the valley and ridge line. Listen for a sound or look for movement. I see vultures. Probably where yesterdays battle was. Wait! I just heard something. I don't think it was a mortar. I sit breathless for thirty seconds and I will know the truth.

If I get more sleep maybe I can relax. I got your package. I ate it already. That spaghetti was fabulous. Ain't that silly. Eating is the only relaxing time. The spaghetti was beautiful.

Well, I got some extra sleep so while on guard I am going to just write the whole guard. Okay. See ya then.

Well, here I am. I am on guard. It is 12:30 A.M. It took me a half hour to get my things ready. I have guard till two A.M.

Well, the moon is bright. I can see good. It looks like a three-quarter moon. It is getting low in the sky. There is a big shadow on this side of the mountain. It is a good night for the NVA to play with us. I don't think he cares about us though.

We have reconn by fire with M-79 grenade launchers every night. We have one tonight. I will fire it in a little while.

One of my old buddies came back today. He cut himself with a bayonet while cutting down coconuts! This was back in January. Only three men in my platoon still remember him. I handed out supplies today and happened to walk by his position. We used to smoke *grass* together. Well, he had some so we sat down and smoked. Wow! did I feel good. The first time since February. It just made me *loose*.

Ma, when I get the chance I will do something about my condition. But until then, well, destiny will be the leader.

Well, I just took the watch we use for guard and turned it up ten minutes. Ain't I tricky.

The radio sounds like number-one. I think it will be fine. Did you send me a few extra batteries, or are they flashlight batteries. It is cool at nights, especially on this mountaintop. Hot during the day but okay at night. I think I may have lucked out having to go to LZ West. We will stay here for a long time, I hope. In case you are wondering, the moon has gone under a small layer of clouds. This is why I can't see the lines anymore. Well, I think I will fire the M-79.

So bye till then

I just fired the M-79 grenade launcher. I got it fairly close to where I wanted it. So now I feel comfortable. I am trying to get a situation report, but then men are asleep or just not on the horn. In case you are wondering, I am in the bunker and am using a flash light with a red lens to write by. We are going to CA to LZ West at seven A.M. I hope I don't have to build another bunker, but I guess I probably will have to.

Well, I better call my report in to the company.

That's finished.

You know I am not the acting Platoon Sergeant any more, but I am staying with the CP group. I think the reason is because I have the will to live and I show it in my work. The men with me aren't going to get killed because I always do that little extra something. The lieutenant trusts me. He is too lazy to build the bunker himself, so I do. He trusts my judgement. This is a big reason why I will stay with the CP group for a while. I might have to go to a squad soon but that won't be for a little while. Till then, I like where I am. I have forty minutes left of guard. I should have fifty minutes, but little do they suspect.

They have a new hand grenade out. The M-33 fragmentation grenade. It is round and small like a hard baseball. It is littler and lighter then the *M-26 frag*. The M-26 is the most used one. The M-33 is more powerful and has more fragments. It is dangerous because it is so powerful. We leave them in the bunkers. We don't carry them around.

You can't see the NVA crawling up to your bunker. They are tricky. I am on the bunker line and there is a small ridge line right in front of my bunker. *Bla!* I hope we are not on line at LZ West. The CP group is usually behind or in the middle of the perimeter.

I have one of those M-33 grenades in my hand now. If I hear anything *Wham!* Then I'll blow my claymore and then start throwing more grenades.

I will mail this letter on the chopper when I CA over to LZ West. If you get this letter than I am on LZ West. Okay. I am going to start resting up as much as I can. When I start those patrols and go into the field I want to be rested.

It sounds like you are going to have a *record year* at the stores. You are over last year, so we will see what sales on Mother's Day ends up like.

You realize I have 196 days left. I have been eleven months in the Army. I am getting there slowly, but surely.

In a few minutes I am going to lob another M-79 out there. Then I will wake up the next guy on guard. I have a compass on order for myself. I need one. I guess soon I will get a map and then I will be on my way. *Wow!* I am getting tired. I only have fifteen minutes left.

Well, I better close. Bye until later.

I should be able to get this letter mailed now that I am on an LZ. So I might be able to catch up with my writing.

I will address it, or wait, I will use the one you addressed. But I will put down SGT. FRED L.BROWN, *not Sp/5.* Okay.

See you soon, Fred Leo

P.S. I am going to check on R&R. I got to get out of this country for a week or so.

—This is a pin from a hand grenade I threw last night.

Dear Ma *7 May 1968*

It is the early morning: 12:15 A.M. I am on guard till two A.M.

Wow! I got the radio! You're so beautiful (the radio!). I love it. I can pick up all the countries, except America. I don't think any soldier over here can say his parents go as far as you do to help me. Thank you so much.

I guess you know that it is too big, so when I go on R&R I will send it back home. Don't worry about another radio. I think I will just pick one up on R&R.

Well luck is with me. I should be guarding this LZ West for maybe a week, so I will use the radio for the duration of my stay there. I will get it to the First Sergeant. He will hold it for me.

Well, we were dropped off early and I worked like mad all day. Again. I put a roof on a bunker. Then wouldn't you know it, I had to change bunkers. On this one, we had to finish the roof, build a wall and fix up a berm in front of the bunker to stop rockets and recoilless rifles.

And guess what I found while digging? A cross. It's real nice and I've never seen one like it. My shovel hit it. I'm gonna put it on my helmet.

This area is real rough. I watched air strikes all day. A jet was almost knocked down. These NVA just keep their guns talking. Today "B" Company captured a 106 recoilless rifle. It is ours! They also captured an anti-aircraft .51 cal. machine gun.

LZ Center is only a few kilometers from me. I can see it good.

The moon is real bright. I can see the lines on the paper!

You know that cold I told you I had. I got rid of it in two days! I just keep going. The rougher it is the more my body builds up. It doesn't know defeat. It used to. Not anymore.

You should see what I have at my bunker. Wow! About fifty or more *frag* grenades. I am going to get a couple of LAW's (Rocket Launchers) tomorrow.

It is one A.M. I think the area might be quieting down. There are no gun ships working the area, so it is getting quiet.

Well, here is a bring down. They changed my orders. I am Not E-5. I am (back to) Spec. 4. Oh well, it was too good to be true.

I can hear the generators running on LZ Center. The night Center was hit, 119 places in Vietnam were hard hit. How can you fight people who don't care if they live or die.

I turned my watch up ten minutes. I might change it back, but I am so tired! I have about a half hour left. *Bla!* My eyes see dots, my lids are about twenty pounds. *UH!*

You know I still have a can of tomato and rice in my foot locker. I wonder if I will ever see it *again*. It has been close to four months since I seen it.

Nancy Sinatra is on the radio right now.

The guy going on guard next just rolled over. He probably knows he has guard in a few minutes.

I think LZ Center is being mortared. It sounds like mortars. I can see the explosion flashes from here.

I haven't washed for about three weeks. I only can get so dirty because I sweat so much.

Wow! My head is bobbing now. I fell asleep for only a second. I have ten minutes left. BLA! I have heard no movement so I guess it will be a quiet night.

Well, you ain't going to guess what is happening right now. a jet just got finished taking pictures with Big Flash Bulbs. They do this so they can spot every movement at night. Good idea. You can't believe how weird it looks.

By the way, I have guard two times tonight. The second time I will have guard for 45 minutes. I will not be able to write during my next guard. The moon is just about down.

Well, five minutes left.

Fly, time, fly

You know what song is on the radio. "Lemon Tree is very pretty and the lemon blossom so sweet, but the fruit of the poor lemon is impossible to eat." You know the song?

Go, Baby Go. Two minutes left.

Hurry, Hurry.

Man, that radio is beautiful. I bet everyone is jealous. Ha, ha. Too bad. See you in the morning, bye.

Today is the eighth of May.

I continue. It is another day later. I am on guard. There is a lot of fog. I guess it is from the South China Sea. I can see the Sea from here.

Tonight is quiet as was last night.

I just found out. The companies in the Valley are taking heavy casualties. The NVA are dug in on this mountain. We pound them continuously but it does no good. The *Big Flash* just made two passes taking pictures. I don't think he can see much.

Well, as I was saying, the companies in the Valley are hit hard. They were being surrounded by NVA tonight. I don't know what is happening now They are being mortared all the time in the field. There are Firefights off in the distance that flare up every so often.

So we might go down and help them. Just my platoon. It depends on how hard they are hit tonight and during the day. But no matter what, we will be down there soon, real soon. I am trying to get extra sleep. I need a lot. I will not be sleeping much in the Valley of Living Death.

For some silly or other reason I am full of confidence. I don't know why, but no matter what, I will come out of it okay. It is funny. How could a person have complete confidence in himself when he is about to go into *living hell*. I do and I feel strong. I have a sense of balance about death, war, and what must be done in certain cases.

I am going to tape two magazines together so when one goes empty I have another. That gives me a total of 36 rounds!

Fighting and dying plays tricks on a man's mind! I go through changes. At one time I don't care if I live or die. Then another time I am so afraid, I shake. But I imagine under those surface feelings, I always care.

I don't know if I told you or not, but I will send the radio home on R&R. I will probably use it during my stay on this LZ.

Your best friend is your ears. Very seldom can you see someone coming. Like just now! Someone or something is giving a yell in the valley. It echoes. It could be a call for an assault. Let them come. I have plenty of fire power and grenades. I need some easy kills.

There is a box of C-rations right behind me. I think I will grab some fruit. Wow! It was *Apricots*. I like *Peaches* the best. Hint. Hint.

You should see the water they give us. It is almost unbearable to drink. It is horrible. We put iodine purification tablets in it to make it drinkable.

Ma, could you send me another watch. Same kind. Okay? It is a good watch. It glows in the dark, that is real good. It winds itself real good. Wait. Maybe you could send me parts for it so I will not need a new watch.

Those two little pieces holding the band broke on me. So I threw away the watch band. So I need those parts. Okay? Or a new watch. Maybe with the date?

Well, another day is gone.

It is now the ninth of May. Does time pass!

Well, they didn't need us in the valley today so that is good. They are going to send our whole company down in a couple of days. By then I hope we have weakened the NVA enough so we will not lose as many men as the other companies.

Well tonight was the first night that I didn't have trouble staying awake. I have caught up on my sleep fairly well. I sleep during the day.

You know even though the rain always soaks us and makes things sort of miserable, I still like the rain. I guess I always will. One night we just finished our foxhole. Then it started raining. Everything was muddy and dirty. So we hopped under our shelter. Then the mortars came. We hopped in our muddy hole. All wet water in the bottom. We got soaked. My blanket got soaked. Then it got all muddy. For about two hours after that, they mortared and threw hand grenades at us. When everything finally calmed down I was all messed up. I wrapped up in my poncho and wet blanket and covered my head and laid in the mud against the bunker.

That night might have been bad, but I still like the rain.

Do you know I have about 190 days left in Nam. I am almost half through. Wow! You know six months is a long time when you have the idea that every day might be your last.

Ma, when I go into the valley I will not write until I am out. Okay? But I will drop a *line*. That is all it will be. It will say roughly that I am Okay and still alive. I must spend all my time and energy trying to stay alive. If you don't quite understand, I will explain it all to you later. Okay.

Well I got the radio right here with me. I am going to try and find a station with some music on it. So wait a minute and I will get some good sounds.

Well, I got good music now. I guess the longer I play the game of war, the more nervous and jumpy I am. This is one big reason that when I am in the field I can't write. I am listening to every sound, watching every movement. I can't take my mind off my movements. Because at that moment a sniper might open up or they might mortar us. You have time to get in a hole - if you listen for mortars. If you miss the sound, it might be the end.

I think they are mortaring LZ Center. So far I have heard over fifty mortar rounds.

All day and all night they are bombing, mortaring, using gun ships. This area is never quiet and peaceful.

I think I will throw a grenade down in front of my position. If no one is there it will at least put their head down and give them second thoughts.

Bye for now, Fred Leo

Dear Ma *10 May 1968*

TODAY is the

10TH of MAY

I

AM

Okay

JUST MISSED

Fred Leo

14 May 1968

"Brown, you got point," Second Squad Leader Sergeant Grauer says, the words reverberating through the air. "Okie, stay close.

"The Canine Team will be right behind you guys," Robin Hood adds.

"Alright, let's move it out," the company commander calls. Delta Company had been ready to move since first light but the Canine Team hadn't arrived until past eight A.M..

Brown takes off his helmet to touch the body of Jesus. Then he places a camouflaging leaf over the crucifix sewn onto his helmet. Pulling the charging handle, he slams a round in the breech of the M-16 and flips the selector switch to automatic. He moves briskly into the pointman position and onto the trail that leads down from LZ Center.

Using peripheral vision to register any movement, he searches the open terrain for booby traps. His rifle moves rhythmically side to side, like a wooden yoke used to find water except this rifle-yoke is searching out the enemy lying in ambush.

"Brown! Dog alert," Okie cautions. The German Shepherd sniffs the air and alerts to the left. The handler points out the suspected location.

"Rattattat!" Brown reconns the area with a burst of automatic rifle fire. Nothing. Brown picks up a brisk pace and again the dog alerts. Brown stops and reconns with fire. After two more dog alerts with Brown expending two magazines of ammunition and nothing to show for it, he signals Robin Hood.

"What's goin' on, man!" Brown says stomping over to met him near the handler their platoon sergeant. "This dog smell something or not! Shit. By now every NVA for in the valley knows we're comin'. That dog trying to get us killed!"

The CO has a short conversation with the dog handler who says the dog is having a nervous breakdown. It had seen too much action lately.

"Chicken shit," Brown glares at the handler as the dog is led back to LZ Center. "That's what I call it. Both of 'em are chicken shit."

"Alright, let's move it out."

Pointman is the lead person in a moving column of infantry. Life expectancy of a pointman at the moment of contact is 1/10th of a second. That makes point the deadliest position in the Vietnam War. If a grunt walks point in a combat zone twenty-one times he is given the distinction of being called a Gunfighter.

A Radio Telephone Operator's (RTO) life expectancy at the moment of contact is 2/10th of a second. That makes it the second deadliest position in the Vietnam War.

Brown has been the RTO through some twenty firefights and combat assaults and has taken point another fifteen times. Those two feats combined make him a Gunfighter. So it was with no surprise that on this crucial day the company commander would want someone of Brown's special ability. Ability you can't get out of a book, a classroom lecture or through intensive training. On this pivotal day they need someone with mettle who could find the trail, stay the course and would remain "cool" in a firefight. Someone like a Gunfighter who understands the dance of death.

Everything appears tranquil like a sun bathed wheat field. Brown can even detect the soft whistle of a breeze as it ruffles the knee high grasses.

Brown quickly outpaces everyone by twenty-five yards with the company spread out all the way up to the base's perimeter. Suddenly, Brown detects a hint of movement left of the trail and just inside a tree line. It might be an ambush.

The ill fated dog episode had already eaten up three precious daylight hours and Brown knows it is up to him to try and make up for lost time. That means he has to throw some caution to the wind. So to negotiate this potentially dangerous spot, he decides it best not to break stride. Pretend he'd never seen it. Then if things worked out right, he can spring the ambush just before they do.

Continuing the rhythmic walk with rifle swinging side to side, always opposite of his line of vision, he plunges fearlessly forward.

He starts to visualizes a dark room with a table in the middle draped with a black table cloth that nearly touches the floor. In the center of the table set in a cradle is a glowing crystal ball. Gathered around the table are several dark figures who stare intently into the incandescent ball. Leaning over the seated mystic, Brown realizes they are playing the odds on something. His eyes focus on the universe within the crystal ball and . . . . It's him!

He raises his eyes skyward to gaze into a black cloud that appeared to be a window.

"Hey what are you doin'? Concentrate will ya," he scolds himself. "And stop this daydreaming before you get yourself killed!" Concentrating once more, he puts an imaginary defense shield around himself like the spaceship Enterprise in the TV series *Star Trek*. "Beam me up Scotty."

If there is an ambush, he needs to appear confident. Then they might hesitate. If that happens, he'll have the advantage and might be able to blast his way thru.

Breezing past the suspected ambush site, he continues on. Something moved! Relax, he tells himself. He knows that if he looks too hard his imagination would create something. He also knows that if he listens too hard his imagination will create a sound. And he knows that if he stays on edge like this, he will not last an hour before getting careless.

Like a ship using a zig-zag pattern to throw off a torpedo submarine, Brown employs erratic behavior. Occasionally he crouches, walks from side to side on the trail. Lifts the helmet to listen better, looks and regroups his senses. Quietly breathing he continues going deeper and deeper.

Nearing another suspected ambush, he swings the rifle with sweaty finger firmly on the trigger. False alarm.

"Shake it off. It's okay. Now keep moivin'."

Coming to a wide, heavily traveled path leading from the main trail, he squats and searches in the mud for signs of recent foot traffic. Deciphering the tread marks he determines the trail has taken heavy NVA foot traffic, but none were formed in the past twelve hours.

Rising from the dink squat, his legs shake. He takes several revitalizing deep breaths and turns to see Okie is now fifty yards behind. The entire company needs to march ten miles through rolling, rugged terrain before night fall. He can't be stopping too often or be overly cautious. That just won't work. He must stay in motion, making himself a fast moving target. That's his best bet.

With a respectable gap between himself and the rest of the company Brown can listen for sounds better. No interfering noise from the other soldiers. And he can, if need be, take a little extra time to negotiate a suspicious looking spot. So his biggest challenge is to retain strength of body and mind. All the rest he puts into God's hands. If this is his day to die, he would die fighting not cowering in some corner.

"You want me?" He scans the terrain. "Come and get me. But I don't run and I don't die easy."

The sound of his heart beating and lungs taking air begin to block his hearing. He resorts to holding his breath or lifting his helmet to listen better. The heart is a different story. But he finds he can keep it paced properly if he uses a controlled gait and slow rhythmic breathing.

Hours later, he achieves the valley floor where the trail bottle necks between two towering rock outcropping. No way around and the perfect ambush. Moving to the left of the trail, he signals Okie to come forward. The remainder of the company is well behind, so they need to negotiate this potential ambush quickly if the company is to keep moving.

He signals for Okie to move past and set up just to the right of the bottle neck. Brown scans the area one last time then without hesitation plunges forward, increasing his stride until nearly trotting and with the momentum attained, plunges through the gap. His body feels like it is bathed in flames as he swings the rifle around in all directions with a scream lodged in his throat. He's ready to jump, dive, roll and give it all he's got.

Nothing.

Okay. That's good. All right now . . . let's calm down a little and keep on moving.

He forces himself to stand straighter so blood circulation moves through his neck and spine easier. "Look and act confident. Everything's gonna be just fine," he says to himself trying to retain his combat metabolism.

Looking behind, he finds no one in sight. He steps behind a tree, squats and waits. Using both ears and senses, he determines the company is probably fifty yards behind. Then he feels himself turning invisible and floats like a white ghost. Everyone will soon come around the bend and walk right through him, through the already forgotten No Name soldier. How many times will he have to die before he's really gone?

"Brownie?" Okie calls just loud enough, his voice questioning the situation. Brown signals everything is fine and to come forward.

"So far, so good, buddy," Okie says taking a position on the opposite side of the trail behind a tree.

"We're still goin'." Normally a soldier wouldn't be pointman in an area such as this for more than two hours. So in a given day there might be as many as four different pointmen. But after five hard miles in four hours with the midday temperature rising to above 100 degrees, Brown is still pointman.

Passing thru a stream, he scoops water into his helmet and splashes it over his head. On the other side, he stops in a secure position and fills his four empty canteens with cool mountain spring water. Then he drinks his fill.

Deciding the company will probably take time to cool off in the stream, Brown moves up the hill and at the first bend in the trail, takes up a defensive position. And of course he is right. That's why he would end up pointman so often. He could understand other peoples needs, often times even before they did.

While the soldiers took turns refreshing themselves, the lieutenant and Doc came up the trail to sit alongside Brown.

"Doc! Doc!" They turn to see a lifeless soldier being dragged into the stream.

15 May 1968

Black ghostly clouds claw their way across the sky, obstructing the full moon, leaving a tenuously lit landscape. The winding mountain trail has become treacherous from the whipping rain. Still pointman, Brown trudges up the incline with a sheer drop-off only inches away. Rounding a corner, his pack catches on a dead tree limb that drags him to an abrupt halt. The eerie sound of rocks tumbling from the trail into the valley below sends jitters through his body.

Backing up slowly, he shakes the rucksack trying to break it free. When it gives, the force sends him stumbling, his foot slipping ever so close to the edge. "Man," he sighs. Then the ledge gives way under foot. He rolls back against the sheer wall as rocks and dirt spew into the dark abyss.

Plodding up to a turn, he glances back to see stooped soldiers silhouetted in the rain squall. Rounding the corner with the grade steadily increasing, he slips with the heavy rucksack throwing him forward into the mud. Standing back up, an excruciating pain runs through his wrenched leg. Finding it too slippery to walk upright, he resorts to crawling the last twenty-five yards to the top of the trail.

Making the crest, he gets bull whipped by a blast of hot air. With eyes clearing he realizes the sky is suddenly clear with a strong moon beam lighting up the valley floor.

In the ethereal light, he sees a lush agricultural river valley filled with four distinctive rice fields.

The first of the four fields is a rice paddy being flooded by two women pedaling water over a protective dike from the adjacent river. Working the paddy are shirtless male peasants in black silk pants balancing atop a wooden plows drawn by water buffalo. Nearby, a child relaxes on the back of another water buffalo.

The second field is covered with delicate rice sprouts tended by Vietnamese women dressed in all black with conical straw hats.

The third field is full of green stalks that ripple like waves in a sea of green.

The fourth and final field is full of lush full grown rice that is being harvested.

Here in this lush blue river valley is the entire rice growing cycle taking place simultaneously.

Around the perimeter Vietnamese pedal rusty contraptions to

separate the rice from the stalks and chaff. Other workers busy themselves with flaying the dried rice sprouts against woven bamboo walls, dislodging the kernels that fall into wicker containers. Other Orientals toss the grain into the air from a wide winnow wicker tray to let the lighter husks blow away. Still others load the rice onto two wheeled animal drawn carts and pole baskets called *don ganhs* for the women to carry to market.

The overseer wears a long black coat, a red scarf around his neck, and a black beret. He has been contemplatively moving about the fields making occasional signals with the his walking staff.

Then transcendentally everything stops. The animals. The people. The breeze. The blue river. The sea of green. It all comes to a dead stop. All except the overseer who pivots to face Brown.

The moon now changes into a pulsating raging ball of fire. The ground beneath the people and animals begin turning crimson as their bodies bleed out and soon join the river of blood.

The overseer pulls back his hood to reveal the face of Brown's father. The blue eyes of his father bulge as he begins laughing harder and harder. Then the flesh rots away leaving a bleached skull, the staff becoming a wriggling viper. The overseer turns into a glowing red tailed walking skeleton.

The crimson red valley bursts into flames that mercilessly swallow animals and the pleading Vietnamese. The horrible dead smell of sulfur pours from the valley to wash over Brown.

The skeleton laughs a diabolical laugh as it gazes upon an American flag draped coffin. He jabs the red hot pitch fork into the coffin with the flag bursting into flames. The casket begins to open . . . .

"U-u-u-u-uh."

"Brown, wake up." Jelly Belly says leaning over. "Your guard. Wake everyone in a half hour. We gotta move out by five A.M." He lays back and is immediately asleep.

The eighteen hour forced march had lasted until two A.M. bringing them to the base of their objective, Hill 350. They had finally night logared in a napalm burnt field with only a few foam covered scraggly shrubs to serve as concealment. Booby trap hand grenades and claymore mines serve as their only true protection. Now it occurs to Brown that the trip grenade is so close that if detonated the shrapnel would probably hit them too.

Contemplating as he looks over the field of fire, Brown realizes the narrow winding mountain trail they traveled upon last night must have spawned the nightmare. It is so strange, now that he thinks about it, that whether asleep or awake he is submersed in this war. No escape. And as time goes by, it is becoming harder and harder to differentiate the line between the two.

They move out by 5:30 A.M., the company splitting into three platoons as they move against Hill 350.

"Brown, you got point," Jelly Belly calls.

"Why not," Brown says tiredly under his breath. By midmorning they are pushing through thick elephant grass that towers ten feet. For the first two hours, Brown had pushed it aside with the machete in fear of making too much noise. After the third hour, he finds himself hacking away with abandonment, the dull knife blade working no better than a stick.

"*Ahhh!*" The razor edged elephant grass finds its mark. Another open cut to sting from salty sweat. His clothes are dark from sweat that dribbles from his shirt tail. Caught within a suffocating wind screen of elephant grass, he swelters in the midday heat.

Without a word, he raises his hand to 'halt' the column. Peering through a tunnel of grass, he sees an open space. With rifle poking, he moves cautiously to the edge of a fifty foot clearing that has been created by a bomb. Moving noiselessly around the edge of the crater, he arrives back in the tall grass. A few steps later he comes upon another crater, then another, and another until they nearly overlap.

"Looks like a lunar landscape," Jelly Belly says coming up from behind.

"Rolling thunder?"

"No," Jelly Belly says. "They say they can't get clearance to bring 'em in."

Ever since their arrival on the rim of The Valley of Living Death there has been the constant rumble of shelling by artillery, bombing by airplanes or jets, and strafing by gunships. Now, for the first time there is an eerie calm.

"The Air Force claims we've used our quota of bombs for the month. They wanna cut back."

"Cut back. Oh great," Brown groans.

Pushing aside the last bit of elephant grass reveals devastation as far as the eye can see. The only thing left standing in the mulch is a fractured tree trunk. A ghastly mist oozes out of the rotting, grotesque hollow craters. Could this be the hanging tree, that Brown had heard about? The one where the NVA hung a soldier after beating and skinning him alive?

They come upon thirty foot craters, formed by 500 pound bombs, that appear like open lips through which one can see the quaking heart of mother earth. It will take a long, long time for the ground to drink in what has happened here.

A pungent smell of burnt flesh fills the air as Brown comes upon the remains of an NVA, charred by white phosphorous. The hideous corpse's face stares with sucked-in eyes, skin pulled taut over protruding bones. The ribs are covered with a thin layer of melted flesh.

"Crispy critter," Jelly Belly comments. Napalm that had once been blazing fountains of death now cover the area with its dried black ash/foam. "If you stand at the base of a napalm column it would suck the air right outta your lungs."

Another dead NVA, partially covered by crater dirt, lay on his side bloated and burned.

As a child Brown would spend hours analyzing Matthew Brady's Civil War photographs. The picture that caught his imagination was one of a confederate soldier killed in 1863 at the battle of Gettysburg. His lifeless body lay with head back, rifle within reach among a rock configuration called Devil's Den. Standing over these ghastly remains, Brown realizes death is no intruder here. This is home to the Grim Reaper where glamour is empty and lunatic. Where a soldier can plod to his destiny.

The crest of the hill comes into view with a gunship zooming over the crest, having made its last pass.

"Looks hairy."

"Drop your pack. Come on, men. Let's go. Assault!"

Dear Ma and Dad *15 May 1968*

Here I am in the *Boonies*. We are doing good. We haven't lost too many men so far. We have taken two hills. We got light resistance. Soon we will try for the third hill which was an old 101st Airborne Fire Base.

I have received Dad's letter and all of yours. *Wow!* "Ha, Brown, can I read some of your letters. I didn't get none!"

That sesame seed bar sure is appreciated. Wow! It tasted good. Ma, I hate to say this but that lemon flavored Kool-Aid *needs sugar*. Read closer. Okay. I had to throw it all away. I don't have hardly any Kool-Aid. Okay. I sure wish it was good because lemon is a good flavor. Oh Well.

Ever since I have been in the field it has been *hump, hump. hump!* When we assaulted one hill I could hardly walk up it, let alone run after NVA. But I have stopped and slept every chance I got. I feel okay now.

Me and the lieutenant are up tight. I guess because I led our platoon up the hill. We were the second platoon up so I only got a few rounds over my head.

When we stopped on the hill the NVA started mortaring and rocketing us. *Bla!* I will not tell you how close the rocket was to me.

It was a bring down. We moved into our night loger and they mortared us the whole time. One Medevac after another. You should have seen me work out on my hole.

Scoop! Scoop! Scoop!

Soon we are going to have four or five companies, including ours take the next hill. We are going to take it Second World War style. We have to go through three barbed wire obstacles and knock out bunkers. The hill is bare! Not too much cover from mortar, rockets and small arms. We knocked out one NVA .51 cal. anti-aircraft machine gun today. The jets just blew it away. There is still another one over there on this tower of rock. I hope he doesn't let us have it.

Everything is rough and rugged. These last three days we have been mortared three times. We are mortared almost constantly.

We are low on *food, water, and sleep*. I went almost one day without eating. We have no food now. I don't know when we will get some.

Everyone realizes the dangers coming. We all are excited. We took two hills, soon the third and last. We have been running them out. We will run all the way up there if need be. We got the smell of *victory*. We will show them what we have. I don't know who is going to be lead company. But if it is ours you know what the chances are. The other company led out today.

I am pushing for R&R. Hurry Hurry. I hope I don't get wounded before R&R. I got $100 cash and $400 in money orders. $500 in all. Good Hu? *Wow!* Clean sheets and a bed under a roof, air conditioning. T.V. Room Service. Wow! I just don't know what to think. But after R&R I don't think I will come back to the field. I will have them break my arm on R&R so I will not have to come back. After this mission, I will have done my share. I want a fair shake. If they will not give it to me, no sweat, I will give it to myself.

Those pictures of you and Dad are nice. I will keep them as long as I have room. Okay. You look thinner than when I was home. Are you?

It is 11:30 P.M. now. I have guard until 12:30 A.M. In the books they say you should not be on guard over 1-1/2 hours, but they didn't take into consideration that I am writing my parents.

Did I tell you I found a cross? I was shoveling inside this old bunker at LZ West and there it was. I sewed it on my helmet. It feels good. It is a real nice cross. Oh, well.

I am working with three new guys. I got them thinking for themselves. They are learning what to do and what not to do. They have turned out good.

Every once in a while you write, brush your teeth and wash. Wow! It has been well over a month since I washed and the same way with my teeth. But I sweat so much all the dirt just runs off. My teeth. *Bla!* I will not mention them.

That was alright for Roxanna to come home wasn't it? I forgot to say happy birthday to her before. Could you tell her okay? I will send her a present from R&R. Good idea, hu? I will send everyone something. Okay.

You should see those gun ships, Jets, and Sky Raiders work out. They are something else. The jets open up with a burst of .30 cal. And you hear it! Then a *wheeee-aaa*. Then the blast of the jet engine. *Sheeee!* Wow! There are bomb strikes over the whole area.

A couple of days ago the NVA were setting-up to mortar one of our companies. I spotted them. We called in the Sky Raiders and they blow them away. They mortared us, but *BLAM!* no more mortars.

Wow! Forty-five minutes left. Hurry time. Hurry, I am tired. They are firing all night on the hill we are going to take.

I feel so good. We are finally doing away with some NVA. They are a hard shell to crack. They will not run but stay there till they get you or you get them.

I realize more and more that this war will not be won by man power. Life is nothing to them. North Vietnam has unlimited man power and China and Russia have unlimited supplies. We only have so many men. Out of these men only one out of five actually fights. The rest stay in the rear with the gear at *Base Camp* under roofs.

Wow! I am getting tired. Bla! Half hour left.

Well, I better close. Thanks for the candy and Kool-Aid and all. Honestly, I don't know what I would do without it.

Bye until later. Don't worry about me getting hit. Bullets hurt. Okay.

I will write soon, Fred Leo

16 May 1968

"Bzzzz!" The sound of a bee buzzes his ear as fragments splinter off a rocks. Then from the valley comes the sound of a rifle's discharge. Slinking lower, Brown knows the sniper has barely missed the intended target—him. He'd been trying to chop out a hole in the rocky terrain, without much luck. With no appreciative amount of soil, the sandbags prove only useful for sitting.

"I know why they say, 'you never hear the bullet that kills ya'," Brown says to the returning Jelly Belly.

"What?"

"The sniper again. You better stay low."

"No one would give up their pickaxe," he says dropping low.

"Well, this entrenching tool ain't cutin' it. We'll just have to wait."

In the distance they heard the sound of yet another enemy mortar volley.

"*Incoming!*" they holler in unison, the word echoing throughout the perimeter.

The NVA have been walking mortars around their perimeter on

Hill 352 since their arrival yesterday. In the last hour the mortars have been targeting Brown's side of the perimeter. Melding around the rocks, they crouch even lower under their steel pots on hearing the sizzle of the rounds dropping-in. Four mortars impact frighteningly close with shrapnel ricocheting off the rocks.

"Medic!" comes a shriek. "He's hit. Medic!"

A second volley comes rushing in right behind the first with everyone holds tight. Testing the air after a third crashing volley, Brown deems it safe—at least for the moment. Rising ever so slowly, he peers over at the CP where the panicky calls are coming. Doc is nowhere in sight and the NFG RTO is frantic.

Brown bounds across the rocky terrain to the CP. Inside the foxhole lays Lieutenant Wade's motionless body.

"Alright, let's slow down. Take it easy," Brown tells the NFG. "Now give me a hand." They hoist the lieutenant's limp body from the foxhole. Getting him laid out, Brown sees blood trickling from the officer's left ear.

"He was on the radio," the NFG explains pointing to the twisted piece of metal ten feet away that had once been a field radio, then to the impact sight and finally the handset which lay in the foxhole. "That's when it took a direct hit."

"Was he wearing a helmet?"

"Yeah."

"Waa*aaaa,"* Lieutenant Wade slurs as he awakens and tries to sit. The prognosis seems good, apparently he has a slight concussion which would explains the languor. They hoist the lieutenant to his feet, his brown eyes watery and expressionless.

"Put a helmet on his head." The NFG takes off his and places on lieutenant Wade's head. "Now listen close. I gotta get him on a medevac. Alright?" Brown talks slow so as to calm the NFG. "Go find Robin Hood and tell him what happened. Okay?" The NFG nods. "And find yourself another helmet."

"Incoming!" echoes through the perimeter.

"Go! Get outta here. This hole is zeroed in."

A rocket whizzes overhead, missing the perimeter as it flies down into the valley before exploding. Then mortars start exploding. Regardless, Brown continues his mission as he drags the officer toward the interior of the perimeter. There is no way of knowing when a chopper might make it in for an evacuation, so Brown needed to be within sight of the PZ—wherever that is.

"Where are we going?" Wade asks lethargically. "Is it time to go home?" Although the voice is pretty much normal, the inflections of the words are spoken by an innocent, trusting young boy. "I don't think my mommie knows."

Though it's a strange thing to be saying, Brown isn't really paying attention. "Don't worry everything's gonna be just fine." At the moment he's trying to determine where the mortars are concentrated. His ears and senses have become so attuned to incoming mortars that he can actually dodge them. And that's exactly what he is doing. This is something only a soldier of Brown's long combat experience could accomplish.

With Wade securely in his grasp, they would drop to the ground just before a mortar would hit. Screams of, "Medic!" and, "I'm hit," would then fill the air. But Brown would be up and dragging his charge to the next depression away from the last explosion.

Through the gunpowder haze, he spots a bald spot on the hill. He can see several KIAs laid where they had been deposited. One he knows had been decapitated by shrapnel earlier. Close by are the exhausted, bandaged and bleeding WIA painted in the same grey pallor of death as the dead. The only true way of telling who is alive or not is to see who flinches when the enemy mortars start landing. And as the mortars rain, the attendants run shamelessly for cover leaving the wounded squirming and huddling around bushes or in any depression no matter how slight. Only the dead didn't flinch when the mortars came calling.

Because of the intensive incoming, the Hueys were unwilling or unable to get in for a landing. So if by some miracle one did arrive, it would be without fanfare and would stay for only a matter of seconds. So the only ones who would get onboard would have to be close. Real, real close. And that's why Brown as well as the others needed to stay nearby.

Another consideration—the NVA once owned this piece of real-estate so had the coordinates of the PZ. Anytime they wanted, they could drop a mortar right on target. Fact is two helicopters had been hit already trying to get in.

The main NVA tactic is to send three consecutive mortar volleys, four mortars to each volley or a total of twelve mortars at a time. Then they pack up and hurry to another location and repeat. The only way to stop them was for someone to see the muzzle flashes. A fire mission from LZ Center would be called in and if done fast enough the mortar team could be killed. But most of the mortar fire came from the lea side of the hill so the artillery from LZ Center would simply sail over the top and do no harm. That's why the F-4 Phantoms or Gunships were used to knock out most of the mortars. And so it had gone for the past two days and still counting.

Dragging the rubbery legged Wade, Brown finds a trench inside some chest high grass.

"Uuh!" Wade trips catapulting headfirst into the depression. The helmet saves his head from getting split open on a rock, but his open mouth ends up scooping dirt. Reaching over, Brown grabs the shirt and props him up in a sitting position. He spits out the dirt, or rather throws-up the dirt. Taking the towel from around his neck, Brown wets it slightly and begins to clean Wade's mouth, neck, bloody ear and face.

Brown hears the puff of another mortar volley sailing into the air. His ears track them as they near the chopper pad.

"Ca-bloom! Ca-bloom!"

By the chopper pad, pathetic screams can be heard from the already wounded. The commotion startles Wade who begins to paw the ground like a dog trying to bury a bone.

"Hey buddy." Brown pats Wade on the shoulder. "You okay?" The lieutenant looks at Brown with puppy brown eyes, then returns to his scratching.

Becoming more jittery following the next explosions, he looks questioningly at Brown.

"That's thunder. I think it's gonna rain," Brown says playing on Wade's loss of memory.

Wade tries to stand.

"Relax, buddy." Brown grabs Wade's arm. "So do you like the rain?" He pats him on the shoulder as he fishes for some way to keep him calm.

"I'm scared!" he says, pouting.

"There's nothing to be scared of. A little water never hurt anyone."

"Can we go now? Please," Wade asks his eyes imploring. "I don't like it here, anymore." Tears roll down his dirty cheeks. He laces his arms around his knees and lowers his head.

"We'll go as soon as it stops thundering."

"I nee-ed you," Wade says muffled.

Brown takes off Wade's helmet carefully and starts running his fingers through Wade's brown matted hair. This isn't something he would normally do, but then again, this isn't a normal situation.

"I ain't got no one," he sulks childishly. "And, and . . . ." He begins crying softly so Brown places a comforting arm around him. The crying turns to unabashed sobbing with his whole body rolling with emotion. Holding tightly, Brown begins to rock Wade as he hums a soft childhood melody.

"Heah, don't be so sad. You're goin' home." Then under his breath Brown says, "And I won't."

"No one cares about me," Wade pouts.

"I care," Brown says sincerely. Unexpectedly, Wade swings around and with trembling hands pulls Brown in for a hug. Continuing to crying, he buries his face in Brown's shoulder.

Rustling comes from the nearby bushes. It might be NVA sneaking into the perimeter. "Shooo," he whispers softly into Wade's ear. "Calm down. Everything will be fine." Not wanting to startle Wade, he slowly pushes him back and pulls the rifle into firing position. More rustling of bushes. Then nothing. Whatever it was has moved on.

"Is something bad gonna happen," Wade whispers.

"Nothing's gonna happen as long as I'm here."

Squeezing him reassuringly, Wade rolls over onto Brown's lap and closes his eyes. Again Brown finds himself stroking Wade's hair while humming softly.

"Could you wake me when mommie gets here?"

"She's be here any minute now. Probably just finishing her errands." A tear forms in the corners of Brown's eye when he thinks of his mother and a story she once told him. As a ten-year-old child she had fallen asleep on the street car—purposely just so her father would have to carry her home. "I loved when he held me," she'd said adoringly. His mother loved the way her father's strong arms could push away the world. How he'd take the time to listen. Take time to say a caring word. Brown feels that same way about his mother.

"I'm real thirsty," Wade says rising and looking over with Bambi eyes.

Unselfishly, Brown hands him a drink from his last full canteen. With no re-supplies getting in, everyone is worried about running out of water. And for good reason.

As Wade drinks, Brown wants to say something like, "Now you scoot right to bed." And, "Sleep tight and don't let the bedbugs bite.

Night night."

Handing back the canteen, Wade wipes his face with a dirty hand. "Brown, you gotta stay with me," he beseeches his memory still fragmented.

"Don't worry, I'll take care of you," Brown croons with confidence. The experience is so moving that Brown realizes that at this moment he really would give his life to save this man.

God, what day is it anyway? Tuesday? Sunday? No Thursday? And what time is it? Is it five o'clock yet—quitting time? Since arriving in Vietnam he has been on constant duty seven days a week twenty-four hours a day. The only way to keep track of time is by counting the days to Deros. Counting the days until he'd fly back to the World.

"Is that for us?" Wade stands when he hears an approaching Huey. Yes, by the sounds of it, a chopper is definitely trying to get in. But then Brown's trained ear detects the faint sounds of an enemy mortar being fired.

"I think it's gonna thunder. So hold tight for a little longer," Brown says calmly, not willing to take the risk. "They'll be another along soon enough."

Seconds later NVA incoming mortars hiss through the air and explode around the PZ. Bandaged soldiers have bunched together and plead for the chopper to land. The Huey gets jolted by shrapnel and the door-gunner collapses over his M-60 machine gun. The chopper limps away descending into the valley leaving a black trail of smoke behind.

"Think they'll be mad?" Wade asks sitting up straight with his helmet back on.

"Mad?"

"I never told 'em what I was doing," Wade's voice has now become almost normal.

Confused at first, Brown realizes the reference. A lot of soldiers would send phony letters home, like it was their sworn duty to lie. It is commonly called the Code of Silence. Brown laughs to himself because he breaks the Code of Silence with every letter he writes. If anyone knew what he wrote, he'd take a lot of ridicule.

"I'm gonna die?" Wade whimpers gazing innocently at the blood on his hands after wiping his face. "I'll never make it home." He squeezes tears from his burning eyes.

"Don't say that."

Suddenly he cocks his head and stares directly at Brown. "I know. You can come with me." Wade beams with excitement. "They won't mind and we could ride our bikes," he blubbers. "Go swimmin' or," he leans close and whispers, "I know this great fishing hole. Never told anyone about it." He leans back with a big grin on his face. "So, how about it buddy?"

"Yeah, why not." Brown gives him a return smile and a pat on the shoulder.

The battalion commander's chopper has been circling at an extremely high elevation, where he's been adjusting artillery and calling in air strikes. Then just as the howitzers begin pounding the enemy's mortar positions his chopper swoops down like an eagle. The M-60 machine guns blazes as they make a strafing run low over the valley. Then swings over and comes in for a hard landing.

"Let's go."

18 May 1968

The three day long mortar barrage finally lifted letting a few choppers land. They brought in much needed supplies along with a squad of mortarmen. After helping distribute supplies, Brown sits to wolf-down two complete C-ration meals, his first "real" meal in days.

Smoking, he pulls back to gaze over Que Son Valley. From their escarpment his eyes drink in the intoxicating view. The mist below sparkles as the morning sun's hot blaze nibbles at its edges. White clouds interplaying with sunlight to send shadows fluttering across the valley floor and walls. It has been a long time since he'd taken time to enjoy the beauty of such an imposing sunrise. The shackles of war begin falling from his soul as he jumps to his feet. "How about a little walk."

During AIT at Fort Gordon, Georgia, Brown had qualified as an expert mortar gunner, so decides to check out the mortar squad as they set-up. Walking over, he find them rather jittery as they clumsily set their 81mm mortar tubes and uncrate the ammo. Their clean cut platoon leader, complete with sewn on insignias, stands with arms crossed watching critically. Combat-wise Brown knows these soldiers should first be digging their foxholes. Scoffing, Brown decides the lieutenant is new to the field.

The lieutenant is instructing his men to turn the mortars tubes toward Hill 354. First platoon had taken the third hill objective early that morning and Brown could actually see them working on their minefield and fortifications. So why set up tubes aimed at your own men?

Taking a mortar round, they attach a charge-three to the fin. Brown knows this charge would not propel the round clear of the Hill 354. So what are they thinking?

Embolden, he goes over and squats behind the tube to verify his suspicions about the direction and trajectory. His worst fears are verified.

"Soldier, are you attached?" The mortar lieutenant startles him.

"Ohh." Brown stands. "Just looking. Qualified as expert gunner back in the states, sir."

The officer makes no reply but his stare makes Brown feel like he's done something wrong. What's his problem? Brown think angrily. Is he waiting for me to salute him or something?

"I just can't help but notice that . . . ."

"Standby," the gunner calls.

"Fire," the officer shouts.

A mortar round is easy to follow when you stand directly behind the tube. So Brown watches as the round arches high in the sky then starts to plunge.

Continuing to follow the trajectory, he holds his breath hoping he is wrong. Dead wrong. Then he's startled to see the gunners fire two more rounds in quick succession. The lieutenant obviously confident with his calculations.

Still following the first rounds, his eyes fall upon a friend, Russell and his buddy who are setting up booby trap grenades outside the perimeter. Both soldiers begin running for cover and then . . . .

The two other round hit right behind and when the smoke clears both men lay moaning and critically wounded on the ground.

"Right thirty degrees!" the lieutenant barks. The unsuspecting mortarmen follow orders. He turns quickly to see if anyone had detected his friendly fire error. His eyes land on Brown.

"Sir," Brown spits, "the next time we get into a firefight the first round from my rifle will be into your head."

19 May 1968

The chopper swoops through a haze of gun smoke to land on a precarious hillside ledge. Brown and three others, the last from second platoon, scramble aboard after loading the KIA. The chopper lifts as the gunners, along with Brown's men blast away at the fast approaching NVA.

As the Huey gains velocity, AK-47 rounds start splintering the windshield penetrating the instrument panel. Momentarily, the ship rolls out of control. The door-gunner reaches over and quickly kicks the two KIAs from the platform in hopes of lightening the load. The Huey shuddered, then races down the incline like an avalanche, the pilots fighting for control. Faster, faster, faster they storm unable to maneuver as they head for a hillside outcrop. The left skids catch a rock and the chopper careens to one side, now skimming the tree tops.

Losing his grasp, Brown slides to the edge of the platform. He frantically rolls around and grabs a seat support. The Huey slaps into a tree lashing his leg as he pulls himself back on board.

"Thud! Thud! Thud!"

The Huey rocks like a boat in the North Atlantic as an NVA anti-aircraft gun opens fire. The chopper gunners return fire, their hot expended cartridges swarming into the air.

The Huey swing abruptly to the right and drops altitude to get under the NVA machine guns. The engine coughs, the cabin begins to fill with smoke. Just clearing the tree tops at full throttle, they swing around in the direction of Hill 354. Their last and only chance. With momentum, they sweep up the mountain side, the bald crown coming into view.

Haphazardly they fly for the perimeter. Brown slides off the platform to balance on a skid preparing to jump. At twenty-feet, the Huey unexpectedly jerks sending him catapulting through the air. Smashing into the ground, he rolls and bumps into a mount of dirt.

"Cabloom!" The chopper explodes sending a heat blast rushing across his body.

"Pop-pop-pop!" The sound of an AK-47 startles him. Flinging off his pack, Brown grabs his rifle and makes a mad dash across the two hundred yard clearing toward the safety of the American perimeter. The last thirty men from his Delta Company fire cover. A bullet buzzes past Brown's head and he tumbles to the ground playing dead.

"Phoof! Phoof!" Enemy mortar fire.

Counting the seconds to impact, he prepares for the next move. Simultaneously with the first mortar explosion, he jumps. A burning sensation begins to goes through his body and he collapses. Feeling around he finds warm blood. Then he rolls over, hears and sees a mortar dropping directly . . . .

"Ahh*hhh* . . . !

"Brown! Wake up! It's one A.M. your guard."

Dropping his hands from his face, he looks over. "Okie?"

"Another nightmare?"

"Yeah, I dreamt I was depending on you to save my life."

"Scary." They allow themselves a chuckle and Brown checks his chest for a bloody wound just in case.

"I don't think thirty guys can hold this hill." Okie's voice trembles as he overlooks their field of fire on Hill 354. Their fortification is a circle trench some twenty-five yards in diameter, dug courtesy of the NVA.

"Hell, we do or die." Brown takes out a canteen and pours a little water over his head and unshaven face. Then he knuckles his matted hair.

. . . As a ten year old, Brown's father would clamp a hand over his head to viciously capture him. Then would move the hand down to Brown's neck and place a thumb under the ear so to direct the line of vision. "Over there!" he'd yell twisting Brown's head while squeezing so hard Brown's eyes would pop with water. "There," he'd point an accusing finger at some obscure object. Brown had already spent the better part of the morning picking up cigarette butts and cleaning papers off the restaurant parking lot. "Get our there and pick it up!"

Black buzzards were still plentiful but pretty birds had long since abandoned Que Son, the Valley of Living Death and with them the song of life. Brown has learned to replace their songs of hope with his imagination. But whenever he'd get pulled back to *this* stark reality, he finds himself an angry young man. A hateful young man. A spiteful young man. But he doesn't fight it because it gives him strength.

With the unique opportunity to watch life run at fast-forward, Brown can watch a person with certain traits live out their short life. For instance, if someone is a procrastinator, lazy or doesn't pay attention to detail, they will end up dead in a week. There are all kinds of judgements to make and then he'd have the opportunity to watch them play out to the bloody end.

All of this fast-forward life cycle adds to Brown's ever increasing brain bank of wisdom. In the game of war, a phony of any type is very easy to spot. Very, very easy. No contest.

And now, he knows for a fact that his father is a full blown phony. A phony of the worst kind. Based on his newly acquired wisdom, he knows his father should have let the sperm run down his leg when he had the chance. That his old man never wanted him born.

So he finds the focus of his anger is usually directed at an authority figure or better yet his father. Yes, hatred directed toward his *bastard!* father gave him the best adrenaline rush. All he had to do is visualize himself bludgeoning his old man with a bayonet. He would grin at the sight of blood running over his old man's chest. His battle cry is, "I'm gonna make it home so I can strangle that bastard with my bare hands."

"Bastard," Brown swears thankful that at least his father is good for something. Replacing the steel pot, he slides off the bunker with the bayonet fixed on his rifle.

"Well we've made it this far, Brownie. We can make it the rest," Okie says faintly optimistic. "Don't let this place mess you up. Keep your cool, man." Okie's eyes close as he drops off to sleep in the NVA trench.

His stomach aches and Brown feels nauseous. Leaning over, he throws-up on a dirt ledge. Finished with upchucking his last meal, he takes a canteen and washes out his mouth and wipes his lips. With his entrenching tool he scoops dirt over the vomit.

"Well, I ain't dead yet." He checks to make sure the rifle's selector switch is on automatic.

Monomania prowls through his mind as he scans the field of fire across the two hundred yards of mud to the jungle. All appears quiet as a tomb. Focusing on a shrapnel shattered tree—it begins to breath. His vision quickly blurs when he focuses on any one object. So using peripheral vision, he finishes scanning the area.

Through experience, he's learned that peripheral vision can detect movement and shapes much better than staring head-on. With scant barbed wire and only a few booby trap grenades and claymore mines, Brown knows that it is crucial that he detect the initial attack.

Seconds would literally mean the difference between life and death.

To the left and at the edge of the tree line is a rock tower some thirty feet tall. The tower had been the perch of an NVA anti-aircraft emplacement that had withstood days of pounding. Brown stares directly at the tower and begins to envision voracious ghosts encircling around it. A supernatural glow starts coming from the top and a foamy goo starts oozing over the edges. Steam and sulfur clouds begin to swirl around the base. The Devil's Den overflows with good fortune.

Scenario after scenario gets reworked and replayed in his mind over and over again. Each time it takes another big chunk out of his soul. In so many ways, as he waits time wastes him.

Raising the rifle, he dry fires at the breathing tree. "I'm walkin' outta here. Ain't nothin' gonna stop me. Nothin'."

DEAL WITH IT

It's having
nothing to
hold, that
hollowness
in his chest, and
he can't tell what's
going down. But he deals
with it. He searches through
unraveling sanity, stuffs down
fat-caked C-rations unfit for a dog,
and does his best to ignore leeches and
mosquitoes that feast on his blood, leaving
welted flesh behind. That's what he's trying
to deal with. Spilling blood, sacrificing
blood, a loss of a limb, an organ, or buddy.
Now that's just asking too damn much. It's
gotten outta control, outta hand! It's all
gone to shit. He can't deal with it no
fuckin' more! Didn't figure it a skate,
didn't figure on getting creamed
either. But he's still a
believer and believes the
Man up above is still
saving a place,
just for him.

Dear Sister Roxanna *20 May 1968*

Well, I have been receiving all your letters. Wow! It is so good to hear from you. I wish I could write you more often, but I have been hanging onto my life with just skinny strings.

Our mission was to take three hills. The first day out we had so many heat casualties we had to delay the mission one day. On our way to a *night loger* we came across a mortar, NVA squad. They were setting up to mortar a company to our front. The Dog we had as point *alerted* and we opened up. We got a few mortar rounds, but managed to knock the mortar out before we got hurt. We then called in the *Sky Raiders*. Wow! They bombed the whole area. The bombs were Napalm and fragmentation. The earth jolted every time a bomb blew up.

Well, the next day came and we started up the first hill. I think we snuck up on them. Well, anyway we dropped our heavy gear and ran up the hill. We threw grenades in front of us when we ran. We killed about twenty NVA. But we had two or three men dead and a few casualties. See, there was three other companies helping us, but we were in the lead. After it was secured the NVA started playing. They mortared us and rocketed us. We had a couple wounded and killed. We put artillery on the mortars so we stopped them.

We found machine guns, AK-47's, M-16's (ours from the men that were killed before we took the hill), a 61 mm mortar tube and ammunition. We found a rocket launcher too. The night went easy. No problems.

The next day we got up at five A.M. and moved out, leaving an element on the first hill. We moved out for the second hill with another company in the lead. They walked right up the hill with no problem. Then - *Blam, Blam, Blam,, Blam*, they mortared the company bad. We lost in our company only a few men. Thirty men wounded or killed in all.

The next day. *The worst day I have ever had in Viet Nam*. We were mortared all day long and into the early night. We lost almost a whole platoon. Our company lost over half of its men.

Well, this day we were being mortared. Our mission was to capture the third and last hill. Our men moved out. But my platoon alone stayed behind. The reason, our lieutenant was shell shocked by a mortar. This is when we, Delta Company, lost all its men. Half way to the hill they got mortared.

One company alone still pushed on. They received moderate casualties. They stopped at the base of the hill at three A.M. Then they got mortared all day. We had a platoon go with this other company to secure the hill. They lost five men.

The next day my second platoon and what was left of the third platoon moved out for the hill. We were to take the 'scenic' route. *Bla!* I took point for my squad and the other squads had their point. The terrain got real rough so I said to myself, Hell with it all, and moved behind the other squad. A few minutes later *BLAM!* Then a scream of realization came from one of the five wounded men.

"I'm hit! Help me, Help me. Oh God I'm hit!!"

We ran up and found two of the five men laying in a pool of blood. One man had a leg blown almost completely off. We hurried and brought in a *'dust off.'* Three men went into *shock*. It was just too, too, much.

Well after this savage scene had passed on we got choppered to the other hill.

Last night, believe it or not, we found an NVA soldier with an AK-47 in a hole. He had been there for four or five days. He was alive, but weak. He was about twenty-feet from my bunker. We grenaded him so another man is dead, even if he was an NVA.

Yesterday we had a patrol go out to find two American bodies. They didn't find them but they found a leg of an NVA. Or was it? Yesterday my platoon and me went and picked up dead men's equipment. Ours, U.S.A. We found all kinds of equipment. It really, really plays with your mind. I put on one of the packs, thinking the last man who carried it was dead! Oh, *man!* What a *place!*

Roxanna, there is only one man in my platoon that has been here longer than me. *One Man*. You see, God must be with me. I am one of the few men in my platoon that has a cool head when something happens. I hope it keeps me alive. I will look forward to the day when I can *look to tomorrow*.

I am getting rough. I am mean and mad at times. If a man steps in my way, I don't think I would shed a tear if I killed him. I don't think I am the same person that I was when I left. But basically there ain't no way this War can change me too much. Okay?

Roxanna, you know I just about died laughing when you said you would come over and break my arm on R&R. Wow! You know what I have been planning? Just that! Break an arm on R&R. I am going to a judo, or karate school and have them do it.

There is no way I ain't going to make it home. Don't forget. Okay? My nerves are still okay and my health is too. So don't worry. I am too small and skinny to get hit.

Roxanna, could you start sending me pictures, any kind. Okay? Be sure you have duplicates. When they get old, I will burn them. Maybe you could send me picture of your cycle and your house in New York City and just anything. Okay. That would be groovy. I look at the same colors day in, day out.

Well, fun time. I am going to chow down. Wow! Big thrill. See you on the other side.

Slobber! Slobber!

Well, I had (yum, yum) hot chocolate. Then I got a little chow from my buddy. I might as well be on a diet. I asked a guy how heavy I looked. One said 170 pounds and another one said 140 pounds. Oh, well. The scales aren't too accurate.

R&R *Hurry!*

I may have gained weight. I am so tired of living and acting like a savage animal. Oh well, this time I am really going to chow down.

Bye for now, Sp/4 Fred Leo

Dear Ma and Dad *24 May 1968*

Man, I have been receiving all your letters. *Wow!* Do I look forward to them. Sounds like we did real good at the store on Mother's Day. Eighteen-hundred chickens is better than last year wasn't it? I bet it was fun working at the store. How many of our stores sold over a thousand on Mother's Day? You tell me one of my letters is in the newspaper. Could you send me a copy. I can never really remember exactly what I wrote. Okay? Tell me how did it get to the newspapers.

No kidding, I don't know if you were just saying it sounded

like college writing, but it makes me feel good.

That Apricot *Life Saver* was fabulous. Keep sending little things. I can't tell you how much it helps.

Well, here I be. We are back at LZ Center. We had *Hell* out there. This is true. We lost over half of our company. You tell me how I made it because I don't know. I wrote Roxanna about it. Could you get it from her? I want you to know what happened, but I can only write about it once. It was bad!

To give you an idea of what happened, we were mortared for over twenty-four hours straight. All I had was a scratch in the ground to protect me. We lost our lieutenant by shell shock. But he couldn't stay in the rear so he came out.

I have no good news except I am back at LZ Center. I am waiting for breakfast. It has been months since I had a hot breakfast. Am I going to enjoy this.

C Company is still out in the field. They are down to about thirty men! They are trapped. No one can get them out. This area is bad - real bad. These anti-aircraft guns are everywhere. We have had many downed aircraft.

I hope I get mail today and maybe a package.

One day I almost *cracked.* After I got finished carrying a buddy, who was hurt bad by a booby trap, I sat down. It was close to 110 degrees. It was hot in that jungle. I carried him for over twenty meters up the hill to an LZ we made. When I sat down I began to shake and tremble. Then my mind began getting funny. So I forced myself to stand and walk back to my gear. When I got back to my gear, there was a soldier pointing an M-16 at me. I grabbed him and he was delirious. He was going to shoot someone, so I took the rifle from him and I carried him to the LZ. Then we put him on the Medivac. I was okay after that. I think I even forced a smile. Wow!

Well, I will level with you. I don't think I will walk out of this valley again in one piece. There is no way. They will kill me, if not I expect to be wounded. Right now I am still okay. I can *think* and *act* yet. I get nervous and weak and the whole bit at times. But this I can not help. I tell you this because I am not pulling a shade over your eyes. Please understand. Don't let anyone else read this part. It is just for you, Ma. Okay?

Well, I am going to chow down now. See you on the other side.

Today is the 23rd of May.

I fell asleep after chow and I sacked out during guard. I was just too tired.

Today we went on a small mission. Go see if we could find any gear left by a company that was ambushed. We only found expended cartridges and a few odds and ends. It took all day and it is now four P.M. I am sitting outside my dilapidated bunker. The sand bags are old and ripped. Many of them have old mortar fragment scars. The ground all around it is beaten by the weight of foot prints. There are hand grenade pins and expended cartridges that have melted into the ground. My gear is lying in a mess against the bunker. My flight jacket is laying down, crumpled up with the WN showing on my name Brown. I can see only part of the bird. The rest of it is covered over. I carry a big shovel with a cut off handle. The handle is laying across my rucksack and the spade is lying on the ground.

Everything is so quiet and calm. A chopper is coming in for a landing. It is silhouetted against the sky. The sky looks fierce, and then peaceful. The sun is shining through at a few places, or making the earth seem like a cathedral with indirect beautiful lights.

Out there somewhere a man died today. I don't know him, his race, background, or name. Perhaps the world will miss him . . . perhaps not.

At times the mountains look like you could reach out and touch them. Then you look at the walk to them. Then the blood that has been shed on that ground. The hopes lost and, perhaps by chance, some hope found.

There are no farmers. The land is going to complete ruins. The dikes are getting old and weak. The soldiers walk on them and they fall down. Some times the soldiers falls. He gets up, but the dike stands there, waiting, forever. Will it ever be fixed? Storms, rains, wind and sun will soon wash it away. No one will ever know about the work that some man put into that long since gone dike. No one will know about what weight and what pains that little dike took. No one will ever know except the dike.

The birds don't sing in this land like in the Land of Milk and Honey. The birds sing weird, unnatural perhaps. You hear them sing their song, but a song you forget soon. Maybe like the song of someone's hopes that are soon forgotten, for everything dies fast here. The earth shudders to the TNT which falls on it, hurting, destroying. The trees bend and break. The grass blades are covered over by blood, flesh, leaves, birds, and all types of dead things.

My mind dreams, thinks, but I get frustrated. More and more I am angry. No one steps on my toes and gets away with it. My mind doesn't like this, but I think it is reaching, reaching for what I don't know. This second I have in my hand right now is perhaps my last. This *perhaps* plays with my mind.

I will go back into Que Son Valley soon. I try to be brave but I hear of so many around me dying. My battalion has been cut in half. We will not get replacements for a time.

Today is the 24th of May, I guess. I am not sure.

Our battalion had over twenty casualties yesterday. We don't have many men left.

I guess you have noticed it is hard for me to write. I just can't write no more. My mind drifts into formidable waters too often now. I cannot control it. I am utterly depressed most all the time. I got the word we will go out again, possibly tomorrow!

Instead of writing I read and re-read your letters. I look at my pictures and just think. I can see how a person could go mad over here.

I received your package. I don't heat my food anymore. It doesn't matter. I couldn't wait to eat the chow you gave me. Those beans and Spanish rice was *Wow!* I ate the apricots too. I will take time later and heat the beef gravy and pour it over the C-ration I eat.

Wow! Did I clean my weapon. I cleaned it for hours. It should fire up a storm. I don't know what time it is. It is late, I guess. It is probably about four P.M., by the way the sun looks.

I feel bad. You and Roxanna write so much and I don't write back too often. I worry. Maybe soon I will pass through this phase. Until then I can't hardly write. I am beat.

I will mail this letter today. Okay.

Ma, could you send me another Magic Marker - black. I lost mine. You know even though I live in the sun, my skin is getting no darker than it is right now. It isn't dark either. I was surprised.

I better end.

Will start another, Fred Leo

Dear Ma and Dad *25 May 1968*

Two more days and I will have been here six months.

I feel good now. I have been catching up on sleep between details and patrols. I guess I have to un*wind!* I woke up this morning and I was myself again. Wow! Every time it takes longer. Bla! R&R Hurry up.

Well, the NVA are up to their tricks again. They rocketed us with 122 mm rockets. If it hits my bunker I could kiss life goodbye. They are powerful.

I was sleeping outside and all of a sudden - *Wheeeee!* What was that? *Whish!* "Are they incoming?" I don't know but they went right over my head and I'm getting into the bunker. Then they started with a short barrage. They missed us - luckily. They also hit two other places close by. Intelligence had it that there was to be a ground attack. But nothing else happened.

Oh wait. I was setting outside waiting for the unexpected, or expected, when an RPG rocket landed about thirty feet from me. Man, did I make it to my bunker fast. An RPG round is a rocket propelled grenade that is a little stronger than a regular hand grenade. The NVA was real close who shot it.

Bad News. One jet and a World War II sky raider and a helicopter were shot down. I was watching the sky raider when it was hit and exploded in the air and fell to the earth. As usual, we have four more men dead and wounded.

We keep on taking those anti-aircraft guns from them, but they get more and more. They get re-supply fast. You know they have better weapons than us. No lie. We captured a light weight machine gun that is lighter and has a smaller round than our M-60. Plus it is faster and has less parts and is easy to clean. The M-60 is almost useless in the field. Ammo is too heavy and the machine gun breaks down all the time.

I have changed my mind about the NVA. They are tough.

Real tough.

I got the beans you sent me. Wow! I am going to chow down tonight. I will make a regular meal, heat everything up and mix stuff together. Man, I didn't eat too much chow tonight so I am still hungry. How is that! Number one.

I finally am getting my gear squared away. I cleaned and put new ammo in all my magazines. Also, check this out. I took two ammunition magazines and taped them together. I will use it when I think I am going into thick stuff, or when on point. It should work out good.

I have been reading some old magazines I found. I feel okay now. I read a couple of motorcycle magazines. I sure would like a 450 Honda Scrambler.

Oh, tell Roxanna that I could buy her Honda 160 for her in Japan. But, she will have to put it together. It will end up about a hundred dollars cheaper or more. That is if she gets it together right! Maybe she should just buy it in one piece though. Something to think about.

I took a shower today and let my feet air out for about three hours. *Bla!* They don't look like Miss America's feet.

I hooked a tear gas launcher to my roof today. Those NVA will have a lot to cry about if they come at me.

Could you send another Magic Marker. Butter Fingers lost it. I mark all my stuff with our *bird*. Everyone knows the 'bird' on the logo patch. In about six months a lot of men from Nam will be stopping in our stores.

Well, we got some beer and Coke today. First Coke I will have had in over a month. I don't like beer unless it is real cold. So usually I don't ever drink it.

You know I was walking around after dark with a buddy. Just needed to be doing something. Needed to let my mind just go. It was beautiful. My buddy said, "Don't walk so slow. Are you sick or something."

I said to him. "How long have you been in Vietnam?"

"About three months or really only two months."

"Well," I said, "I have been here six months and I just want to walk nowhere, do nothing. Just walk and think. Six months is a long time from the World. You will know what I mean in another four months."

He didn't say anything after that.

You know, I will only have to go out to the field until I get my R&R. Then I will take R&R and break my arm. Then, home here I come. Sounds good! Well, we will see.

You wouldn't believe the sunsets here. They are so, so beautiful. The mountains make part of the scene but the rolling, thin and sweeping clouds bring the true beauty. Well, I am in my bunker right now. I am going outside to see it better. See you soon.

Here I am. I got me a Schlitz Beer. *Bla!* Bad tasting but all I have right now. Some jets are passing overhead. They have been bombing that valley over there. It is out of our AO. Am I glad. We have enough problems.

Wow! The 105 Howitzer just fired. It bucked like wild. You should have heard those guns talk last night. They really put the brass out. I see some apricots from the C-rations. I think I will eat them. Hold on.

Sanitary me, I grabbed a spoon that was laying in the dirt and wiped it off. Wow! Ain't sick yet. I am going to open the can with my dirty can opener.

I just found out something. If it happens, it will be wonderful. I can't tell you about it till it is an actuality. Okay? I will keep you in suspense. You will find out in about two weeks or less. I got to put out some trip flares now. So bye until later

Well, today is the 27th of May.

I went on an all day patrol yesterday and I am going on one today. They are going to give us two days off after this so I will be at LZ Center till probably the end of May.

Well, I got to go get breakfast and leave. We got to go all the way down the hill to where we were ambushed one time. It will be a long hard day.

See you in a day, Fred Leo

Dear Ma, and Dad *30 May 1968*

Well, here I am in the Boonies. But not in Que Son Valley. We are back around Hill 218. It is 100% better. Intelligence has it that when we were in Que Son we were fighting a *regiment* of NVA. Now they are down to one company size. But also another NVA regiment is on it's way. So I am glad I left. It is peaceful here. They are going to get replacements and build us back up.

We were snipered at and we killed one NVA soldier who was carrying a new AK-47. So you can see it is better here. We have been out a day now. We were not mortared last night. So that is good. I don't think we will tonight either.

Wow! Is it hot. Must be over 100 degrees. I sweat so bad that my pant legs are drenched. We haven't humped much today.

We have a new captain. He doesn't know much, but he should be okay. Our lieutenant went to the rear. He was attached to us for six months. I have been here longer than him though.

Man, you sent letters after letters when the going was rough. I don't know if I would have been able to make it without them. Usually I save a letter to read for a week. I must have had ten or more letters on me and I read them so much I memorized them. Sounds silly, but I did. Could you send me more pictures of you and dad. The other ones got messed up. So just keep on sending pictures of everyone okay?

I am still pushing for R&R. I am not going back to the field if I can help it. I will get R&R in about a month, I hope. I will have been here seven months. One month for R&R and four months left. We get out of the field one month early so I will have three months to stall. Well, they are moving. See you later

Well, we are taking it easy. Am I glad. I have been on patrols almost all the time I was at LZ Center. So I am beat.

Wow! I seen the weapon they got from that dead NVA. It has a chrome bolt. Maroon hand guard, and a fold down butt.

It is about three feet or less long with the butt. About two feet with it folded. Those NVA have the weapons!

I bet it is warm in Chicago. The sun shining and the birds coming back. I bet it is beautiful. Business sounds real good. Say Hi to everyone. Tell them the number-one Chicken Breader is still around. You know, I am one of the few guys without a purple heart. Some newcomers already have two. Keep going, Fred!

Well I haven't got sick yet. I feel good, but all played out. I imagine it will take a long time to get back my strength. I can't hump as much weight as before. Could you call Roxanna and tell her I am okay. You know. I have been closer to just going berserk than ever before. My heart, strength and mind turns to straw! But I just think about home and you and Roxanna and realize many, many little things of life. But now it is getting too much. I keep on yelling about R&R. I hope soon.

You know that red Ford truck, which I rebuilt the engine by myself, brings back so many good times. I really liked that truck.

My M-16 is clean. Cleaned it this morning. The outside is bad. But the inside is clean.

Man, I could eat anything. I am so hungry. I have to get something. I don't have any food. I can't carry the weight.

Man, those leaches really bother me. One was crawling on my flight jacket. Everyone is talking to each other a lot. Talking about anything helps you feel better.

You know I sure would like to see you or Roxanna on R&R. You and Roxanna are the only ones free to do this. But I have determination, no matter how I feel I must, if possible make a whole year. If I feel I will be ruined by it, I will tell you. On R&R I will call everyday and send all kinds of things. Okay. When I leave I will say you can stop writing, because the letters will be lost and I might miss something.

Tell Uncle Raymond thanks for buying my food. Is he back on the farm? Now I know where he picked up the words, "Oh, my aching back." I think of him and the farm often. Tell him I might not get a letter to him, but there is no way I don't think of him. The Rambler working good? It should last him another ten years.

OH! Could you send me some spaghetti and beans. Find some good stuff. Cookies okay and whipped cream! Send me some funny books okay. Man, I look forward to them so much.

Wow! I get hungry thinking about it.

You might wonder what happens to all those envelopes you send me. Well, some seal from the moisture, so I lose a few like that. Keep on sending them okay and a lot of paper because sometime I will be able to get out some letters and I will run out of paper. Okay? THANKS, tell me how is Linda Key doing.

I will continue, Fred Leo

June 1968

Dear Mom *1 June 1968*

Well, God was with me last night. I killed two or three NVA. They had a machine gun and an AK-47. I shot them with my M-16. My gun jammed and I got them with a grenade. I don't know how I got out of it without a scratch. When I leave this area and go back to Hill 218, I will tell you about it.

Chopper coming in, must get letter out. See you.

I can't believe how lucky I am. We had men killed and wounded. I am okay.

Ma, I lost my rucksack. Could you get with the bank and cancel those bank drafts. I lost them when I was in contact. Send me about $600. I lost my regular money too - $100. Oh, *man*.

Who cares. I am here to talk about it.

Ha, I got a brand new week old M-16. I lost mine.

Wow!

The old M-16 was a *dud*. I got a good one now.

Bye for now, Fred Leo

1 June 1968

Jumping from the chopper at LZ Bayonet, their new battalion base camp, Brown hurries across the tarmac. In the field they couldn't even get enough to fill a platoon so Brown is shocked to see so many soldiers milling around.

"Brown!" Sergeant Denning hollers, a beer in hand and a cigarette dangling from his lips. "Damn man," he says rushing over. "You were reported dead. She*eet!*" Grinning from ear to ear, they clasp hands. "It's really you?"

"Sure is, Sarge. In the flesh." Brown smiles pleased to see his old friend.

"No rucksack?"

"Lost it last night during the firefight."

"Is that a bullet wound?" He looks at the bandage on Brown's left wrist. "I listened to the whole thing on the field radio," Sergeant Denning beams. "They say you should get a Congressional Medal of Honor. Why you saved the whole goddamn company."

Brown shakes his head modestly. "I guess." His green eyes flash with emotion.

"God Brown. I was checking body bags for ya, man. So how ya feelin'."

"After firing off eight hundred rounds of ammunition during the firefight, I'd say I'm beat." Brown, unable to handle emotion, makes a hard right turn and inward. "Looks like a regular National Guard week-end around here."

"Yeah, things are a lot different than I thought they'd be," Sergeant Denning says as they walk toward Delta Company headquarters.

"How's that Sarge?"

"Well, I think you hit it right on the nail head. Nearly half of the battalion is back here shaming. They won't go into the bush."

They pause under an afternoon sun to view a twenty-man battalion award ceremony where the harangue has just been delivered. "So what's going on over there?"

"Politics as usual."

Brown looks questioningly.

"It like a big club around here. Certain soldiers . . . certain officers . . . the ones who suck-up. The ones who fit the profile."

"What in hell?!" Brown exclaims, not really paying attention to

Sergeant Denning, as he recognizes a soldier. "That's the mail clerk for chrissakes." They have just pinned a Bronze Star for valor on his uniform.

"Another good kiss-ass," Sergeant Denning says. "Got out of the bush after one month?"

The Presenter stops in front of their re-supply soldier, the one Brown had de-panted in the field. His Bronze Star for Valor citation reads that he unloaded supplies while under fire.

"A Bronze Star, for kicking rations off a chopper?" Brown is appalled. "These REMFs really take care of themselves," he turns to his former platoon sergeant, "don't they."

It is a form of Chinese water torture for Brown to watch the GI Joes of the battalion get medals of valor pinned onto their clean, pressed uniforms. It isn't jealousy he feels—well maybe a little. It's . . . well—he'd always respected soldiers with medals for valor. Now in one swoop it all becomes a lie. Where are the heroes now?

"I didn't wanna leave ya out there, Brown," Sergeant Denning says apologetically. "But I had a chance. And like most everyone else back here, they got out of the field after three months. But being a base camp warrior ain't what it's cracked up to be."

Brown isn't paying much attention because he's intent on trying to recognize someone else at the twenty-man award ceremony.

"They constantly threaten to send us back into the bush unless we bend over and grab our ankles. Know what I mean?" He takes a drink of beer. "That's what the lifers have over us. And it works. But lately its gotten a little outta hand. Now they run things like a little Mafia around here. And the lifers don't trust no one. So they . . ." He takes a contemplative draw on his cigarette. "They have old grunts like me protect 'em."

"Protect 'em? You're a body guard?" Brown looks over amazed.

"Yep. They're afraid of getting fraged. I'd much rather be in the bush except," Sergeant Denning gives a sly grin as he finishes the beer, "except . . ."

"Except what?"

"I can't get enough beer."

"Shit Sarge, it's only noon and you're already drunk." They laugh.

"Yeah, I'm drunk alright but get a good look around ya." He swings his hand leaving behind a trail cigarette smoke. "We're surrounded by a bunch of drugged-up, burned-outs, gutless . . . ." Sergeant Denning doesn't find the need to finish the statement.

"I was talking to Buddy Rogers," Sergeant Denning says placing a hand on Brown's shoulder. "He told me what you did on that hill last night in Dragon Valley. Said it was the bravest thing he'd ever seen or ever heard of. You standing up there alone, silhouetted against the black sky and just pouring it on. He said you dropped at least a dozen NVA and that's only while he was watchin'." His eyes fill with warmth knowing it is truly a miracle that Brown is still among the living.

"Sarge, you gonna get me out of the bush," Brown implores. "A six months stretch in the bush is a long time."

"We're buddies, right?"

"Yeah, Sarge, we're buddy."

"Well, how should I say this?" He takes one last puff on his cigarette then field strips the butt. "They train you to kill, right. Then they send you to Vietnam and you . . . well, you kill. Follow me?"

Brown listens not knowing where it will lead.

"So," he takes a drink of beer, "let's say for instance, you have this no name soldier that has killed more enemy than any other person in the entire battalion. No Name soldier has taken point over twenty-one times so they call him Gunfighter." Sergeant Denning looks at Brown.

"Go on."

"So this Gunfighter turns out to be so good that he takes on sixty NVA soldiers, and single handedly saves the entire company."

"Sarge what are you talking about?"

"Well, what would you do with that soldier?"

"I'd give him a Congressional Medal of Honor then I'd take him out of the field," Brown says understanding the Gunfighter is him.

"See, that's the catch-22." Sergeant Denning stops talking and takes out a pack of Marlboro. He offers a cigarette to Brown. They smoke in silence while they continue to watch the awards ceremony.

"Eighty percent of all soldiers should be sent home to their mommies. Ten percent are good followers and the other ten percent are good fighters. Out of all those men you might get one gunfighter." It isn't easy for him to say what he needs to say but continues. "Brown you're the Gunfighter. You're dangerous. And you scare the hell out of people."

"Sarge, one minute you're complimenting me and the next you're . . . you're what? I'm just doing my job the best I know how. Hell, most of the time I'm just trying not to die." Brown finds his voice shaking with anger. "I'm trying to survive and I'm not gettin' much help here."

"You threatened an officer on Hill 352 didn't you?" Sergeant Denning accuses.

"I can explain that," Brown says with blood draining from his face. "He fired mortars and . . . ."

"You don't have to explain," Sergeant Denning says cutting him short. "That only proves what I've been trying to tell you. See good soldiers follow rules. And gunfighters, well they're dealers of death. They make up the rules as they go," he says. "Tell me the truth. If anyone gets in your way . . . you'd kill 'em. Right?"

"In the bush the law is written in lead, not on some fancy piece of paper."

"Brown this isn't easy on me either. I'd hoped that you were in that body bag because . . . ."

"I think you've said enough, Sarge."

"I need to finish okay," Sergeant Denning pleads. "Just let me finish. You need to know this."

Nodding, Brown shrugs and listens.

"They figure you're gonna get killed. And Purple Hearts and medals of valor are worth a lot of money to the right person. Someone who is alive and . . . well fits the mold."

"I have four Purple Hearts coming and at least two Bronze Stars for valor and you say I deserve a Congressional Medal on Honor but . . . . but." This has all unnerved Brown. This certainly did not turn out to be a heroes welcome. Instead everyone is frightened of him. They wanted him dead. "Oh*hhh* my God. This is insane."

Everyone in the formation has come to the position of attention. The officers and NCOs salute, which signals the end of the ceremony.

"Brown one last thing. Everyone knows about you—The Gunfighter. But they won't use your name and they'll pretend like you don't exist. They'll try to provoke you into a fight. Then they'll have a hit put on you for fifty bucks."

"Let 'em try," Brown says stone cold. "Just let 'em try."

"You can't stay back here. You belong in the field. You'll be safer out there. Gotta didi," Sergeant Denning says abruptly.

Apparently not wanting to be spotted, he hurries to a deuce and half truck that has, *Stay High* painted on the hood. "Take care Brown," he hollers over his shoulder. "Just remember, I'm on your side and I'll see what I can do."

"Thanks Sarge. I appreciate any help I can get." A hollow emptiness fills his heart making him despondent.

The ceremony soldiers, puffed proud as peacocks, begin filing past. Grudgingly, Brown realizes that in their own way they feel they have earned the medals.

At the command hut Brown introduces himself to the company clerk. "Brown?" He turns to a clerk sitting at the desk and asks, "He's looking for Brown. That's the guy killed wasn't it?"

"I'm not looking for him, I am Brown," he says trying to remain calm. "I was told to report here."

Both clerks look puzzled and then begin checking the roster. Finishing they say, "No Brown here."

"Hey you, soldier! Clear that goddamn weapon!" a lifer sergeant in starched fatigues yells on entering the hut. Whiplash-quick he snatches Brown's M-16, ejects the magazine and clears the chamber, the round clanging onto the wooden floor.

"You some kind of NFG or something?" The lifer—who has just arrived from the award ceremony has a medal for valor pinned on his uniform—glares at Brown. "Talk to me shit for brains!" Their eyes lock. "This ain't no hippy commune either. So get your goddamn hair cut," he growls through yellow chipped teeth, his eyes ablaze. "And while you're back here, don't let me catch you . . ." He waves a threatening finger.

"Brown, here's your orders," the clerk says finding the incountry R&R orders. He's about to hand them over when the rifle is suddenly slammed into Brown's chest. Brown closes his hands around the rifle and stares hard-eye at the lifer.

"You grunts are all the same." His demeanor has changed markedly after hearing Brown's name. "You come back here," the lifer now speaks in a low even tone, "and think you don't gotta follow the goddamn rules! I'm warning you, you better not piss me off!" He storms out, the screen door slamming behind.

With orders in hand Brown says, "Well, I guess a man's gotta do what a man's gotta do." Locating his foot locker, Brown finds the lock broken and everything in the foot locker has been stolen.

"You Brown?" comes an indignant voice. "I need to check your rifle serial number." Brown's M-16 is propped against a stack of foot lockers. The soldier takes the rifle and checks the number. Then he accusingly states, "This ain't your rifle."

"No shit Sherlock," Brown says trying to control his temper which has been pushed near the limit.

"You lose your rifle?" he asks.

"What?"

While examining the rifle he says, "You should keep it cleaner if you want it to work right. I'm gonna issue you another M-16."

Brown follows him to the armory encased in sandbags. He reappears with another rifle and props it against the sandbags.

"I don't want it," Brown says a bit perplexed by the whole proceedings. "I want the one I had."

"Well, that's not how it works," he says stubbornly. "And don't lose this one."

Anger steams through Brown's veins and his mind interfaces with death. Seeing red, he swears that he will seek revenge, that he will doggedly wait, and one by one take out these REMFs. One by one he will seek and destroy. With teeth clenched, he takes the weapon.

Striding away, he happens upon a little one room PX. Inside he finds pens, paper, envelopes, toiletry, cigarette, gum, candy etc. "Gimme a pack of them cigars over there," he says congenially.

Moving from the PX, he lights and puffs the cigar to life. Leaving the battalion compound, he crosses a large open space and starts up a hill headed toward the engineer's compound. Reflecting on the days events, he realizes that six long months of personal sacrifice in the field will go unappreciated. That it was all for naught.

"But my blood spilled on that ground and I know what I did," he shouts under his breath. "And I guess that will have to be good enough."

All his life he felt he needed to prove himself. Now that he had, they treated him in exactly the same way—like shit. At that moment he concludes, "I've done all the proving I'm gonna do. From here on out they'll have to prove themselves to me."

Far from the naive boy who arrived six month ago, Brown stalks in the manner of a veteran who know odds are stacked against his survival. Like in an Old West cowtown, the pallet sidewalk clanks under the heels of his worn leather combat boots. War is the real game of muscle, will and steel. This stolid figure has walked down the sage brushed streets of Tombstone, Arizona alongside Doc Holliday and Wyatt Earp into the gunfight at the OK Corral.

The passing REMFs gaze at the shrapnel riddled steel pot and shrapnel scared fragmentation jacket. They stare at the ripped jungle fatigues, the unmistakable shoulder-warp and the pistol belt with hand grenades. And finally they notice the M-16 which against all regulation is again loaded with a round in the chamber and a full magazine. Noting the adroit way he handles the war gear, the passing REMF's know all too well that this is a gunfighter, a dealer of death.

But does anyone dare stare through clairvoyant green eyes to the molten matter behind. Yes, the passing men knew it, they could feel it. No mistake about it. This is the real thing. An authentic American gunfighter. "Don't get in my way, asshole!" is written all over his demeanor.

Turning into a nicely kept barracks, he spots three engineers huddled at the far end. After a cursory glance, they continue talking in low voices. Brown collapses on an empty canvas bunk, the first one he'd been on in six months.

"Gimme a chance. Just one chance! That's all I ask," an engineer spews vengeance. "I'll frag 'im. I swear to God I'll do it."

Fragging lifers and officers is apparently a base camp warrior's idea of a cure-all, Brown decides.

They begin saying their final goodbyes.

Brown recalls the farewells he's experienced that were very, very different. " . . . *ahhh*!" comes the screams from the mud caked bloody poncho, a hand reaches out from a pulverized body. It locks onto Brown's arm his eyes pleading. "Ahhhhh!" The kind of shriek a soldier makes when his brain has been ripped loose from the cranium of sanity.

And how do you explain the goodbyes whispered in the blade wash of stinging dirt from a Medevac Huey. And the expression on a grunt as he cleans the blood from a dead buddy off his hands.

War is ultimately the business of killing. So the military pulls good men out of society, psychologically alters them, then has them kill on command. "Charge that hill." But after first blood, can the soldier really go back, melt into *normal* society? Based on the changes Brown has seen in himself, the odds are highly against it.

Unafraid of that first breath of new life, a soldier is baptized by fire and embarks on the incredible journey. They have confronted a mystery of death, but could they ever tame it? Brown is finding there are few ways to stop the march of fate once the line has been crossed.

Regardless, America has sent it's Peace Keepers half way around the world to South Vietnam so the Vietnamese might enjoy the same rights as they have to freedom, liberty and justice for all.

"Hey, buddy," a soft spoken GI stared down at a Brown, "don't wanna miss chow do ya?"

"Chow?" Brown sits disorientated. "What time is it?"

That night at the Enlisted Men—EM Club, Brown bought a beer which is opened, like all beers at the club, before it is shoved over to him. He walks through the tent around a maze of fold up tables to where Sergeant Denning sits.

"Glad you could join us Brown," Sergeant Denning says as the other soldiers stare unfriendly across the table. "I've slept more times with this grunt than with my wife," Sergeant Denning jokes. He punches Brown jovially on the shoulders.

For the next few minutes, he embellishes Brown with swear words as if they were the kindest words ever spoken.

" . . . Those two combat photographers Dana Stone and Sean Flynn didn't like what they saw. Said we looked a little lax or something like that. Can't say as I don't agree."

"But things would be different if we had a PR department. For one thing we wouldn't be goin' through all this shit."

"Well, right. That's the real reason we're a prime candidate for the blunt of the casualties. They could kill us all and no one would know anything about it."

"Rent a Battalion. That's what they should call us," another soldier adds sarcastically. "We've done the dirty work for the Marines, First Cavalry, ARVNs, 196th, 11th. I don't know who else. Shit, and they all get the credit."

From another table a soldier blurts, "I was in three firefights too many. I'm tellin' ya right here. Ain't no way they're gonna get me back into the bush. No way, man."

From another table of inebriated soldiers, "Blam! I sent a short burst into the bushes. Then I pushed my way through to find this dink holding a dead baby." The soldiers at the table lean into the story when the narrator finishes with, "Man, how was I to know?"

"I wrote Yamane up for a Bronze Star," Sergeant Denning says leaning over. "Ya know, I miss old Same-same." They both sigh.

One GI at the table begins talking about how some gunships were make unapproved assaults on suspected VC hamlets similar to the vigilantes of the Old West. "They take justice into their own hands."

"I was with 'em one time when they swung out over the river to this fishing boat looking for contraband. When they pass the pilot yells, 'We took incoming!' It was a lie. I know it for a fact. They looked at us but never shot at us. Anyway, the chopper spun around and the gunner opens fire. One dink was killed right off and the other gook jumps overboard.

"You shoulda seen him swim, the gunners take turns fanning bullets all around him. Tutututututut," the narrator makes chattering noises to simulate the machine gun. It was effective in giving their imagination a moment to decide what might happen next.

"The dink slithers from the water and then the chopper just hovered over the poor sucker. They gave the dink a little goodbye wave." He raises a hand with only the wrist moving in a curtsy wave. "Then . . . "

Everyone visualizes the dink being cut to pieces. Arms, legs and body flopping around on the ground like a puppet on a string. And finally Brown sees the dying man's fingers clawing into the sand.

An argument breaks out at a nearby table. "Yeah okay. I'll give it to ya. So he did something brave for once. But if the lieutenant is so goddamn brave, why hasn't he ever been pointman? Huh? And why aren't the officers ever humpin' the boonies? I'll tell ya why. Because an officer's life is more important than yours or mine!"

Going for a fourth beer Brown overhears another conversation. "But that ain't the proper way to kill 'em. Should've just blown 'em away on the first day, right? Then there wouldn't be any questions asked."

On the way back. "Yeah, talkin' about dink bitches," one says, "they've got a real cute one down at the vill. Just came back from Saigon. She got her tities enlarged and her eyes rounded. She costs a little more but from what . . . ."

The conversation drifts to soldiers trying to contract sex transmitted disease to get out of the field. Then they mention the dreaded, black sylph.

"Every hear of anyone who got it?" one soldier asks.

"No. But if you do, I hear say they'll send you to this deserted island somewhere and wait till you die. Then they'll send you back as a KIA. If you don't die soon enough, they make you an MIA."

Eavesdropping on another conversation. "I don't know about the Bloods around here anymore," one man says. Ever since Martin Luther King was assassinated they've changed."

"Some of the Bloods are getting letters from the Black Panthers telling them this is a white man's war. And they should refuse to fight."

"If that's true then why did Washington, re-enlist after gettin' a panther letter?"

"Well, the letters are all fine and good but first you gotta get outta the field. And the Brass dig-it cause it makes it look like everyone in Nam enlisted and volunteered."

"I've heard they put formaldehyde in the beer so you can't have sex," Sergeant Denning says as Brown sits back down. "Say, let's go to the NCO club."

Brown is left listening to a crescendo of conversation from the stoned, drunk and over medicated soldiers.

" . . . survive, man. Cover your own ass first," a drunk slurs.

The rest of the strung out soldiers continued telling overly dramatized and exaggerated stories. "I put a booby trap on my screen door and a claymore under the step. No one is gonna sneak up on me," a paranoid soldier says dryly.

"Our own guys killed him during the mortar attack. I swear to God. Just before he got killed, he told me he was gonna break up this drug and prostitution ring." Brown concluded that the medics were the key distributors of drugs, legal or illegal.

Vintage Vietnam. Everything is true and nothing is true.

" . . . the reason our meat is rancid is because the cooks sell off the good rations to the officers. Side money. Shit, ain't no secret. Everyone knows it. Hell, I was over there one night and they were grilling steak and lobster and at the same time we were eating shit-on-a-shingle."

A helicopter door-gunner sits alone at a corner table with no one to help dissolve the sadness or turn pain to laughter. Instead the horror that lurks inside the soldier stays suspended and jiggles like raw nerves from a dismembered limb. Brown knows his stories have no beginning, no ending. They are stories about the faces he has seen. Faces of the guys who couldn't get to the chopper. Those horror ridden faces that have the devil holding onto their legs dragging.

In contrast the ones who saw little or no enemy contact, are heard the loudest. After listening to so many fake war stories, you can't help but wonder if there's anyone left in the field to fight.

Standing, a drunk Brown loses his balance and tips the table sending all the empty beer cans clanging to the ground. Using the M-16 as a cane, he makes his way with half shut eyes through the maze of tables and chairs.

Under a midnight sky, his practiced ears detect the faint sounds of enemy mortars tube firing. "Incoming!" he shouts. Spotting a bunker, he wobbles toward it.

"Incoming!" come more shouts across LZ Bayonet.

Brown trips. "Uhhh!" His face smashes into the dirt his steel pot rolling away. "Shit!"

With the mortars crashing all around, he pulls on his steel pot and falls fast asleep.

Dear Ma & Dad *3 June 1968*

Wow! Guess where I am now. In the rear with the gear! I am next to the Chu Lai air strip now. Where am I going? *In Country R&R!*

It should last about two weeks. I hope. Man, I am lucky. I leave tomorrow.

I scrounged up some money, so I have over a hundred dollars. I have been at Chu Lai for almost two days. Haven't been able to relax yet. I hope in a day or two maybe.

I got your packages. Man, I had beans and spaghetti. I am going to have the beef with some beans tonight.

I am here with Sgt. Denning. He got a Bronze Star for Da Nang. That was during the Tet Offensive.

Ma, did you get my ring yet. It should be there in two weeks or less.

I went to the PX. Guess what I got. After shave, comb,

suntan lotion. *Wow!* I haven't used any of those things for months.

Tell Aunt Maude I got her Brownies. Scaled them in two minutes. They are the best brownies I ever ate.

I am going to write everyone while I'm on R&R. Finally, I guess.

You know, Ma, I have done most everything I wanted to do in Viet Nam. I have killed a man and they have tried to kill me. I am lucky. Ninety men have been killed in my battalion since Da Nang. This is not counting the wounded. There are very few that do not have Purple Hearts that have been here as long as I.

I just set here in disbelief. How?

Well, you might wonder how I *might* get a medal for valor. Well it was about eleven P.M. on May 31st. Everyone was scared to take point so I did. We had night logers on this particular hill before, so I knew the way. I walked up the side of the hill and when I reached the bald part of the hill I went to the left and the next man to the right.

I continued to walk to the top. All okay. Suddenly I am standing next to a trench line. I thought to myself the last trench I seen like this was at Hill 352 near LZ Center. I then looked to my left. I saw two men. Not realizing at first who they were, I said, "Hey, you guys from Charlie Company?"

The men turned grabbing their weapons. I then opened up on them, wounding both. I jumped into the trench line. I listened and then I jumped up and put another burst into them. Then I grabbed my hand grenade and lobbed it on them. But it was a dud. Then I started firing like mad all around to keep anyone from coming up on me. The NVA on the other side of the hill, realizing what was happening started shooting rockets at us. The NVA started advancing, throwing hand grenades. Then the NVA next to me that I had wounded opened up on me with a machine gun. Seeing this I grabbed my last grenade and threw it. It exploded, silencing the two NVA and the machine gun.

Now the NVA put us in a cross fire from another hill

with a .51 cal. machine gun. They started over the hill and I picked off one and the rest of the men got some more.

Wow! I forgot but right before I threw my last hand grenade at the machine gun, my M-16 jammed. I threw it away and jumped up and ran for another M-16. This is when I shot the other NVA.

It was time to pull off the hill now. So we backed off with grenades and bullets every inch of the way. We finally reached thick shrubbery where we held up for the night.

Wow! That was hairy. I made it without a scratch. We have a couple men wounded, but none killed.

By the way, one NVA had left his rifle and was crawling to talk to another NVA. They were looking at each other when I happened to walk up on them. Would never happen again in a million years.

Remember what Hemingway said, "You are not a man until you have killed a man." *Wow!* I killed a man, not saying I am a man, but now I am on the way!

Let me count my money. I got $129.35. That should be enough for In-Country R&R. I will not be doing much. I want to save my money for Out-of-Country R&R. I am going to change it to Hong Kong or bank notes.

I am going to get the top people to work on my re-assignment to Germany. I should get it.

Ma, get this! Sgt. Denning and Captain Price and Lt. White and Lt. Livingston are trying to get me out of the field and into S-4 Ammunition. If they can swing it I will get the job in July. I hope I get it. I know I will see you in four months then. But as always, if I ain't there, don't take it for absolute.

Ma, you should see my new ID card. Wild. I look like the picture enclosed, but I am holding my name crooked on a piece of paper that looks like a picket sign. My hair is uncombed, definitely the wildest ID card the U.S. Government ever issued. I look like a draft dodger. Wait till I calm down and I will write another letter. Till then. I'll write you from R&R.

Bye, Sp/4 Fred Leo

P.S. I will make sergeant stripes, I hope in three months or less. But if I leave the company and go to S-4, I don't know, but I am not worried.

Dear Uncle Ken, Maude & Karen *10 June 1968*

Well, I received your cookies and brownies the night before I went on R &R. So I skipped supper and ate them all night. My buddies liked them too. They were real scrumptious. *Thank you!*

Karen did you make both cookies and Brownies? You did a good job. The guys wanted a picture of you with the next ones, okay? See if I can't fix you up with something. Oh well, just a thought.

You still going to climb those church steps. I hope, or wish I could be there. You miss everything when you are in the Army. I will be home for the next Thanksgiving and Christmas. Let me look at my calendar and see what it says okay? 170 days left. Not long now.

Right now I am in Vung Tau on R&R. *In-Country* kind. If you work it right you can end up with a week or so off. I am going to try for two weeks. You have to miss your plane and everything else. Tricky. But they expect it from us, so why not give it a whirl.

So the cars are still cranking out. I bet it is nice for summer to be here. No cold cars to sit in. *Burrr!*

They have full length good movies every night. *Clambake* staring Elvis Presley. *War Wagon* staring John Wayne. I wonder what will be on tonight. Most of the guys go mad over here. You know why. All the women are little shrinked up people. Some come up to my waist. It is so nice to see a girl from another land your height.

Wow! When I leave here I ain't coming back. *Glug Glug Glug Bla!* I feel sick. That is about all I do. Drink.

There is usually a man to meet you at this R&R Center. "Well," he says, "there was a colored guy killed over there." Then, "This is off limits at this time." And, "You can't go here, here, here, here, here, here or here."

I asks, "Where can we go?"

"Nowhere."

Too many restrictions. I have the beach about 300 meters from me, but it is "off limits." So I got to go to the other side of town to a beach. You will not believe this. They have slot machines in the R&R Center. You pull the crank and three lemons show, and you get money. Las Vegas all the way! I lost two dollars. The machine has a dent on the left side now! I am not going to breakfast this morning. I drank it last night.

The M.P. thought we got a little rowdy last night, so we started making sounds like incoming mortars rounds and all.

"You guys don't worry about mortars and guns." We shouted at them. "Why don't you let us alone. We ain't hurting no one."

Most of the guys who get In-Country R&R have a hairy story to tell. Mostly there is only a few left. "The guy in front of me was killed the other day." Kind of stories.

Oh well. There are cattle and horses running around the streets. Horses and buggies are everywhere. I rode in one. Well, got to go to the bar for some more R&R. I call it "Rum and Riots." Others call it "Rape and Rampage."

Oh well, 'tis life. See you in a few more days, when I write.

Fred Leo

Dear Ma and Dad *11 June 1968*

I am leaving the R&R center. I feel like this is home. I get the *old feeling* in me of leaving something. I already signed out. I am waiting to check my rifle out.

It is funny to see the men. They look at their gear. Slowly they put it on and assume the soldier image. They don't have much to look forward to. They wonder if their company will be in the field. Wondering about if another friend is gone. Then, am I going back for my turn at eternity.

The moon is bright, but it seems to give a black light. The clouds are broken and mysterious.

I am going to put in for my Out-of-Country R&R in September. Then when I get back it will be almost October. So I will have a little over 1-1/2 months left. Wishful thinking. I guess I better check on my rifle. So wait a minute. No, I don't think I can get it yet. I'll write later.

Well, it is now seven P.M. I am in Saigon in this compound.

After picking up my M-16 at the desk, a bus came. So I left. I took a Chinook to Saigon. Got here about ten A.M. So I dropped my gear and went to the PX. I tried to get a radio, but they didn't have any. So I walked back to the heliport and got a bed and sacked out. I woke up and went to the movies, a regular movie house. It was funny. The first two rows of chairs were under *water!*

It wasn't a bad movie. When it ended I had forgotten everything about where I am. This is the first time this happened for a long time.

Well, it is raining hard. I am in a steel roofed hutch. The rain just sounds so loud. It is coming in all the windows.

Wow! I wonder if I will get away with this little delay in routes. I am going to stay here two more days. Who cares! I like it here. No one asks for ID's or anything. I do what I want. No restrictions like at the R&R Center. I didn't really like R&R. I didn't rest. I felt pushed because I only had three days. I feel better here.

These people here in Saigon don't know a war is going on. Everyone seems to "know what I mean" when I say something they haven't experienced. The old bit "I know what you mean." I will never say that anymore. I used to. Now I say, "I understand" or something, but that person talking is the only one who knows how it really is.

The EM Club is within walking distance. But I don't want to go. The smell of food and drink is in that whole building. People smoking, drinking. I can't handle it. So I came to my hutch and here I am.

Ma, I want to ask you something. I am completely serious and I know what I say.

Could you come see me when I go on Out-of-Country R&R. Okay? I really want you to come. Okay. Bring some friend. During the day we could have a real good time. At night we might split up or we can arrange things. I don't know where I will go. I will put in a new R&R application when I get back. Perhaps for this September. Okay? Then a few weeks after R&R and I will come home.

I haven't cracked. You know. I wouldn't ask you to come if I didn't think I could make it. I'm just looking at it different.

I was hoping Roxanna could come, but she will probably be in school or something.

Ma, did you hear more people in the US are killed in a day than in Nam. Fifty people a day in the States. About one every half hour.

I stepped on a scale and guess what. I weighed 150 lbs. About 140 is what I weigh when I hump the field. I don't know where the pounds are, but they are somewhere. Tomorrow I will go to the air terminal and sign-in. Then I will take-off for the rest of the day and hide.

Tricky, wow! I probably will get caught . AWOL! I will take my chances. Don't worry.

Guess what I have for luggage. A little bag I got from

the *hospital*. Shaving Cream and razor. Then my helmet and weapon and web gear. I travel light. Some of these guys have a duffle bag. Wow!

Don't mind that Polaroid picture I sent you of me. I just came in from the field a couple hours before. I look a little ratty!

I think I will find the shower and clean up. See you later.

Oh, I forgot. You should see the PX. Huge. It is as well stocked as the ones in the U.S. They sell cards and everything.

Everyone has a cycle around here. Honda's go good. I rode on one. A South Vietnamese Air Force guy gave me a ride. It was groovy.

Well, shower here I come!

Went to see James Brown do a live concert at another theater and it too had water up to the third isle. He was real good. Sweat like a pig. By the end of the show he looked like we do in the boonies. When I got back to this compound I'm staying at, the gate was locked so I climbed over the barbed wire fence and get in.

Today is the 12th of June.

I had an abrupt awakening last night. About 4:30 A.M. we had incoming rockets. This place isn't safe. No bunkers to run to. I just jumped to the floor and hoped my luck would hold.

I leave here tomorrow and go to Da Nang, stay there a day and then to Chu Lai. You just got to know your way around. But before that I will go to a movie show in the morning.

I might end up in Chu Lai on the fourteenth, maybe later. If I think I can swing it, I will stay out longer.

Wow! I better get this letter mailed. I will mail it as I go into the show. Well, wish me luck. I hope Da Nang doesn't have many rockets.

See you later, Fred Leo

Dear Ma and Dad *15 June 1968*

Well, I must be writing so much I bore you. I guess you can tell when I have some spare time. Well, yesterday I decided to go to the Aviation Center. They couldn't get me on a flight to Da Nang, so I will try again the seventeenth. There is a good movie on Sunday, so I am going to stall till I can see it. The movies are no good after Sunday so I probably will try harder to get back to Chu Lai.

I walked for a mile or so yesterday. I about ruined my legs. With no weight I walk *sloppy*. I pulled my legs out a little, seems funny.

I can see the smoke from bombs exploding from the PX. I can feel them too. By the way I am at the PX waiting for the show. Oh. Boy. They better look out now. A *B-52* just lifted off. The bombs the B-52 drops aren't big but he drops over six hundred of them, I am not sure. It shakes the whole earth for miles. The smoke goes about a mile high and huge! You don't want to be a mile from these jets.

I have been cleaning up every night. My skin is in fairly bad shape. I have a lot of scars. I guess they will slowly disappear.

It is nice to see people riding bikes. They are so practical here. But back in the states people always worry about what other people think. A major and a captain just rode by on a bike. It doesn't look funny. An old Sergeant got off his bike, smiling all the while, locked it and walked away.

People are willing to swallow their pride here. No matter how old, young, or what you did in the world, you roll up your sleeves here. If you were a cool playboy, or a college graduate with honors, you were still expected to do what the others do.

That old major can't seem to get the hang of the bike. He is in front of me. He put on sunglasses. Taking out a cigarette, he just lit it. Well, there he goes. Happy as ever and riding slow. Doesn't care.

You know I got to hurry back to read some letters. The

last one I got from you read, "I hope you are on R&R when you read this letter." *And I was!* I just found out I had R&R two days before I went in for it.

Well, can you just mark off the old *money orders*. I hope so. I didn't actually lose $400. I will kill myself if I did. Well, I better go. Bye

It is now 3 P.M. I seen the show. It was okay.

You know I have found out something. I am exactly the same. I haven't changed at all. I was at the PX and was going to buy a soap *dish*, but I didn't.

The watch you gave me is still running nicely, but the spokes are broken. So I took a watch band and put it around it. I then hung it on my shirt. There is a watch repair at the PX but I didn't get it fixed. If we get together on R&R you will see the same old me.

You know I might end up a researcher. I will go places and find stuff. I hope maybe I could get in with the *National Geographic*. Then I could travel and be rid of those little things. I have thought about this, because I have grown to like the woods and trees and wild life more than ever before. Those long, winding, forever forgotten roads into yesteryear have so much to tell me.

But when I go to the U.S. I will first go to college.

I really don't know if I will be able to come to the business for many, many years. Maybe this will change, maybe sooner than I expect but leave it at that.

Today I have 164 days left.

It is the 16th of June. Another day gone. I've been in the Army one year.

It is hard to get a flight out of here. I should make it tomorrow. So it will be the 19th before I get to Chu Lai.

I found a clean shirt today, so at least I have a clean shirt.

I get a little more short tempered every day. Viet Nam

could drive a man wild after a while.

There are too many *War Heros* here. You know what I mean? I better close.

See you soon, Fred Leo

Dear Ma and Dad *17 June 1968*

Here I am at Quin Yon (don't know how to spell it). It is growing dark. You can feel the heat from the sand. The wind is blowing out to sea. There are a few palm trees. They blow so beautifully. Makes you think of Florida.

I am in an old deserted bunker. No roof. The breeze blows freely all around it.

No matter how long you are away from home loneliness gets you down at times. It was so lonely on the plane here. I wasn't sure I was going to get a ride to Chu Lai from here. I didn't know where I could sleep, eat or anything. I was taking a chance. When I got to the airport I asked to go to Chu Lai, so now I have a reservation. I hope I get there tomorrow.

I left the airport to try and find a bed or something. I came across a USO. I checked in my gear for over night. I read a few books and watched T.V. Then I went for a walk.

It is so hard at times. But I think of home real hard and write a letter. Then I am on my way to recovery.

When I walked into the airport I asked where I could get a bunk. No one knew. Then a couple of fellows said I could go with them. I could get a girl for five-dollars plus a bed. I guess that is what made me feel bad. They laughed at me for saying, "No." I can't make love for one night because I am not true to myself and I don't care to associate with a girl who thinks she has to love to get along.

So, here I am in this bunker alone. Everything strange. I

haven't been able to talk to people candidly for two weeks. Thank God I have my parents to write to. I got to get back so I can read your letters.

You know, I only have a very few friends. Most of them are dead and gone because of wounds. It gets you if you think about it.

Oh, well, I better go for a walk. I like walks. I can't hardly see what I write anyway.

Bye, Fred Leo

Dear Ma and Dad *18 June 1968*

Well I'm back in Chu Lai.

Wow! I have been reading your letters. You are really getting organized. I can hardly believe how fast. You said you have the insurance and accounting all wrapped up. *Wow!* I might even come back right after college.

Oh, about my radio. I sold it for $150. I need to pay some guys back and so I would have some ready R&R cash. I am sorry I cannot keep it. It is too big for a guy who is in the field, but I used it all the time on R&R. I didn't want to let it set in the re-supply hutch. So since my buddy would like to have it, I sold it. He said I could use it when I came in. He's a guy from Chicago. The Doctor. He is one of the guys in the picture of all four of us.

I got the $600 money orders. Thank You. I have it in the safe with the First Sergeant. I couldn't find my foot locker, but I found my duffle bag. It had my khakis.

Well, first bad news then the good. I am going to the field in a few hours and I will not be able to swing *S-4*. The Good. We are back in the Chu Lai AO for a hopeful three months. We're working out of Hill 69. No one has been killed or wounded since we have been here. So the field has nothing in it. A few booby traps and VC but nothing real bad.

I have my R&R in August. I might make it October. I am not sure yet. I have got to play it by ear so that I will perhaps miss the move up into the hot areas.

By the way I am going to Australia. I get six days in that country. Only five in Japan or Bangkok.

I am going to be RTO. That is about the safest job. You don't walk point. You get the breaks if there are any to be gotten.

Ma, I am glad you saved the assassination papers on Bobby Kennedy and King. I was hoping you would save them. I imagine you got the *LIFE* with the ads in it about our stores. That ad will be around for a long, long time.

Tell Roxanna I got her package. We ate it up that same night I got back. We heated up the bread and put cheese on it, then we ate the sausage with beer. Roxanna, maybe you could send another one similar. Okay. Sausage is uncommon around here. Pepperoni sausage everyone loves.

So you're home for a while, Roxanna. Where are you staying. Has Lorraine told you of the surprise she has for you about Danny? Well, I will see you tomorrow.

Well, I don't think I will go to the field today, so my next letter will be from the boonies. RTO again. I will be traveling lighter than anyone. Oh, well

So long, Fred Leo

Dear Ma and Dad *23 June 1968*

Well I am in no other place than the field. We move at night and hold up all day. I have had a cold the last few days. I don't know how I keep going. My mind is a little messed up. I can't seem to write.

I have found, *BLOOD, TEARS, AND GUTS* keep men like me in the field going.

Blood - Our buddies get killed or wounded. And we kill and wound.

Tears - Our home, when we think of it. The agony of the things we see and do.

Guts - What keeps us going. Hard Core! Willing to Die.

Take point and realize the consequences.

Brief descriptions. You know what I mean. I will go to Australia on R&R. I hope I get six days there, only five in Japan or Hawaii.

By the way R&R didn't help. I might have been better off without it. My body and mind are beyond repair in just a few days. It will take at least a year now.

Nothing is happening. I am the platoon RTO. I feel it is about the safest job. The radio is heavy but I am coming home. It doesn't matter.

Bye for now. I am alright. Just am a little sick and am a little frustrated.

Bye until later, Fred Leo

P.S. Received the $600 money order. Got all your packages. I used them in place of C-rations for two days!

Dear Ma and Dad *27 June 1968*

I got your letter where you talked about your office down by Leon's Restaurant. It sounds like a good office. I commend you on a very good idea. It gets to be too much of a hassle around everyone while you are trying to think. That is one thing I will have to do. Learn how to concentrate good. At this time I am less and less able to concentrate. At times I even mess up on the radio. I could be the company RT0 but I turned it down because I am too worn out to concentrate.

I think Roxanna should stay with our business. It sounds like it is so big that no matter what you do you can fit in some way.

Well, I got back from R&R and found out how worn out and depressed I have become. I cannot walk with over 100 lbs. on my back anymore. I have no extra strength.

Well, things are different in this new A.O. It is near Chu Lai. It is the easiest AO in *Viet Nam*. Not really, but we haven't had anyone wounded or killed. But the other companies have had a little trouble. I think two or three men have been killed and about five or six wounded.

Our operation in this AO is different. We walk all night and hold-up during the day. The trouble is you can't sleep good during the day. It must be over a hundred degrees now. I am in the shade but I am drenched. By the time 6 A.M. comes around I feel like a hundred years old.

By the way, I've spent enough time as Pointman and am now the platoon RTO. For me, I feel it is about the safest job to get.

For the last couple of days we have been going into a village at dawn. A couple of days ago we captured twenty young men. We only shot at three. We didn't kill them, because we don't like killing. If they were in easy sights when they ran it would have been different.

Ma, you feeling okay? The last letter doesn't sound like you are depressed, a little lonely. Don't know maybe it is my imagination.

Yes, I sent the flowers from Saigon and Chu Lai. They were nice ones so I bought them. Ma, do you put the flowers in your own office?

You know for some reason your letter is about the nicest I have gotten. Maybe the time and place is right for it.

As time goes on I become more and more anti-social.

LZ Center just seemed to blow me apart. After that experience I have not been able to get my strength back. Ever since than I have become more and more withdrawn.

I have 150 days left.

It doesn't seem like this will ever end. I am glad I went on In-Country R&R. Now I know where I stand. I might have gone to Australia R&R without meeting you. I sure miss you. I hope you can come to Australia, or wherever I go. I imagine it will be in September. I will have my arm broken after R&R. I will keep it broken till I go home to the U.S. September is only about two months away.

I hope time passes. Fast!

Well, I have to bring some empty water cans to the chopper pad. See you later.

Well it is about seven P.M. A couple nights back it was raining real hard. So, I separated my steel pot from my helmet liner. Then I balanced the steel pot over it like an umbrella. This guy bet I couldn't balance there while I slept. He woke me for guard and it was till there. I only sleep on my back. If it's cold I cross my ankles and arms. And I never move. They can't believe it.

Anyway, we will move in a little while. We don't have to go too far tonight. Our platoon is shaping up again. It was bad at one time. But it is shaping up *again*, but our platoon sergeant is going to leave in ninety days, so it will go down again because of a new leader. I got to get out of this company when that happens. Well, got to change the battery in my radio and pack up. See you tomorrow!

Today is the 29th of June.

I am supposed to get paid today. It doesn't look like we will get paid though. It is in the evening. It is a little cooler today. I got good shade. I sacked out most of the morning.

I don't do much now, ambush at night and sleep during the day. This is free time. I hope it stays around. I have done all I have wanted to.

I guess it will be hard to leave the office if you come on R&R. I will be home a few months after. If it will be too much of a mess to come, too much office work. That is okay.

But when you come bring a lot of money and a friend. It should be a lot of fun to run around in another country.

Well, nothing else. 149 days left

Bye until later, Fred Leo

Dear Ma *30 June 1968*

All the cars cranking out? The Toronado working good? Maybe you will get a '69 model? What does Roxanna use for transportation, the Ranch wagon? How is she doing in the office? Is she slowed down a little, or what. Have you taken any new pictures lately? I bet the green grass and everything is Boss.

Can you get a picture of the lawn with the new flowers?

I haven't heard anything on S-4, the supply job in the rear with the gear. I might get it, but it doesn't look too hopeful.

Boy, we have become sort of a slipshod troop. I don't know when we will get to Base Camp. It will not be for a while I guess. I didn't tell you I went to the beach. We went in for about eight hours. They brought us to the Chu Lai USO on the beach, but the waves weren't high. Oh, well. It was fun anyhow.

It is late, about five P.M. We will stay here until dark. Then go to our ambush. No contact yet. I hope we never get any. But the Intelligence reports say there are three-hundred Sapper Troops about four kilometers from here. I don't think we will have any trouble.

I was talking to my platoon sergeant. He is from Canada. He has done a lot in his life. But he got married to the wrong woman and felt the only way out was to be in the American Army. He was a fur inspector. He ran rackets on the side though. Like taking a mink here and there. He was a miner up near the North Pole. The shaft was over 4500 feet down. He drove the little trains. He said they had a garage and vehicles down there. Part of the mine was going under a lake.

He worked on the ocean docks. He did a few little things on the side. He is about 28 years old. He will re-enlist because he is trying to get back on his feet. He is a cool little guy.

He said a lot of school teachers went to the mine he worked at. The mining towns are isolated. A train every three days go to this town. I imagine a person could have time to collect his thoughts and read and write. A miner gets lots of money. Sounds good. I might try mining for a summer. Read books for college. I imagine I could hear some wild stories.

I have decided something. Someday, I don't know when but I will ride a bicycle across the U.S. I always have wanted to do this. Maybe I will end up using a *motorcycle*, but I will go across the U.S. on two wheels.

If I get to Germany I will not have to join the Merchant Marines. But if something wrong happens, I will join them. Oh, well. Time will tell.

If I work at mines for a while maybe Dad could come up and fish near it.

Oh well. Dream on. Dream on. I imagine I will end up at Southern Illinois or Northern Illinois University. It is cheaper. I will see.

Linda Key is a junior in high school isn't she? Time flies. What does she do in her spare time? Does she work at any of our stores?

Four of the old guys left these last few days. Three went to be MP's in Saigon. I guess they need men bad. MPs I think they have it rough in Saigon. When they drive around, I heard VC throw hand grenades in their jeeps.

One guy went back to the rear to S-4 (supply). Three of us supposed to go. He is the first one. I don't know if I will though.

You know that we have codes and everything. The most used one is the *Shackle* code. They give you two words consisting of ten letters. It changes every month or so.

Example: F A R M I N G BOY
0 1 2 3 4 5 6 7 8 9

If I have twenty-six men in my platoon, the Shackle will be RG. On the map they pick different coordinates every week or so. They give names to these.

Example: You just give your location in relation to these coordinates.

Our call sign at this time is

Vulcan Delta 2-6 Kilo.

It will change to

Kansas delta 2-6 Kilo (Name for me)

This is to keep Victor Charlie on his toes, if he tries to figure out the men by these call signs.

Also the frequency changes every month. From 61.35 to 75.01 for example. We have all these goodies. Sometimes it is hard to keep track. All this information is kept in an SO-One. 1 don't know what it means.

Well, bye till tomorrow. It is raining.

Bye, Fred Leo

July 1968

Dear Ma *2 July 1968*

Yesterday was a *fun day*. We left the AO for eight hours. I went to the PX and USO. I didn't go swimming because of not enough time. I will get a cut-off pair of fatigues and go swimming next time. I got your small package. The Raisons were number-one. I couldn't believe how similar to a watermelon taste those candies were. Ma, that can of Spanish rice was too big. Can't eat all that at one time. Okay.

Well, in a few days we will be changing AO's. I think we will go into the mountains this time. I haven't heard much about the place, but the company that is there right now hasn't had much contact.

You will not believe what I heard. A company of ARVN's in Saigon took a plane to Chu Lai. Then they disappeared. No one knows where they are. It is believed they were a VC Company. Wow! What a bring down.

It is about noon and I am waiting for re-supply. Ma, I don't know if you have heard much about the 198th, but the 1/6 has been carrying a big load. You probably hear how other battalion kill all kinds of 'dinks,' but not the 1/6. The reason is we do not have a publicity manager. The others do. I get so mad when I never see the 1/6 in the *Stars and Stripes*. It gives the impression we never do anything

Well, I better close. I will mail this on resupply chopper. So I will start another. I will probably be in the mountains this next letter.

Fred Leo

Dear Ma and Dad *4 July 1968*

"Okay men, saddle up. We're movin' out. We got to get to our day loger," Sarge hollers.

The sun had just come up and was shining uncertainly through the clouds. It gave off a light red color that moved like fingers under and over the clouds.

"Okay, third squad you lead out. Try and find that trail between these knolls," Sarge said.

Last night we'd been coming down this steep mountain side and couldn't find a level place to sleep. So we walked sluggishly because of little sleep and a rough night.

"Delta 6 this is Delta 2-6 Kilo. I am moving out for my day loger at this time," I said over the radio.

"Roger is there anything further," came the reply.

"This is Delta 2-6 Kilo, Nothing."

"Blam! Wait, I think our point just hit a booby trap," I said.

All the men suddenly had that sick, uncertain look on their faces which is present when we get contact.

"Get down!!"

"Get some cover!!"

"Medic! Medic!"

"Get the Medic up here, hurry!"

"This is Delta 2-6 Kilo," I said. "I think I will need a medevac."

"Rodger, how bad are the men."

"This is 2-6 Kilo. I am not sure, wait. Roger. Word was sent back we need it fast, over."

"Okay, I need a location and the number of men."

After the transmission was over I went up front to see if I could help.

"Keep cool, Rothwell. You will be okay. A bird will be in

bound in a minute. Hey, Blakesley, hang loose, you didn't lose any limbs."

The men hit a bobby trap. It probably will cripple the pointman's foot for life. The man behind him was hit and has multiple leg and face wounds.

Not bad, considering. We pulled back and sat down.

"Brown, do you have a pen?" I give it to him.

The guy took off his soft cap and turned it to where I could read the name *Mary*. He took the pen and darkened the name so he could see it easily.

Different men have different ways to keep their *cool!* By this time everyone realized what had happened. They all looked uncertain about life. As always, "You know the only reason I wasn't him was I wasn't feeling good."

So much for a wonderful 4th of July.

"Delta 2-6. This Hatchet 2 on your push," the company commander said.

"This is 2-6 Kilo, over," I said.

"Rodger, I have a few questions I have to get cleared up. Now was it a delay fuse or did it have a trip wire."

"This is 2-6 Kilo," I said. "The man remembers stepping on the mine. It blew-up under his foot. Shrapnel went through his boot and tore the leg up badly, over."

"Rodger...."

Today is the 5th of July.

One of the guys had a *nightmare*. He was a good buddy of the man hit yesterday. He yelled his name out in the middle of the night. *"Blaksley!"*

It is now eleven A.M. I slept all morning. I got up and was fixing some hot chocolate when a small Vietnamese boy came over. *"Hi, No Name."* It doesn't matter what your name is, you are known in life by your personality traits. These kids don't know personality in the G.I. so any name is *No Name* to them.

Change one. I am now going to Bangkok. The rumor has it that Japan is too expensive and Hong Kong has the some thing but cheaper. Then Bangkok has the same thing as Hong Kong but cheaper yet. Bangkok is supposed to be the number one spot.

Chopper is in-bound.

Bye, Fred Leo

Dear Ma and Dad *8 July 1968*

Well, another day gone. We don't do much of anything. We are still in the same AO. No contact. The moon is a full moon now, so we have changed out tactics a little. We walk until two A.M., then set up an ambush and sack out. We have been walking close to 8000 meters a day. *Bla!* It hurts. I can't hump no more.

Guess what we did a few days ago. They dropped these 55-gallon drums of CS gas. Then we put on our gas masks and walking into it and stayed there for the whole day. It was miserable trying to eat and drink with that gas mask. My eyes were watering like crazy. It's hard trying to sleep wearing a gas mask. *Ugh!*

Things changed a little. We will stay here an indefinite amount of time. I am glad of that. No one in our AO is getting much contact, but they don't want us to get too used to this AO. We'll see.

I just woke up. It is about 1:20 P.M. I am waiting for the re-supply bird to come in. I got a letter from you yesterday, Ma, dated June 30th. I have letters back for weeks. I will answer all the question which I usually don't do. Okay.

That village the VC wiped-out is being taken care of by the 1/52 198th. It is near here but no sweat.

I am glad you liked the flowers. Only the best for my Ma.

Never found my foot locker. Maybe next time in I will. I don't brush my teeth. But I had a hair cut a week ago. It will be the last time until R&R.

I should know if I have R&R in about a week or two weeks. Okay. I got paid but it was raining and the voucher got mutilated, so I won't mail it home.

I don't know if I made it clear but I am back to platoon RTO. Being an RTO I think will bring me home safe. I don't take point.

That is the main thing. I try to travel lighter than before. All I carry is a poncho liner. Then just my radio and combat gear.

We had a *hot* meal. Some potatoes, green beans with bacon, bread, a cookie and some kind of eatable meat. It was alright. We haven't had milk but once for about a month. I heard there is some kind of shortage.

Could you be sure and bring my ring with you on R&R. I really want to see it. It looks big, huh? It is size 10-1/2.

Wow! Roxanna can come on R&R! Boy, we will have a blast. Bangkok is number-one. It is wild.

Don't worry about me now. Okay? I am in a safe place. I am a seasoned trooper. It is harder to kill me than a new trooper. Because they haven't shot anyone or killed anyone yet. So I am straight.

I got the comic books. I will read them tomorrow. They look good.

I put in for Germany. So tell Roxanna to hold on and we might get together and she can go around in Germany. Sounds *good,* huh? Well, I will mail this on the chopper. I will write again soon.

That pineapple/grapefruit juice drink looks good. Tell you how it tastes tomorrow.

Bye, Fred Leo

Dear Ma and Dad *9 July 1968*

Guess what! Wow! Tomorrow we are going to Dragon Valley. But tomorrow is a big day for me. I am going to NCO school. I will be grade E-5 or E-6 in two weeks. The School is on the Chu Lai Beach. I will not get back to the field till the first of August. Then R&R in a month. Wow! I am so *happy!!*

I will have made sergeant faster than an Instant-NCO. I will clear over $300 per month. After two years in service I get $279 base pay. So, if I go to Germany I will get over $300, like here in *Nam*.

I have a chance for E-6. Then I will get $318 base pay, and

because of over-seas, I will get close to $350 a month, plus you have it made if you make *E-6*. That is the same rank as Sergeant Denning!

If I play my cards right now, I will leave Nam alive and not severely wounded. It is all too good to believe. I can hardly write I am so *happy.* I will only have four months left in Nam after school. I get out one month early because of my rotation. I get close to a month for R&R. So I have to find some way to get rid of two months!

Wow! Wish me luck.

Everything seems like a fairy tale. I will write when I get to the NCO school. Okay.

See you then, Fred Leo

Dear Ma and Dad *12 July 1968*

Ma, Viet Nam is like any place. They have fertile soil, sand along the coast and around, and clay and rocks.

Well, I lost my foot locker. I should say–they lost it. Couldn't find it. Oh well, *tis* life.

Ma, straighten Roxanna out. I don't want her to put one foot on this soil over here unless she is willing to kill. No place is safe! Nowhere. It is kill or be killed and I don't think she wants to kill. This land is nothing. The people are in pitiful shape and the war is harder everyday.

I read all the time of Vietnamese *civilians* getting killed because they want to make a stand on the war. You can't when it is as intense as it is now. Okay?

I got your package. I ate the spaghetti last night with apple sauce from the C-rations. And I have the watch on my wrist. I gave the old one to my buddy Shepard. He came here the same time as me.

It is nice to have a watch in one piece. Ma, could you bring my *ring* on R&R. Okay? I would like to wear it.

Well, my buddy Ryes wants Bangkok so I took Australia which means I get two extra days. Good huh. So right now R&R is from the 21st to the 28th of August in *Australia*. You can meet me at the *R&R Center*. They say any taxi will know where it is. But if something should happen, we can both call home. We can coordinate through the *house*, okay? Now you have to get a flight and get your end squared away.

Australia is the land of the *endless* parties.

My buddy Okie can vouch for this. Roxanna might pick something up good in Australia. I imagine she knows ways to get around, since she is half way around the world it is only a few dollars to get to Hong Kong or Japan. That tricky sister of mine!

I don't have much to say, but I will go to NCO School in three days. The trick about the school is you have to be in the upper third to get promoted. It might be rough. I know two smart guys who didn't make it. I hope I do.

Well, I am not doing much. I am right in the middle of everything. I am unable to make opinions or think about much. It is all new to me.

So I will say bye for now, Fred Leo

P.S. Tell Aunt Lillian I am really looking forward to seeing her again. Okay.

Dear Ma and Dad *15 July 1968*

A day to remember.

I am at NCO School. I will do nothing today but relax, shower, watch a movie and polish my boots.

It will be maybe two days before I receive any letters. Maybe three days because they will collect them and then give them to me.

You know, I feel I have gone through this feeling a hundred times before. But it continually reoccurs. I feel lonely. I feel misplaced, and I know I must learn how things *are* and fast. If I miss something, I will not be able to pick it up later.

The class will consist of about forty men. Three of these forty will get rank. The rest mark it off as experience.

Did you know the 101st Airborne is not *airborne* anymore. I mean they don't parachute out of airplanes. They work with the *Air Cavalry*, or Air mobile, similar to the 198th Light Infantry.

I will clean my weapon real good today. My weapon is the only one my first sergeant passed everyday so far. My weapon is *clean!* I put a new camouflage cover on my steel pot, but as soon as I finish, I'll put old 'trusty' with the cross back on.

Ma, I would like you to send me an enlarged picture of us four guys. Remember the one with Sergeant Denning. Also I want a good picture of "Thor" the War God of Greece. Okay. I am going to have a painting of us guys and "Thor" standing in our shadows. It will be a beautiful picture. Please send it as soon as possible. If you do I might get it to you on R&R. Okay.

By the way *no more* film coming. A guy stole the camera. I have no locks, foot locker even. He just went through my gear and that was it. Oh, well.

I am going to clean my weapon. See you later.

Well, it is 1:30 P.M. my rifle is clean.

A day just passed. It is the 16th of July.

I have had a big low-down on speaking, and all kinds of good techniques. This school is beautiful. I know of no place I could get this knowledge but in the Army. I do not think I will make *Sergeant* here, but if I pass, I will get the next citation. I hope I get it before R&R but I might not.

I have to give a three-minute speech in about an hour. That is at six P.M. Before I leave, I will have to give a twenty-minute speech. So if I dig in and keep the notes for later, they will be very valuable.

They had a movie last night *Mounties Go Home* by Walt Disney. It was good but they showed the first reel of film then the last, then the second reel. What a bring down. Plus it was ragged. Kept slopping around in the projector. Oh, boy.

Well it seems almost for sure the 1/6 Infantry will go back to Hill 218, which is *LZ Bowman.* So Dragon Valley here I come. But two weeks of that then R&R.

You know a guy from my platoon who got here in February just got out of the field to a rear job. I have been here about 2-1/2 months more than him. So, I will have to make my own breaks.

It just isn't fair to have a guy in the field for one whole year while some of the new guys get jobs in the PX. Or guys become mail clerk after two months in the field. Then a lot of guys get out of the service after eight or ten months here.

I wonder what will be on the movie tonight. I hope it don't start before I get a shower and polish my boots.

Well, we will have formation in twenty-five minutes.

Bye till tomorrow.

It is another day. Today is the 17th of July.

We will go thru the gas chamber. No sweat. I brought my gas mask. I hope it works.

You should see me scale up the food here. I drink over a quart of milk every day. Today I can say, I feel better than I ever have in Viet Nam. Right now I am carefree, have my own bunk, good food and recreation—which is the beer hall and a show.

Last night was the movie *Dirty Dozen*, but in the middle of it they turned it off and had a floor show. A couple of Red Cross girls dressed up as Cowgirls. I went to bed after the floor show. Had a beautiful night.

There is a constant, slight wind here because of the sea. In daytime the wind goes toward the sea and at night it comes landward. I stay cool. You even need a cover at night.

You know I have realized something. I cannot be a leader. I always need someone to cling to. I cannot break away and be a leader. I do a good job and my platoon likes me and I have a great deal of respect. I got this respect because I always do a good job. The reason RTO is so good for me is because I can cling to the man I RTO for. I feel lost when I need to lead because I don't have the most essential thing a leader needs, *confidence*. This I lack when put in a new place. But when I find a person to cling to, I am able to express myself, and be very useful as a guide.

I think the reason I came to Nam was to try and find independence and lose my need for someone else at all times to talk to and so on. But I am afraid I will not.

I don't consider this a fault, but a fact. A car may be able to run good, but if you don't have the right supplements it is not up to capacity. That is the correct gas, driver, and so on.

I will now try and find out the things I need to function right and to my ability. This, of course will be trial and error. That is one of the reasons I must do many things. I must go and do everything possible. I will be a *hood* as before, a drinker, a combat veteran, a truck driver, a cross country cyclist, a miner, and so on and so forth. I might by chance get through early but this is doubtful.

At home, a good job at the store, a wife and kids will, I hope it will, be the eventual end. But a good life it will be.

Well, so much for thinking ahead. I will close and mail this letter.

See you in a month, Fred Leo

Dear Ma and Dad *18 July 1968*

Today marks 130 days left. Just had chow. Chicken. You should have heard the replacements. "This is the worst chicken I ever seen." These guys will soon consider it a luxury if they're infantry.

Well, we are going to have a test today. From here on in we will be working hot and heavy.

I will probably not get to see the show but a few more times. But they have bad movies half the time, so no big sweat.

It is now 1730 hours. I am going to have a test. It is supposed to be easy, so I am not worried.

You know I must have gained ten pounds since I have been here. Maybe only five. The watch you gave me is working good. Roxanna should be home by the time this letter gets to you. How is she? All right, I hope. She have fun?

We have PT (physical training) in the morning. I can pump close to twenty push-ups. A lot of work, huh? The highest I ever got was about 75 pushups. But twenty isn't bad for what I have been thru. Bad food and all.

Everything about R&R is the same. Australia from the 21 to 28. Meet me at the R&R Center. I will get there about noon. Okay. It will be slightly cool. Bring warm *clothing*. Okay. Bring my *ring!*

I hope everything is okay. Everyone safe and okay. Remember if anything goes wrong, contact the *Red Cross!* I can go home from here if the Red Cross okay's it. Don't hesitate if anything is wrong.

I got two packages from you and two letters. Dad is in Tennessee?

Everyone was jealous. I was the first one to get letters or anything. I skipped chow and opened the packages. That apricot nectar was good, real good. Then I scaled the beans and Spanish rice, then the whole can of peaches. *Wow!* I don't know how I got it down.

I am glad Linda Key is working good. She never tells me about what she does. Oh, well. I am glad you clued me in. She likes office work?

We will zero our weapons here. I haven't had a zeroed weapon since I have been here.

Wow! War stories and more *War Stories!* Bla! I am so tired of hearing them. Silly people. Some are from the 1/52 Infantry 198th. They don't know there is a war. But from the sound of it you'd be surprised anyone was left alive in the field to fight. You would swear they have done more time in the boonies than me.

Oh, well. Time to study. See you later.

Well, I almost maxed one test and almost failed another. So I am still passing. I guess.

It is another day, 129 days left.

I woke up with my legs hurting. That PT helps. I guess that shows what shape my legs are in. Bad shape. Oh, well.

I just got finished with talking to an NFG. He is scared. He was almost shaking. It is sad to see people like this, but they know a guy can get killed all too easy. I don't think I was that bad, because I didn't know enough to be scared.

You know what my old buddies used to say, "Brown, you still have milk behind the ears." They think differently now. Oh well. Tis life. See you later. Must go to class.

Another day gone. It is the 20th of July.

I will go out to the firing range, then at eight P.M. we come back in.

Tomorrow we will again stay out after dark. Even though we get up at five A.M. we stay out. By the time you get squared away it is about ten P.M. They just never play it cool with you. Enough already.

Re-learning how to read a map. I already know, but it is a good review.

Just filled my canteen. I imagine it will come of some use tonight, since we will have C-rations for chow, but not me. I am going to scale the chow you sent me. Good idea, huh.

Two cans of chili. Boss. I also scaled some lemonade! It is my last package. *Hint hint.*

The sand really generates heat. Some places you can hardly breath, but you get near the wind and you stay cool, if you have a hat.

You have all your gear squared away for Australia? Is August about the best time to go on a vacation? Summer is almost over.

Ma, I wish you could send me some pictures. I sure would like to see some. But maybe it doesn't matter now because I will see you in less than a month. Matter of fact in about four weeks. Can hardly believe that *fast*. Soon it will come to an *end*. Nine months is a long time—too long. We will be together on the ninth month. Remember I got here on the 27th of November.

Well, I am going to get this mailed, so I can start another page.

Bye for now, Fred Leo

Dear Ma and Dad *22 July 1968*

Well, today I learned how to adjust artillery. Yesterday I had a refresher on the map. So now, I'm pretty good with both.

Dad, would you like to come to Australia? They say it's fifty-years behind us, but I think it would be okay. If you wanted you could go ocean or river fishing. I would like to have you if you can.

If you didn't like it you could go home early or something. It would be refreshing perhaps to be with people from another country, in their country. It should maybe just let you stop and think. Perhaps, thank God I live in the U.S. If you can I sure would like to see you.

Well, right now I am on a mountain top next to Chu Lai, Highway One. A wind storm came up and the sand was thrown up in the air, almost to the clouds. It drifted for over four miles in one big sand storm. Now I have an idea how the sand looked in the Sand Bowl of Kansas in the 1930's. The wind was about forty mph.. Strongest I've ever felt it in Nam.

From where I am, I can see fifty miles out to sea. The convoy on Highway One looks small and I can imagine how much sand is getting in them.

It just started to rain, not bad, just a light sprinkle. We will be choppered out of here and back to the beach in about an hour.

Did I tell you I scarfed up a *Robin Hood* hat? It really isn't a Robin Hood hat but it looks very similar to one. It is a South Vietnamese High School hat converted to what it is now. It is a neat little hat. I have it on right now.

I had a speech yesterday. I got *ninety* out of *a hundred* points. That is real good. So I am sure now that I will pass the course. Then when I leave the school the next sergeant citation that comes down, I get. I am taking a risk becoming a sergeant, but it is a risk I am willing to take. Well, I will write tonight. See you then.

Tonight I am waiting for a floor show. It should be good. Starts at nine P.M. Hope I can stay awake until then.

Today is the 22nd of July.

Tomorrow I will have only 125 days left. Funny thing is when 125 days is over I will come home for a month, then be gone another year. But I guess it has to be that way.

Did I tell you I got that *Readers Digest*? I can't read them in the field. I travel light. Every ounce is taken into consideration. But it happened to come now, so I just about have it all read.

Most of the guys are drinking *suds!* Sometimes I love beer and other times I don't. When I am faced with a new or old situation which bothers me, I scale some. It doesn't help. I just forget about the situation, sleep good and then go and do it. What a way to live!

You know that malaria gets pretty bad. There is an LRRP Airborne here with us. He has been here almost three years straight! He has had malaria four times. Now the fever and shakes come every four months like a time clock. I guess it will be with him the rest of his life. I wasn't taking pills but since I heard that, I started taking them.

Oh, well, going to get some beer and go see the floor show. See you in the morning. *Bye*

Today is the 23rd of July.

I have a little disgusting news. I will *NOT* be getting a medal for the Hill. The guy behind me will! He was our platoon sergeant. And two officers that were there will too. If you have rank and know people you can get medals for nothing. It is a fact. I can tell you about it in less than a month!

Roxanna, she feels good now? Great! I know how much fun it is to ride a motorcycle. Durban's place is in Fredericks Town, Ohio. It's a beautiful place. The house is old and very antique looking. They say it was built as a stage coach stop and that President Washington slept there. You feel like you are in the past just being in the house but the future is also the present.

I have a test today. Artillery adjustment. "Right two degrees and fire for effect." I will have some time now to study and do nothing. So I will close.

See you later, SP/4 Fred Leo

Dear Roxanna *24 July 1968*

Well, Santa Claus is here with all kinds of surprises. I talked to a Base Camp Warrior today and a hand grenade riddled his bunk last night. That isn't all, they threw a grenade through the screen and it went out the other side. One landed next to the guy, but it was a dud. Also, this is Santa's big surprise, they thought the first Sergeant was in the 'john' (outhouse) so they threw a grenade in there. It is like the Fourth of July. These are but a few of the happenings in our U.S. Army Base Camps in Viet Nam.

Now that sounds bad but a whole company is up for rape and murder. Believe it or not it is true. This company found three NVA nurses and kept them for seven days. They were made to walk point and the guys would take turns with them at night. Then they set up a firing squad and killed them. This is not the Army or U.S. way of killing the enemy. Kill them right away, it is more merciful.

Oh well, that is another thrilling page in the story of *Viet Nam*. This place is mad!

I can't believe it but it is true. Roxanna, Viet Nam has people like any place else, but we have ammunition for the taking. Roxanna, don't even think of coming here. Okay. Well, I went to a village I seen for the last time six months ago. The girl I used to see there remembered me. Wow! After six months all the *dink* women just like me. *Ha Ha.*

Get your clothes and gear ready. August the 21-28 this R&R.

I wanted Ma to come because I would feel selfish if I didn't let her come. You and Ma have stuck by me all the way, so here is a chance to get you half way around the world, why blow it.

I can hardly wait. Australia doesn't have too groovy threads but they are okay. It will be cool I am almost sure. It will not be summer. Okay Just to give you a hint of the weather.

Bring an instant *easy to use* arm breaker. Okay. I have found out they are not going to give me a break. I am the only one who will. So I will break it. Sounds good. I am serious The guys who have been in the field as long as me are already dead or wounded. I will try not to let 'Charlie' get me anymore.

Roxanna, you said you hear that most of the action is going on in Saigon. Well, Saigon is the capitol. So everything is told about what happens there. By no means is Saigon the only place of action. I have seen airplanes and choppers shot down up here. It is just that the fighting is in the mountains. We have B-52 air strikes here and everything. We have many men who are killed and wounded.

The 198th 1/6 is one of the most *alph*a kicking battalions in Viet Nam. We don't have a reporter in our battalion. That is why you don't hear about us in the States. The men are proud to say the 1st of the 6th Infantry has over two-thousand kills.

My battalion has over one hundred KIA and over 1200 WIA. We have a record of about one to one in hand to hand fighting. The air strikes and artillery even things up. It takes three GIs to take out one dug-in NVA. Saigon has more heavy equipment then we do so they get more kills.

You get what I am saying? There are four divisions in our I-Core area. They are going to be poised for a new offensive this month or the next. Four divisions is close to twenty-thousand soldiers.

Well, I will get this mailed tonight. Oh, I have been out of my mind for two nights from mixed drinks, beer, pot. *Wow!* Been a long time.

Take care. Don't get in any trouble, *Little Sister*

Big Brother, Fred Leo

Dear Ma *26 July 1968*

I got your letter saying you didn't know where I was going to be in Australia. My mistake. Sydney Australia? It is the biggest, if not the only big town, in Australia.

Well, tomorrow is the day, the 27th of July.

I will graduate. I have passed. I do not know my score, but I will get a promotion shortly.

My Base Camp - LZ Bayonet has been hit hard by mortars two out of the last five days. One day seventeen GIs were wounded and one killed. I might sleep in a bunker until I get back to the field. This is the first time it has ever been hit like that. Bring down. It might mean the beginning of something worse. Well, just wanted to get this letter out.

Remember, It will be in Sydney, Australia the 21st to 28th of August. Meet you at the R&R Center. I guess around noon. Okay? Take a taxi to the R&R place. They all know where it is.

Australia is the big island off the tip of Vietnam. Okay. I can hardly wait. The next letter will probably be from the field.

Well bye, Fred Leo

P.S. Tell Roxanna I got her Sausage, cheese and the bread. I will scale it tonight. Must celebrate my graduation.

Dear Ma *28 July 1968*

Well, today ended this course. I'm supposed to go back tonight but I am going to skip out. I will go back tomorrow night.

I will leave with an engineer buddy and spend the night at his barracks. Then tomorrow I will spend running around. At night I will go back to my company at LZ Bayonet.

Then I will tell them I must get dog tags. Then go on sick call. You name it. I will know the scoop on what is happening out in the field when I get back. Could be good news or bad? I don't know.

I have enclosed my Certificate of Graduation. A two star General from the Americal Division gave it to me. *Wow!* He wasn't thrilled about me though. Kind of a bored look on his face. I don't think he even *saw* us.

Be sure to tell Roxanna I received her package. I ate it all up last night. I missed supper so I could eat a lot.

Right now I am sitting on a picnic bench. I am hiding out here so they can't find me.

Tomorrow - 120 days left. Wow! I can't even remember anything about the field. It is funny. I have been here eight months.

Can't say I actually learned anything at this school. Anyway, nothing I can put a hand on. I had all kinds of wild ideas about what I would learn and do and how I would change. I feel that there is something missing yet. I don't know what.

A Day just passed!

You will never guess where I am. You know the *Bob Hope Show?* I am sitting on the stage where it was given. I can almost feel their presence. The stage is really quite small. I don't know how many it seats. But there are rows and rows of benches. The stage is empty now. There are old cigarette butts on the floor, sand, communication wire and rocks. The floor creaks when you walk on it. If it could talk I would know all about the show. The light sockets are busted. The paint is chipping.

I can see what he saw. The South China Sea is near. I can see it's waves rolling in. There is a small rock island and a sailboat out there in the distance. Those waves will play music for anyone who wants to listen.

The Chu Lai Evacuation Hospital is right behind the stage. I imagine Bob Hope saw a Medevac land up there. Not a sound can be heard here, except birds and an occasional creaking of the boards.

Wow! What a feeling this stage has.

The day the show was given I was out shooting at VC. That seems like such a long time ago.

The wind whistles in the trees and through the stage, a lonesome sound. A person doesn't hear that sound in the city with so much other noise.

An M-16 sets against the wall and a torn, shrapnel ridden helmet. It stands with respect because it will *talk* against what it doesn't like. Like a giant, all alone. But I know that weapon has been silenced once. It does have a heart. But now I have it and it has spoken again. Will it ever stop? Will the lead stop flying out of it in anger and revenge?

Well, I am going to the hospital and have some chow. I can talk my way in. I have done it before. Bye

It is night and I am going to the beer hall.

Once again, I am going to Sydney, Australia, the 21st to the 28th. I will meet you at the R&R center. I should be there about noon.

Ma, I really don't think you need anyone. We will have the fun of a lifetime for seven days.

Well, must go.

Bye, Fred Leo

August 1968

Dear Ma *1 August 1968*

Back in the boonies. Nothing happening. No one hurt while I was gone.

Just waiting for R&R. I think about it all the time.

The field drives me mad. *Bla!* Got to get out.

Oh, well. I ain't going to get hurt before R&R See you then.

Bye, Fred Leo

Dear Roxanna *2 August 1968*

So how is my anemic silly little sister doing. Well, anyway you will not have to be too energetic in Australia. I am beat. Tell Ma, or could you bring some extra vitamins. I might take them for a while to see what happens.

I got your comic book. Boy, that was good. While I was reading it I was thinking about the relationship between it and our society. Then I noticed you wrote on the front of it. Thanks for sending it.

What a hassle. The chaplain just came in. He will tell us not to worry! Don't think about the little things (killing, NVA, VC, etc.) be happy. It does so much for me. *Wow!* Sarcasm. I am getting bad.

We got a new Platoon Sergeant. He asked me to be his RTO even though he already had one. He also wants me to always pull guard with him. He is really alright, but I don't like the way he does things. I am going to try and get away from him.

Hey, tell Ma I received the pictures she sent me of my buddies and all. They were good for a laugh. I guess I will never be a movie actor. I can't even take a picture right without screwing it up. What a bring down. I will be laughing at them all morning.

Today is the 5th of August.

Well, believe this or not, we are going in for a *seven-day* stand-down at the USO Beach at Chu Lai. I can't believe it. By the time we get back to the boonies, if at all, I will be going in to get ready for R&R. Boss!

Roxanna, I bought this bracelet today. When you come on R&R to see me wear it. Okay. I have one just like it, except yours has a nick in it. So I took the best one. After all!

Nothing is happening in the field. I hope it stays *boring*. We hold up all day and walk to our ambush at night and back to a day loger. Well, I have built up a frame of mind against going back to the field. I will tell you about it when I see you. Only nineteen days from right now. *115* Days left in Nam. Wow! Getting short.

Hey, I just lost my frame of mind. What a hassle.

Well, tomorrow will be my last day out. We are going in to the beach for a week. I imagine I will not make it back to the field till the 14th. I should go in for R&R the 17th of August.

Well, I will run through it again. I am going to Sydney, Australia from the 21st to the 28th. I will arrive about noon. It is cool there. Have some warm clothes.

Meet me at the R&R Center. Get a taxi at the airport. It will be the same one I come in at, so they should be able to help.

If something goes wrong, I will call home. OK

Well that is it.

See you, Fred Leo

Dear Ma and Dad *6 August 1968*

It is night. We worked fairly hard on our bunker. We have the best bunker on this hill. It is strong. Right now I am inside of it. The rocks have stones flaking off them. The ground is uneven. The whole bunker is built around a big rock that we chopped through. We broke it up in some places and couldn't in others.

The sand bags are grey and dirt falls from a few. The strings tying them are smashed in between other bags. Others look as though they *squeezed* out from the bags and lay there limp and lifeless from exhaustion.

The roof has steel beams on construction stakes. They look as old as our clothes. They have sharp edges on them. They strain against the weight of the sandbags. The sandbags seem to be trying to squeeze between the stakes, but fail.

There is an old torn combat shirt blocking off the crude window. It hangs precariously. It could walk away if it lets loose. Another window has a box marked 'fire works' on it. It had trip flares and wire in it. But now it serves as a storage box. The other window has the almighty C-ration box in it. "Date May 68 - Lot 36." It knows tomorrow will bring its existence to an end - unlike us.

An old grubby poncho liner blocks the door way. I am writing this letter by candle light. I am cramped and rocks and dirt are getting my pants dirty. My legs hurt now. I must quit. I will see you in the morning, or on guard if the moon can get through the clouds. See you *tomorrow!*

Another day gone. I know I will be on this hill at least another day. I can't believe how hot it gets. You can only stay in the sun for a few minutes without a hat. Well, I will get this mailed. A chopper will be inbound in a minute.

See you, Fred Leo

Dear Ma *7 August 1968*

I have been receiving all your letters, Ma.. To say the least I am happy to get them. I get to feel like a kid. I look forward so much to them.

I will go-in to get ready for R&R in ten days.

Well, you will not believe this. We went to the beach for a seven-day R&R. We were there for less than twenty-four hours and we were called on *Alert*. So now we have took over this hill, built bunkers and we are waiting. By the way, we have our bunker with roof and all done in one day. We are the best bunker makers. We will work on it more today.

There is supposedly a regiment of NVA on the way to Chu Lai. We are the *Out Post*. I am Platoon RTO again. Today I was asked for the third time to be the Company RTO, but I will stay with *my platoon*.

Today, 109 days left!

For some reason it is beautiful here. I have never felt so good on a hill before. There is a small creek down on the bottom. There are a couple of water buffalos in it. Swimming. There is a rice patty which extends for miles. I cannot see the end of it. The mountain flares up on one side and on one side stands a huge rock with an eagle's head on it.

I can see the South China Sea. On the other side is *Chu Lai* Air Base. You can see the Jets screeching as they land. A chopper is passing over us now. It is 2000 meters high. There are roads that have long since been abandoned. They stretch for miles between the mountains.

We sent out a patrol. We can see them over in the distance. About 2000 meters away. You can tell the old guys. They are as skinny as a board. My buddy (we call him Jelly Belly) weighed 230 lbs. coming in the Army. He weighs about 170 or less now.

Well, I am going to scale up some *Turtle Tangerine*. See you later.

Boss... Real fine. Tasted great.

There is a guy, Bill Fotis, who just got to Nam who brought a tape recorder with him. He has some good sounds. The *Mama and the Papas*

Well, I feel good. That is all I can say. I can hardly wait for these next nine days to pass.

I can hardly believe I am going to see you and Roxanna in such a short time. It is going to be weird to see you both in another country, after not seeing you for nine months!

Well, I guess I will try and catch the next chopper.

See you then, Fred Leo

Dear Roxanna *11 August 1968*

Well, what am I doing? Well, I am on a platoon size mission. This is my third day out. I climbed this mountain by taking a rocky stream bed. Air distance from bottom of mountain to top - or rather map distance it reads about 500 meters. We climbed straight up almost to a height of *365 feet*. That is name of the peak. *Hill 365.* I am an OP *(Observation Post)*.

The last two nights we have adjusted artillery on enemy mortar positions. I hope they don't decide to adjust their mortars on us. But if everything goes alright I will walk back down this mountain and we will get another platoon to take over tomorrow. Not long now. I might get back to the rear early if I get a chance. I should be aloud to get in the 16th if my plan works out.

Oh, well, We got an LZ set up here waiting for a "Bird." Resupply - the big time of the day! Everyone works up to that time of the day and when the "Bird" leaves us we start down hill until the next day. True Hassle. Well, I guess that wraps it up for now.

See you in Australia.

Wow! Be sure to bring my ring and our grandfathers watch. The gold one. It is in my jewelry box. Okay. Bring the chain for it too. I will write again soon.

Well bye, Fred Leo

Note: Fred Leo is in Australia on R&R for remainder of month

September 1968

Dear Ma *4 September 1968*

Well I can hardly believe it is the fourth of September already. I will have less than eighty days when you get this letter. Hope your trip home was fun. Did you stop anywhere?

Ma, I don't know if you realized this or not but my R&R would not have been complete without you. It will be so good to get home. Hope you enjoyed yourself, like I did.

I still have a slight cold. It will gradually go away. As for as my *ring worm*—well, they are disappearing. I am taking pills for them. The monsoon has closed in. It rains everyday. I guess I will have to start carrying a heavy poncho again. It gets cold. But not cold enough to see your breath yet.

When I got back to my company I went on sick call for my cold and the ring worm. So I ended up sleeping for two days. Just getting up to eat. I didn't go back to the field until the second of September. The reason was because my company was in rough terrain. They had to put down a landing zone with knives and a chain saw.

The day before I came we had two men killed and one wounded. The other platoon had four men killed and one wounded. Some of the men I knew well.

Today is the third of September.

We are by no means taking it easy. My company alone has

killed thirty NVA during this mission. Yesterday we found a tunnel complex. We also found four dead NVA. They weren't able to find them until now. They had packs and all kinds of gear, writing paper, maps, diaries, stamps and four sets of clothes and entrenching tools, hammocks and first aid equipment. Plus mortar rounds and Ak-47 ammunition. One guy was blown to pieces. We found his foot about three feet from him. It was a horrible sight. It gets you nervous. By the way I got an NVA belt buckle. Boss! We took it off the dead man's waist. *Bla!*

Oh well, all kinds of things are around here. We will make a Fire Base here to keep the NVA from rocketing Chu Lai.

Well, I can proudly say that I have spent more time in the field than anyone else in my platoon. All the old timers are gone. Also I will get the first citation for E-5 Sgt. that comes down to my platoon, but I will still try and stay RTO.

I hope Aunt Lillian is okay. Tell here I think of her often. Tell everyone hello. Okay? I am as good as home right now. Okay. Don't worry.

Bye for now, Fred Leo

P.S. Send some spices okay? Garlic, onion powders!
This is what happened while I was on R&R. We lost two men dead. "C" Company lost eight men dead and about seven wounded. I am on a hill "A" Company took. The whole Rocket Ridge is one big NVA bunker line. I wonder what they are planning?

Dear Ma and Dad *8 September 1968*

Received your package. I can hardly wait till my next meal to try out the chili powder. That mosquito repellent surprised me. I can spray it on my clothes, but we get cans fairly easy here. I didn't know what kind of meal I will make for chow. I will try to make something up real good.

Could you send some garlic and onion power too. Okay. The guys love that stuff.

Roxanna said you went on a hydro foil ride after I left. She said it was wild.

I am still on this hill. As an OP. I am going to stay here about five more days. I am in no danger. They have the NVA plotted about 5000 meters away. We have been putting B-52 strikes on them. A total of about four-hundred to five-hundred of the thousand pound bombs.

Boy, it is real cool up here. We are seven-hundred feet up.

Remember Pine Tree Island where I was about two months ago? Well, my company is split up. One platoon on this hill, two near Pine Tree. We should be here for about, or rather at Pine Tree and the OP for about a month. Sounds good. Also if we make an advance on this battalion of NVA, I will not have to worry about anymore fighting after that. Wow! Sounds good.

The company commander asked me personally to be his RTO. This is the fourth time I have been offered the job. But I want to stay with my platoon, so I said no.

I got a *good* idea. Since I can't get a delay in route at Hawaii, I will head for Washington state. Then down to San Francisco to see Aunt Martha. Then back to Hawaii with my airlines discount *Youth Stand By*. The Army pays for my plane ride from San Francisco to Chicago so all I pay is about $150.00 round trip. I will stay in Hawaii one week and then I will come home. I just can't pass up the chance to go to Hawaii. So, we will see.

Well, it is getting dark. See you in the morning.

Well, it is morning of the 10th of September.

It is midnight. I had a lot to do today. I had to change my location, so I had to build another hutch, set out trip flares, and all kinds of things.

I seen another B-52 bombing at another place. These NVA are all over.

I feel like I am committing suicide just being on these hills. A whole battalion pulled off these hills in one day. They could sneak back up and take it from us with comparative ease.

By the way we are up against a regiment of NVA. I don't know how many that is but it is a total of over ten battalions. The B-52's should even us out.

Remember *Chippewa*—Christmas Day? Well, I can see it

from here. Also Hill 385 and Bien Son Bridge. The Song Tra Bong River, my old AO last December. Also the whole Chu Lai area. We can see everything - River North - River South - Hill 69 - Pine Tree Island.

This morning I had the beans, beef stew and Vienna sausages mixed with the chili sauce. Some good old stateside chow. I had the corn tonight with a can of beans and meat balls.

You know my platoon sergeant, well, he is going home for a month starting the 22nd of September. Then he will return to Nam for a six month more tour in the field. He has only spent six months in the field but still it takes some guts to extend in Nam in a line infantry company, especially since we are supposed to go to the DMZ in January.

When he gets back, I will be too short to go to the field. I am looking forward so much to the day that I step inside a car and just drive.

Tell Aunt Lillian I think about her all the time. Okay. Tell her I will be home soon and will fix a meal for her. Okay

By the way, I feel great. My ring worm is slowly disappearing. I haven't taken anything for them or put anything on them, but they are almost gone.

I hope you were able to catch up on work okay. I don't know what I would have done if you weren't there.

I felt so out of place in Australia. Did you? I was or had been stereotyped there. A GI among six-hundred in the city. It was depressing. I never felt completely at ease there. I felt I had to run every minute, so I would have no regrets when I returned.

This is the first time the moon has been bright since I got here.

I can hear the generators from LZ Chippewa from here. That is wild.

Would you believe I had a communication and I lost my pen when I answered it.

So that Democratic Convention in Chicago sounded like it should have been held on an isolated island.

We will not get any resupply today. The choppers will be on a combat assault. I think they are going to attack the NVA regimental headquarters. We found out its location from a captured NVA. The NVA was delirious. He was shell shocked. I imagine the dead will be piled three high after those B-52 strikes.

You will not believe this. The whole division has changed its call signs. We are numbers now. Like third platoon is all numbers from 87 to 94, also our call sign is "Pallid Naggin". So when I call anyone I am "Pallid Naggin 6-1 Kilo." *Wow!* Battalion is now known as *'Stall Trap'*. Got to relearn all new call signs.

Well, the clouds keep covering the moon and my guard is almost over. So I will see you later.

Well it is now 4:15 P.M. The fog has rolled in and it is raining slightly. The wind is rustling the trees. The trees around here are shattered by shrapnel. The limbs look almost human, but the tree is dead now. Just the skeleton remains.

Other trees have dead limbs hanging on them, as if they cannot face the reality of death.

I am sitting next to my fox hole. It is about four feet wide and three feet deep. I dug it myself. The other men are not willing to work. The clay colored dirt brings back memories of NVA holes in Que Son Valley. There is a dead NVA about two feet away from my hole. I covered him up.

I use the corn can as a water cup and hot chocolate cup.

You can almost hear the dead walking through the trees. The silence is ominous.

Artillery echoes in the distance. I wonder if I will be able to recognize the enemy incoming mortars?

Well, I better not make this letter any longer. By till next time.

Today is the eleventh of September. I should get this mailed tomorrow. Tell everyone Hi. Don't catch a cold. Okay.

Fred Leo

Dear Ma and Dad *16 September 1968*

Well, it is night. As always I can hardly see what I am writing.

The moon is not up yet. I don't imagine it will be up for over two hours. I am hoping Aunt Lillian doesn't die before I get back. Ma, if something happens, go to the Red Cross. Tell them anything. I would like to be there okay? Don't tell Aunt Lillian this, but remember.

Dad, how was fishing? Catch some big ones, or are those the ones that got away. Just kidding. I don't know if I will ever take up fishing again. Ma told me you were getting a new boat, the last one was too small.

Tell Raymond it will not be long now till I get some of that good old gizzard stew. The winter must be closing in now. You have any snow yet?

Well, here I am in the boonies. I wish I could get out of here but I will not. I talk-back to the guys in the rear so they don't like me. They wouldn't help me.

We came off the big mountain. One guy fell off a cliff and broke a leg. He was new, but he will never see the boonies again.

Right now I am in the Rocket Pocket. I came out here after our platoon had a two-day stand down. I am setting right next to the mountain the NVA use for a path to come down from the mountains for food. We are going to starve them a little.

I was doing a little figuring. My platoon has lost nine men dead. About thirty or more wounded, and lost about ten men because of them going to the rear.

That is about fifty men I have seen get wounded, killed and leave. This is just my platoon of about thirty men. You start thinking when all of a sudden you are the oldest guy in your platoon. The men have all seen less action than me. Wow! Am I proud.

I stated my rights today, and pulled some hard held strings. I made it clear I was platoon RTO and I was to be treated as such, and I would be picked last to do an extra job.

Wow! I guess I am absolutely squared away You should have seen the uproar when I wouldn't shave my side burns and cut my hair. If I tell them I will not cut my hair again, I will get an Article 15. Oh boy. So I will have to shape up next time I go in.

We were choppered back to Chu Lai for a few hours. That's when I seen the Air Force test a jet engine. They just had the engine put on wheels. Then they tested it. It looked weird out of the jet. Tonight I am going on a Rat Patrol. We get up at 4 A.M. and walk around till dawn trying to locate VC or NVA in the villages. It is tricky work.

Are you sending some garlic and onion powders? I am looking

forward to them. My chili powder is almost gone.

Well, nothing else now. I will write tomorrow morning.

It is morning, I will write later, Fred Leo

Dear Ma *24 September 1968*

Well, it has rained for the last three or four days regularly. We have walked thru rivers to our neck and picked off leaches. It is getting real cold out. It feels like forty degrees out here.

I heard about Argo High School. That is a bring down. Shooting at police and riots in my old school. How is it affecting us? Bad, or are we outside of the troubled area.

HAPPY BIRTHDAY!!!
AND
ANNIVERSARY!!

Ma, did you get the flowers I sent you? Hope you had fun.

Well, my feet are starting to rot. I have lost close to three layers in one spot. I am going to let them get real bad. They will be my excuse to get in *early*. My feet will be back in shape after a month.

Well, the NVA are getting bad. One of our platoons lost three men yesterday. We went after rocketeers two days ago. They were so close we heard the rockets blast off. They shot four at a time! Rockets that is.

Then we went to check out the hills we knew were booby trapped. It just blows your mind. It is unbelievable how it plays with your mind.

Well, last night we set up in an ambush after a hard rain. I was laying in a river. It is virtually impossible to keep dry.

I have started to put my writing materials in my helmet again. My back is weak so I can't hump! That's another excuse to get in the rear. Also my teeth! They are rotting away. So I will make a move in about thirty days or less.

By the way I am going to the mountains tomorrow or so. Don't worry. I only stay there a week. Then I will be in the lowlands for the rest of the time in the field. So if I play it cool, everything will be okay.

Let me think. Today I have sixy-two days left. When you get this letter I will have about fifty-five. *Time Fly*

That bottle of seasoning salt is fabulous. Could you send some more. It is half gone already. Makes cooking more fun.

Can hardly wait to see some of the pictures. I will probably send a couple back if I can't keep them dry.

The sun is clearing up the rash on my legs.

Tell Lorraine I received her letter. Sounds like she is doing great.

Well, I will leave now. I will write soon.

Bye till then, Fred Leo

Letter From Father

Dear Fred *25 September 1968*

I still find it difficult to think of anything to write about. It seems to me that it's just about the same every day. Not that the days are dull however, as for the mama she is getting to be quite a wheeler dealer since the last of you kids have gone. I guess Roxanna must take after her in that she seems to have the same inquiring mind and adventuresome spirit. She plays golf, sometimes twice a week, plays cards of evenings two or three nights week and has joined a bowling league.

We are getting along fine in the stores. Except for the hold-ups in our store and in the store Lynn Harris manages. We will soon have one in Joliet. (A store - not a hold-up).

I went fishing alone up in Wisconsin a couple of weeks ago. All I caught was one northern pike about thirty inches long. I was trying for musky. I may give it one more try toward the end of the week. After that I intend going to Florida. The weather will be cooling off enough to lure the fish out of deep water and back long the mangrove trees. I noted in your last letter that you doubted you'd ever take up fishing again. Likely that is a wise choice. Unfortunately for me a fishing trip now and then seems to do something for me that no other form of recreation can seem to replace. Maybe it's because I'm so poor at them that I can't seem to get into step.

I was down to the Cains during the hot weather and stayed about three days. I didn't get a single fish. They have sold all of their livestock and no longer have anything to do. It is true that Mr. Cain is beginning to feel pretty bad since he had a light heart attack. Mrs. Cain has the palsy. It looks as though they haven't much left to live for.

Things down there in Tennessee are beginning to take on something of the same lively tempo which we have around us. They have a lot of the hills staked out and are selling them for building lots.

I think of you a lot and look forward to the day when you will be out of the danger zone. November won't be long coming up. It will be nice seeing you, but more important you will then be out of the firing line.

Richard Russell is working over to the store in Westmont with Ray Wilkerson. He and his wife have separated. I think they are going to get a divorce. Lorraine and Ray and their babe are getting along fine, with another babe on the way. Lorraine seems to be real happy.

So it goes. And that's about all of the news for now. Oh yes, Linda was in the store today. I was telling her mother the other day that I figured you was going to bring back one of those little Vietnamese girls with you and she said that she wouldn't have to worry about getting mixed up with the Brown's that way.

I understand you're writing to a few other pretty girls. And we got a few more new ones you haven't seen. One of them is named Barbara Connolly. Well that's about the limit of what I can think, of so for now.

Goodby, you father
J.B.

Dear Ma and Dad *27 September 1968*

Dad, I got your letter. I was sorry to hear about the 'Cains', but I expected as much for their age.

I have your picture and Ma's in the top of my helmet. When I set it down some of the new guys see it and think you are a cool "Gramps" or "Pop's." Just kidding, they think you are 'cool'. So what did you do on your wedding anniversary? You didn't go fishing did you? Have you got that new boat yet? I think if I get the time I am going to Florida and go skiing and all. Sounds good, but I don't think I will have time.

Well I am on this hill now. I am not sure of the name, but it is near *Hill 707.* It hasn't rained too bad the last few days, but in a month the monsoon officially starts. They are blowing down trees and bushes with *Bangalor* Torpedoes made during World War II.

Say, Ma, I used up the last of the seasoning salt. Could you send some more. Okay? Oh, about that picture I sent of me. Could I have a copy?

Nothing has happened. First platoon lost four men but that is all.

I feel great. The longer I am in the field the healthier I get. My ring worms and rash has went away.

I am buying a roll of film from my buddy. So I will mail it home when I get them taken. Well nothing else.

See you in 59 Days. Tell Aunt Lillian Hi!

Say, could you send me a $200 money order. Okay. I want to start getting money for when I come back to the States.

Also it sure would help if you sent my drivers license to Aunt Martha, and my Youth Fare Cards to fly the airlines for cut rates.

Well bye for now, Fred Leo

Dear Ma and Dad *30 September 1968*

Well, let me start out with a request. Could you send me a wrist band, the type for a sprained wrist. I was working on clearing this perimeter out and my hand sprained on me. I cannot even use it. I have it wrapped up but it doesn't help. Remember it is *one piece*. All you do is slip it on your wrist. Okay? I will not go into the rear so I need it bad. It is my left hand.

I got your package with the garlic salt. It is about a quarter gone already. All I had for dinner was the can of beans you sent me. They were good. I put garlic on them and salt.

I am still on this Hill. It is windy. It must be about 30 mph. It stays like this. I built a bunker yesterday. We got the roof on and everything built in the same day.

We have been having trouble with the 'dinks'. They keep bugging us at night. We have one man dead *already!* He was new.

We keep the *dinks* back with grenades. Every time one goes off I jump. I am like a guy with red ants all night.

I am eating those prunes you gave me. They are good.

I can't believe this wind. And RAW! We have been on this mountain for four days. I will be up here about ten more days. then we go to the rear, for I hope a three-day stand down. That will bring me to the middle of next month. I have decided to start shamming the first of November, or around then.

Well I will stop writing for now.

See you in a while, Fred Leo

October 1968

Dear Mom *1 October 1968*

My hand has gotten better fast. No sweat. I don't need a wrist band. I will keep it wrapped up a few more days and it should be strong again.

Nothing happening. I should be on this hill for about nine more days, then we will head for low ground. It is almost safer in the mountains now. Hill 69 got mortared and rocketed. It is all torn up. First time it was mortared for *ages*.

I don't know what the VC or NVA have planned, but I think they are going to try a *big push*.

Oh well, I'd better go. Chopper will be around shortly.

Bye till later, Fred Leo

Dear Ma and Dad *6 October 1968*

Well, I am still on this hill. It is called LZ Moore in honor of the man killed here. Everything has been quiet in these mountains where I am.

Everything is hanging in the air right now. I don't know what is going to happen. Half of our company consists of new men. We get about three every third days. Our strength is up to about thirty-five now or may forty! Which is phenomenal. So to be serious, they can't be putting us into anything thick for two months, so our new men can get used to Nam.

I got word from very reliable sources today that I will probably make Sgt. E-5 this month or next. In other words, I will without a doubt come home with E-5 stripes on my arm.

That is one of the best things I have heard in a long time.

As far as leaving the field. I could get away with leaving the field as soon as November first. But it depends on the situation. If I am somewhere easy I will stay out. If we are going into something bad, I will go in.

Today I only have *50* days left.

I am already changing my idea about Hawaii. I imagine I will stay at Aunt Martha's in San Francisco a day or so, then try to pick up some clothes and then make it to Chicago.

I guess I will be having Thanksgiving with Martha. I got a roll of film from my buddy. I have two pictures left to take. They are good ones of us on a patrol along Rocket Ridge, of LZ Moore and of Chippewa and the view from here. I will send them 'free' of charge to Kodak. When I get them back I will send them home. It will be maybe two weeks before I get them home.

You know I almost go batty pulling two hours guard. You just listen and look. A guy could go crazy just being mummified for two hours each night.

Tomorrow we aren't going to do anything. I will play it cool tomorrow.

Well, that is all for now.

30 more days - I can hardly wait.

See you soon, Fred Leo

Dear Uncle Ken, Maude and Karen *9 October 1968*

You will never guess what I received. A package I could put the *Empire State* in.

The Chocolate Chip cookies were fabulous. I ate them before I opened the Brownies box. Then I couldn't stop eating the brownies. I ate them up in a very short time.

Thank you so much. They taste real fresh. They got here in about ten days or less.

Well, right now I am on a hill. All I can say is I get plenty of fresh air. *No smog problems!*

I am going to march off this mountain tomorrow. It is about 728 feet up. The straight line distance to the bottom is only about 3000 meters, but you should see what we have to walk on. We will probably take a stream bed that drops into waterfalls and things. It ain't easy. Last time we had a man break his leg. Most every one broke their rear coming down. It will end up about 7000 meters or more, only a days 'hump' for my platoon. It takes other platoons longer to get to the bottom.

"D" company, 1/6th Infantry Second Platoon has a humping record. No one has out-humped us! This is no lie. The colonel congratulated us.

We have gone over 13,000 meters through rice patties and woods on a search-and-destroy mission, in under ten hours!

I guess this is why my back is getting weak. I can't hump like before. So I don't carry anything to sleep on, or keep me dry. I have a light weight blanket. So I imagine I will be water logged soon.

Oh well, I can stand anything for only *47 days*.

I can hardly wait to leave this country. It will have to go so far to get organized. It is so uncoordinated. Such is Viet Nam.

Well, a chopper will be here shortly. So got to get this mailed. Hope everyone is okay.

Bye for now, Fred Leo

Letter From Father

Dear Fred *15 October 1968*

The Mama and I came down to Florida Thursday morning, and this is late Sunday. The time is getting closer when you will be coming home. I can imagine how anxious you are to get out of there. Here at home the political situation is heating up. I hope Nixon gets in. If Humphrey make it I believe that our country will be headed straight down the "give everything away" road. It will make the surrender of our country to militant minorities, further laxities of law enforcement, while the labor leaders consolidate their positions at the expense of the rank and file.

Well I can only hope that my gloomy predictions are just that, overly gloomy. We are trying to buy a piece of business property in front of a shopping center down here in Florida. The center is about the size of the one were Frank Jr. has his store in Villa Park. The property has 250 feet frontage on a well traveled street and has ideal entrances plus meeting up with the shopping center parking. We plan to put up a hot dog stand like Dick Portillo's. Also a nice Brown's Fried Chicken building like the one in Wheeling. So maybe after you get out and get a bit of experience you would like to try your fortunes in Florida.

Mr. Jasper and Max are going to meet me at the airport in Miami on Sunday night. The Mama is going home Sunday morning. We are going down on the Keys and to Key West for a couple of days and then out to the Everglades for about a week.

Don is doing pretty well. We just raised our prices to what they are in Chicago. I hope everything turns out allright. We'll know in a couple of weeks if our volume cuts back.

Well, I'm suffering from the same old problem of not being able to think of much to write about. So I guess I'll just say I'm getting anxious to see you. I'm wearing your medal and saying prayers for you. The chain on the Mam's medal broke and I patched it up for her.

You father John R.

Dear Ma and Dad *15 October 1968*

Well, I have been receiving everything okay. I have the seasoning salt. Now I need some Garlic. Okay. This will be the last time, or almost the last time I will ask for spices.

Tell Lorraine I got all her letters. Baby Danny looked like an Indian. Soon I will start getting Christmas packages. Wow! I can hardly wait.

Well, here is what happened. I left LZ Moore on the eleventh. We walked 2000 meters to Hill 707 and then down 707 in less than a day. It took the other companies *three days!* So my platoon really surprised them.

Next morning we humped for about 4000 meters in two hours through patties and then another 4000. We set up for the night and next morning went 4000 more meters to Hill 69. And then to *Anton Bridge!* (That's the bridge where my buddies were killed during Tet Offensive.)

I can't believe it. I have a bunker that three people live in. It is boss. I borrowed my Trans Oceanic Radio from my buddy. Plenty of candles.

It is one A.M. First day here and we had a 2-1/2 ton truck hit and a jeep. *Bla!* No one hurt.

I been reading a lot. I read about three books last two weeks. Read *The Great Race* yesterday. I just started *Blood Brother.*

Say, I couldn't believe it but I weighed in at 160 lbs. I humped pretty good these last two days. Probably recuperated on LZ Moore. We had one man drop out and one go in on extraction. Only lost two men.

Say, today we are going to receive a lieutenant. I hope he is okay. I don't feel like being messed with. I am not sure how many days left, but about 40 today. I will clean my rifle tomorrow, have the guys buy me chow at the PX, and read all day.

Well I will be here till the 21st. I have it unbelievably nice.

See you soon, Fred Leo

Dear Ma and Dad *October 18, 1968*

Received your package and car magazine.

I heard it said it is an insult to say 'thank you' to your people that are closest. So I'll say it like this: Ma, you are one of the few people who stood by me without faltering. Thank you.

You said you wanted to come and see me in San Francisco. There are certain things I must do before I see you again, and before I come home. I must do them alone.

I will not go to Hawaii, and I will not stay in San Francisco long. I will be home shortly. I will tell you in advance when I plan to get home. Okay. Don't change your plans because of me. It would be short sighted of me not to realize you are trying to help me, but I will be fine.

I was happy to hear Lorraine liked the gift you bought her and said it was from me. I don't think too quick sometimes, but I might learn some day.

I am on guard in my bunker. I have only one hour to go. Tomorrow I will go around town. I have been close to this bunker for four days now. I am not bored but I get very angry at these other soldiers at times. I am very angry now. I will tell them my feelings and loose my OP job. I do not care to have it, if I feel the soldiers around me are unjust. I will wait a while to see.

Today I have but *38* days left. I have less than a month left in the field. Less if I decide to.

Bye for now, Fred Leo

Dear Ma and Dad *24 October 1968*

I been receiving all your letters. I have very high spirits. Physically I am in real bad shape. My back is in bad shape. A muscle is pulled. I will be in soon though.

I have orders for the 22nd of November. I report to Cam Ranh Bay. So I legally get out of the field the thirteenth of November. I have a dentist appointment the seventh and of course my back being as it is I will not be venturing back to the field. So I must wait two weeks at the most. If my back gets any worse I will go in sooner. But when I do make a move it is the final one.

I am not exactly sure where I will go. But I heard it was *Fort Polk, Louisiana*. Basic training or AIT. I am not positive as yet but that would mean I would become a Drill Instructor. The orders are in the rear.

I got a sheet from the Veteran's Administration for the money given to Veterans of Nam. It is $100. Enough for a down payment on a car maybe. I will have to get a car. I imagine a VW is my best bet. I am not making much money so I am not going to spend it all on a gas eating car.

As far as San Francisco goes, it is necessary that I be alone so I can gather myself together. *Wow!* I am so happy. I can hardly write anymore.

So I will go now.

See you soon, Fred Leo

Dear Ma and Dad *27 October 1968*

Well, I have been over here for over eleven months. *Wow!* I have only nine more days left in the field. I will get out of the field the sixth of November. Legally the thirteenth, but I should be able to sham a measly week.

I have my Orders in my hands. Wow! Do you know where I am going? Well, I am going to Ft. Polk, Louisiana. I will be teaching AIT.

My DEROS has been dropped to the 22nd of November. I will leave my Company about the 20th.

Oh, I will take only a week home from Nam, so I can take Christmas time home without using up all my leave time.

I will have to get a car! I think I will get just a VW till I get organized. Think about it and if you have any good ideas I will listen, but a car is a must! Also, if you are in doubt about what I need, well, a Remington Electric three-speed with side burn trimmer. Okay? I need a good brush like Roxanna has. Also, maybe you could help me with some accessories on my car, if I get one, which I will okay. So no sweat.

I would rather get a bigger and better car but I will wait till the summer. Okay. A better and more convenient time. Okay.

Well, of course I am still in the 'sticks'. But we have had no contact. Nothing out here. We will go in for a stand-down, which will last for about sixty hours in a few days.

I feel great except for the famished and weak feeling I have. I know how an old man feels. I must sound like a fanatic writing. Well, I think I am. I only have twenty-five days left in Viet Nam.

Less than a month! ! I will write later.

Oh, before I forget it, will Doctor Swanstrom be in Chicago the first of December? If so I would like an appointment. I must see him okay? If he leaves somewhere I could plan to get there sooner or something. Please tell me as soon as you receive this letter. Bye till later.

Well, resupply came in. I will get this out on the next bird. Did I tell you I read *Gone With the Wind?* What a beautiful book. It was fabulous. I read *Blood Brother,* about the Indian Chief Cochise and Tom Jeffords. It was good, but not like *Gone With The Wind.*

I been thinking I am going to be a truck driver for a few years. Trans-continental. All kinds of plans are clicking in my mind. Can hardly wait to try them out.

Well must go now. Take care

Say Hi to everyone, Fred Leo

P.S. Give me the answer about Dr. Swanstrom. I must see him when I get back.

Say, never thought I could get this far without Dr. Swanstrom my Naprapath! Me neither.

Letter from Mother - Only one saved

Hi Fred Leo Brown: *27 October 1968*

I can't quite figure out where you are. Are you out in the field? You said you borrowed your radio back again to use, so maybe you're at the rear? For a while?

You asked me not to come to San Francisco to pick you up. O.K. I'll send your driver's license, money order, and Youth card to Aunt Martha's for you. Will you call as soon as you get in though? I don't think we'll be going to New Orleans. Maybe we will go later on during the year.

Daddy, Max, the breadman, and Mr. Jasper are down in Florida fishing. They hired a boat at Key West and went out into the ocean to an island called Ft. Jefferson, and fished around there for two or three days. Daddy said it was beautiful way out there. Now they are back and going to go to Flamingo for the rest of the week.

We raised prices down in Florida and they called me yesterday and said that business hadn't dropped off a bit and so they'll make a good bit now at the store...

Business here is going along very well. We have an ANNIVERSARY that all the stores are celebrating this month. We are giving a coupon worth $1.00 on our Chicken and a Half Dinner. The ad is running in the LIFE Magazine in the Chicago area, in both of the TV Guides for the Tribune and the Sun Times, and we are all running it locally. I'm enclosing a copy of the Press Release that is running in the papers too. We're getting quite a large response from it, and business is really good this week.

Well, take care of yourself - brush your teeth, etc. wash you face and neck. 160 lbs. Wow! It must all muscle.

Today is real windy - about 45 to 50 degrees and sunny. I think I will go to church this morning.

Well, goodby for now, Fred Leo: Are you still a radio telephone operator?

Mom

Dear Ma and Dad *28 October 1968*

Guess what,

I am in the hospital. Well I couldn't last for ever.

I got hit bye a booby trap.

Don't worry.

I will be well soon. Nothing permanently damaged.

I got hit on my right arm, between the eyes and through my ear.

I will write later when I can use my arm. No sweat.

I can walk and I feel good.

Fred Leo

Dear Ma and Dad *29 October 1968*

Say I have been sitting here thinking.

Could you meet me in San Francisco?

You and Dad could get a flight to Martha's. I am not sure when I will be there but get a flight the 22nd or 23rd.

Have reservations for the 22,23, & 24. OK.

If I find out anything else I will tell you.

Say, I am getting a Bronze Star for Valor.

I should be able to use my arm in about a week.

The man in front of me, when this happened, is dead.

Well, tell me as soon as you know if you can make it. If you can't, tell me. I understand. I am a man now.
Don't worry at all. Okay.

Fred Leo

Dear Ma and Dad *31 October 1968*

Believe it or not
I am coming back to the States.
By the time you get this letter I will be in the States.
They have to operate on my arm. It ain't bad.
Don't worry, I ain't worrying.

See you soon, Fred Leo

P.S. I am all smiles.
I weigh 148 lbs. Funny how weight plays around.

CHANGE ONE:
I am going to Japan! !
I will be home when I get there!.
Oh, well, tis life.
See you in about a month.

Fred Leo

Ha! I just made Sergeant.

Code of Silence

A young man went to fight in the Vietnam War. While resting along a muddy jungle path under a leaking poncho, he writes, "Mom, it sure does rains a lot during the monsoon."

Reading between the lines, she writes back, "Watched the Evening News and the war looks pretty bad. Tell me, what's really going on over there?"

. . . continued on next page

On the edge of a flooded rice field, he watches
as the last of the KIA are loaded onto the medevac.
He writes, "Wow, you ought to see these rice
fields. They flow in the distance like a lake of green."

To which his mother replies,
"Don't hold back, tell me the truth.
I can not rest until I know."

In the midst of heated battle with the stench
of decaying flesh filling his nostrils, he writes,
"You should see the sun as it rises over
the white rolling South China Sea Fog."

In the next letter his mother pleads,
"Son, I know you and I know when
you are leaving things out.
Pl-*eee*-ase, fill in the blanks."

Reeling from an earlier firefight, he
stares with blood-shot eyes over the field-of-fire.
"Tomorrow we combat-assault the hill. Truth?
I don't know how much longer I'm gonna last."

To this his father fires back,
"Don't write such depressing letters.
You're mother doesn't need
to know all those things!"

So, after eating his first rations in days
he writes, "The sky is blue, the truest blue
you could ever imagine. And the sunset,
why they're simply amazing. It's like. . . ."

Appendices

Appendix 1

Golden Rules of Combat

1. You are not superman.
2. Recoilless rifles - ain't.
3. Suppressive fire - won't.
4. If it's stupid, but works, it ain't stupid.
5. Don't look conspicuous - it draws fire.
6. Never draw fire - it irritates everyone around you.
7. When in doubt, empty the magazine.
8. Never share a foxhole with anyone braver than you are.
9. Your weapon was made by the lowest bidder.
10. If your attack is going really well, it's an ambush.
11. If you can't remember, the claymore is pointed toward you.
12. All five-second grenade fuses are three seconds.
13. Try to look unimportant. They may be low on ammo.
14. If you are forward of your position, the artillery will be short.
15. The enemy diversion you are ignoring is the main attack.
16. The easy way is always mined.
17. The important things are very simple.
18. The simple things are very hard.
19. If you are short everything except enemy, you are in combat.
20. No OPLAN (plan of operation) survives first contact intact.
21. When you have secured an area, don't forget to tell the enemy.
22. Incoming fire has right-of-way.
23. No combat-ready unit has ever passed inspection.
24. No inspection-ready unit has ever passed combat.
25. Teamwork is essential. It gives them other people something to shoot at.
26. If the enemy is in range, so are you.
27. Beer math is 2 beers x 37 men = 49 cases.
28. Body count math is 2 VC + 1 NVA + 1 water buffalo = 37 KIA.
29. Friendly fire - isn't.
30. Anything you do can get you shot - including doing nothing.
31. Make it too tough for the enemy to get in, and you can't get out.

32. Tracers work both ways.
33. The only thing more accurate than incoming enemy fire is incoming friendly.
34. Radios will fail as soon as you need fire support desperately.
35. If you take more than your fair share of objectives, you will have more than your fair share to lose.
36. Both sides are convinced they are about to lose -they're both right.
37. Professionals are predictable - but the world is full of amateurs.
38. Murphy was a grunt.

Appendix 2

Number One is:

1. You're socks are dry
2. Your boots are off
3. A Saigon bar hostess who doesn't like tea
4. A USO show with 20 dancing girls
5. Pre-filled sand bags
6. Being next in line
7. An incoming dud hand grenade
8. B-52s - gunships - Spooky Jolly Green Giant
9. R&R
10. Beer (any kind, hot or cold)
11. Your choice of C-rations
12. Can of mixed fruit
13. Plenty of heat tablets
14. Sleeping anywhere but on the ground.
15. Day in the village with the boy's sister
16. A letter from your girl (anybody for that matter)
17. Rolled marijuana joints
18. Being a short timer
19. Freedom bird
20. Huey

Number Ten is:

1. Monsoon
2. Hitting the dirt in a rice paddy
3. A USO show with no girls
4. A walk in the country
5. Un-sweetened Kool-Aid
6. A dud hand grenade
7. Incoming
8. Empty bottle of bug juice
9. Ham and Mothers
   Choke and Puck
   C-rations
10. Steak cooked in Nuoc Mam sauce
11. Combat Assault
12. Ambush
13. Mine sweep
14. Bunker guard
15. Tunnel rat
16. MOS-11B40
17. A Dear John letter saying your girl is engaged to your best friend who is 4-F
18. Your rifle is a Jammin' Jenny
19. You're an NFG
20. LP or Out Post
21. Pointman

Appendix 3

"A question RFK shouldn't forget: Who are the Americans?"

Boston Globe April 15, 1968
written by syndicated columnist Joseph Alsop, Staff Journalist with the *Washington Post*

Quang Tin Province, South Vietnam — By some standards, perhaps the scent was sadly banal. In a dusty clearing, on the flank of dusty Landing Zone Baldy, the formation was as smart as wartime ever permits.

The honor guard's uniform showed the scars of combat, though they had done the best refurbishing they could, and the guard commander's hand was messily bandaged, for he had lost most of his finger waving on his men in the Tet offensive near Da Nang. The men to receive decorations had been given a bit of help with their spit and polish, so they looked like peace-time soldiers—though the deeds for which they got their Silver Stars and Bronze Stars were high acts of warlike valor and sacrifice.

Here, one noticed all the strains of our America were gloriously represented—Irish and Yankee, Jewish and Puerto Rican, German and Central European and Negro, last listed, but by no means last in act and presence. The officer reading the citations was exceptionally impressive, very young Negro lieutenant, who is making the Army a career.

The Stars and Stripes drifted gently in the bright air in the iron grip on an even younger Negro draftee, who rather resembled Cassius Clay—powerful, ramrod, erect, proud of silken and symbolic burden. And at the head of the list of Silver Stars, along with Captain Francis X. Brennan ("Heroic Actions") and one or two others, was 1SG Hubert B. Ramier ("Heroic actions and personal example"), a giant veteran Negro who had led his platoon with such incomparable dash he and his men overran a whole hornet's nest of enemy-filled bunkers.

The unit being decorated was the 1st Battalion, 6th Infantry Regiment, which descends directly, albeit by the transformations, from the new-raised Regiment of the War of 1812 that the British Admiralty named "The Regulars." So, the unit colors, along with the Stars and Strips, were heavy with battle-honors from the old times.

Canada, Chippewa and Lundy's lane, The Bad Axe River, where

they fought the Black Hawk Indian Wars, Vera Cruz, Churubusco and Chipultepec, Manassas, Antietam, (Fredericksburg), Chancellorsville and Gettysburg, Santiago de Cuba and Panay in the Phillipines, Alsace-Lorrain, Sait Mihiel and Oruel Meuse-Argonne, from Algeria via bitter Anzio to the Po Valley where Wehrmacht broke at last in Italy—all were there except Korea which the Regiment somehow missed.

Now the 1st of the 6th was receiving yet another honor from its deeds in Vietnam. As the unit-citation was read in the standard, flat, military voice, the breeze grew strong, the old pennons fluttered out, and one could read the battle names embroidered on half a dozen of them. Thus vividly reminded of the long American past, thus simultaneously face to face with youthful patriotism and brave endurance and our country's strange accomplishment, and old men's eyes perhaps ludicrously misted.

That was over soon, however, with the concluding address by the Americal Division Commander, Major General Samuel Koster, a tough and able leader in the field, but not exactly a Churchillian orator. Or was it really over, after all? For as the helicopter lifted off again, one found oneself almost desperately asking, for the 100th time, the question that Vietnam always raises: Who are the Americans?

In this war, the question presents itself in novel guise that may have some importance for Senator Robert F. Kennedy. For the contest, this time is not the usual one, between the fat, forgetful comfort of home front and the hardiness and bravery of the field. That customary contrast is there, too, of course, but now there is another.

On the one hand are the large group senator's supporters whom someone flatteringly (or was it unflatteringly?) described as "chicly or leftish," who greet reports that their country has been successful on the battlefield with happy derision and almost eager for an American defeat in war. On the other hand are the people of every American strain, who stood proudly beneath the colors at LZ Baldy, serving their nation in war in the old American way.

In this way Senator Kennedy has his own credentials as, God knows, both his elder brothers did. Yet, there in Vietnam among the men of General Westmoreland's much vaster academy—so different in many ways from Berkely—the conclusion is unavoidable that Senator Kennedy cannot afford to forget the question: Who are the Americans?

Appendix 4

DEPARTMENT OF THE ARMY
Headquarters Americal Division
APO San Francisco 96374

AVDF-CG 27 May 1968

All Personnel of the Americal Division

It is with pride that I accept this opportunity to address you, the men of the Americal Division, on the occasion of the initial publication of our division's newspaper — The Southern Cross.

You have compiled a most enviable record since the division came to I Corps Tactical Zone as Task Force Oregon last April. You have consistently met and defeated the enemy on the battlefield. Your aggressiveness and zeal have been proven time and again, and have added laurels to the heritage of the Americal Division.

The Southern Cross is intended to recognize and publicize your exploits and achievements. Read it with pride -- pride in yourselves and in your Division's accomplishments.

I extend to you a hearty and sincere "Well Done," and the future Godspeed.

S. W. Koster
Major General, US Army
Commanding

Appendix 5

AVDF-BCNV (8 August 1968)
SUBJECT: Letter of Commendation

DA, HQ, 1st Bn 6th Inf, 198th Inf Bde (Lt), APO SF 96219

TO: Officers and Men

I take this opportunity to express my heartfelt admiration and appreciation to each and every "Regular" for the commendable manner in which you have accomplished the challenging missions assigned. The attached letter of commendation related but one of many impressive victories you have achieved in the past ten months. You prevented a major attack on the city of Danang by killing 268 enemy from the 60th Main Force Battalion during the Battle of Lo Giang (receiving the Valorous unit emblem). You killed 118 enemy from the 70th Main Force Battalion during the Battle of Op Bahn I, which resulted in the routing of the entire enemy force. During your 39 days on Operation Burlington Trail, you were credited with 145 enemy kills and 144 captured weapons, which turned back the 1st VC Regiment and allowed the road west to Tien Phouc to be opened for the first time since 1964. During the Second TET Offensive, while operating in the area around LZ Center, you killed 145 enemy and captured 50 weapons in 22 days of extremely heavy fighting against the entire 3rd NVA Regiment, 2nd NVA Division. The 31st Anti-aircraft Battalion and the 2nd NVA Division Reconnaissance Company were also encountered. Intelligence later revealed that you decimated one battalion and stopped the entire Regiment from accomplishing its mission. In your latest venture you have proved the night does not belong to "Charlie" and have successfully prevented his maneuver in the critical Chu Lai Area of Operation. You can be justifiably proud of your accomplishments and as the member of this elite unit I wish you continued successes in all future combat.

William D Kelley
LTC, Infantry

Appendix 6

DEPARTMENT OF THE ARMY
Headquarters, 198TH Infantry Brigade, AMERICAL DIVISION
APO San Francisco 96219

AVDG-BC 8 August 1968
SUBJECT: Letter of Commendation

Officers and Men
1st Battalion, 6th Infantry
198th Infantry Brigade (Lt)
APO SF 96219

I wish to commend you on the fact that it has been exactly two months since rockets were fired at Chu Lai. It is significant that the last rocket attack took place the night previous to the day the "Regulars" were assigned the responsibility for the "Rocket Valley" (Rocket Pocket) area.

Your aggressive spirit, determination, and tireless efforts have been the primary factors in deterring the enemy from attacking with rockets the important Chu Lai Base Complex.

I congratulate you on the successful accomplishment of your primary mission. I wish you continued success in all of your endeavors.

/S/Charles B. Thomas
Colonel, Infantry
Commanding

Appendix 7

DEPARTMENT OF THE ARMY
Headquarters, 1st Battalion, 6th Infantry
198th Infantry Brigade, Americal Division
Apo San Francisco 96219

AVDF-CH 20 October 1968

Subject: First Anniversary Memorial Message

To the Officers and Men
1st Battalion, 6th Infantry, 198th Infantry Brigade
APO San Francisco 96219

In the short six months I have served as this battalion's chaplain over half of its casualties have occurred and I have often been asked, "Why?" Why did these good and brave men have to suffer and even die?

Each man had his own private set of reasons I am sure but this I know: the men who "poured out their rich wine of youth, and their years yet to be" did so for a dream too good to be true. Theirs was a dream of the earth without war, without the taking of lives in battle, a dream of a world in which every human being would be able to live in peace, honor and justice, in true brotherhood as happy, healthy, mature persons. Did they dream the impossible dream or reach for the unreachable star? I hope not, for I dream that dream too!

Since the "Regulars" have been in the Republic of South Vietnam one hundred and four men have given their last full measure of devotion for their country, but why you ask. Perhaps the War Memorial in Glasglow, Scotland, gives a hint:

These died in war, that we at peace might live,

These gave their best, so we our best would give.

They died for you! So keep them in kindly memory now, but do not stop there. Hear the ancient prophet Jeremiah speak:

> **You, that have escaped the sword, go, stand not still. Jeremiah 51:50**

Please do not stand still—do something: be concerned, informed and poised for creative action, America needs your help.

What can we do to rightly honor our war dead? Resolve that they shall not have died in vain; but that this nation, under God, shall have a new birth of freedom and justice for all, both where you are and where we are right now. Remember the "Regulars" and the part your loved one had in bringing us to where we are. We pledge to you and yours that we shall do our part, the best way we know how, so as never to bring shame or embarrassment to any of its members, both past and present, but rather to bring honor and peace. And help me, their chaplin, to help them through your prayers and concern for us.

Glenn Paul Hargis
Chaplain (CPT), USA

Appendix 8

DEPARTMENT OF THE ARMY
Headquarters, 1st Battalion, 6th Infantry
198the Infantry Brigade, Americal Division
Apo San Francisco 96219

AVDF-BCNV 22 October 1968

Subject: First Anniversary Memorial Message

The men of the "Regulars"

On 22 October 1967, the "Regulars" came ashore and remained in the Republic of South Vietnam little cognizant of what the future would bring. Many men have come and gone, but their individual and combined efforts are still gratefully remembered today. On this first anniversary in Vietnam I want to take this opportunity to express my heartfelt thanks and appreciation to each and every "Regular" for the excellent manner in which you accomplished your many diverse missions. Because of your hard work and splendid effort "The Regulars March On" with their heads held high, their chests sticking out proudly, their guidons waving bravely for all to see. No matter the length of your service, you did your part to help the battalion to do its challenging work in the highest tradition of the military service.

I take this opportunity to express my thanks to you and to wish the battalion the very best of luck. I assumed command of the unit on 1 April 1968 and will be departing soon to my next assignment. As I think back upon my tour with the "Regulars" I am deeply impressed by the high caliber of performance in all elements of the command. Thanks to you we opened the road west to Tien Phuoc which had been closed since 1964 and denied the enemy vast quantities of rice and weapons. We blunted and then shattered the NVA in their Second Tet Offensive. We destroyed a NVA battalion-size unit and stopped the entire 3rd NVA Regiment around LZ Center. We faithfully guarded the Division's northern perimeter against VC rocket attacks on Chu Lai. Thanks to you, we have done a commendable job in every respect.

I am honored to be your commander and you can be justifiably proud of your many achievements. I also am mindful of the terrible cost in wounded and dead we had to suffer. I have asked our chaplain to prepare a memorial listing of the officers and men who gave their all. Please take a moment to read this list and offer a prayer or two for the men and officers of the "Regulars" as we carry on what they started. And pray for peace, a just, honorable, lasting peace. Remember the "Regulars!" I will, as I bid farewell to the most courageous men with whom I have ever served. Good luck and God bless you all.

1 Incl

William D. Kelly
LTC, Infantry
Commanding

Appendix 9

DEPARTMENT OF THE ARMY
HEADQUARTERS AMERICAL DIVISION
APO San Francisco 96374

GENERAL ORDERS 19 April 1968
NUMBER 2065

AWARD OF THE SILVER STAR

The following AWARD is announced posthumously.

YAMANE, BENJI
SERGEANT E5, United States Army,
Company D, 1st Battalion, 6th Infantry,
198th Infantry Brigade APO 96219

Awarded: Silver Star
Date action: 16 March 1968
Theater: Republic of Vietnam
Reason: For gallantry in action against a hostile force in the Republic of Vietnam. Sergeant Yamane distinguished himself by intrepid actions on 16 March 1968 while serving as a squad leader with Company D, 1st Battalion, 6th Infantry. On that date, Sergeant Yamane's squad was the lead element in a search and clear operation conducted by his company in an area southwest of Hoi An. Sergeant Yamane had positioned himself directly behind the point man where he felt that he could best observe and control the members of his squad. As he led the company toward their objective, he spotted a booby trap directly in the path of the point man. Immediately, Sergeant Yamane shouted a warning to his men, then turned and shoved a nearby squad member to the ground, using his body to protect his fellow soldier. In spite of his warning, the mine was tripped and the explosion mortally wounded Sergeant Yamane. His actions, taken with utter disregard for his own life, saved the life of

the soldier he had shielded from the blast and allowed the other members of the squad to get down and escape injury. Sergeant Yamane's courageous actions, unselfish concern for the lives of his comrades, and devotion to duty were in keeping with the highest traditions of the military service and reflected great credit upon himself, the Americal Division, and the United States Army.
Authority: By direction of the President under the provisions of the Act of Congress, approved 9 July 1918.

FOR THE COMMANDER

NELS A. PARSON, JR.
Colonel, GS
Chief of Staff

OFFICIAL:

DONALD Y. B. CHUNG
LTC, AGC
Adjutant General

Appendix 10

CITATION

By direction of the Secretary of the Army
The Army Commendation Medal

is awarded to

Specialist Four Fred L. Brown
United States Army

Who distinguished himself by exceptionally meritorious service in connection with military operations against a hostile force in the Republic of Vietnam. During the period

February 1968 to November 1968

he astutely surmounted extremely adverse conditions to obtain consistently superior results. Through diligence and determination he invariably accomplished every task with dispatch and efficiency. His unrelenting loyalty, initiative and perseverance brought him wide acclaim and inspired others to strive for maximum achievement. Selflessly working long and arduous hours, he has contributed significantly to the success of the allied effort. His commendable performance was in keeping with the highest traditions of the military service and reflects great credit upon himself, the Americal Division, and the United States Army

Appendix 11

A list of some landing zones, places and base camps the "Death Battalion" (1st of the 6th) passed over and fought from. From 4 Oct 67 thru 10 July 70.

Chu Lai . Duc Pho . LZ Carentan . LZ Bronco . LZ Gator . Nuoc Mau . Binh Son Bridge . Camp Bravo . LZ Colt . Da Nang . Lo Giang . LZ Baldy . LZ Cacti . Que Son Valley . Hiep Duc Valley . LZ West . LZ East (Hill 488) . LZ Center . Tam Ky . Hill 218 (LZ Bownam) . Hill 270 . Hill 488 . LZ Bowman . Hill 352 . Hill 350 . Hill 353 . Tien Phouc . Quang Tri . Burlington Trails . Dragon Valley . Rice Bowl . Hill 69 . Hill 76 . Hill 45 . Hill 50 . Hill 54 . Fat City . LZ Ross . Rocket Ridge . Rocket Pocket . Rocket Belt . Hill 707 . Hill 661 . Hill 720 . LZ Angle . LZ Moore . Larson Field . LZ Chippewa . Pine Tree Island . Paradise Island . Ky sang . Ky Phu . Son Tra Bong (River South) . An Ton Bridge (River North) . Om Bau Bridge . Ly Tin . Ky Tra . Bong Song . Sa Huhyn . Batangan Peninsula

A GRUNTS
VIETNAM WAR
DICTIONARY

The U.S. military has used several phonetic alphabets. The one that follows is the one I'm most familiar with.

Alpha	Golf	Mike	Sierra	Yankee
Bravo	Hotel	November	Tango	Zulu
Charlie	India	Oscar	Uniform	
Delta	Juliet	Papa	Victor	
Echo	Kilo	Quebec	Whiskey	
Foxtrot	Lima	Romeo	X-Ray	

Note: There are four basic origins of words and phrases.

1. Derived from our American "pop" culture.
2. Military language.
3. In-country vocabulary.
4. Mispronounced, slang and otherwise bastardized words from the Vietnamese, Japanese, and French languages.

Abrams Crighton: The General distinguished himself during World War II when he served with General George Patton. Last commanding general of the American forces during the Vietnam War.

AC-47: *See*: Puff the Magic Dragon, Spooky

Ace of Spades: Known as the *Dealer of Death* card. During the Vietnam War, as a form of intimidation, the Ace of Spades would be placed on an enemies body so everyone would know who did the killing. Not to be outdone, the Vietnamese enemy came up with their own version of the card to place on dead Allied soldiers.

Acid: LSD or similar hallucinogenic drug.

Acute Situation Reaction: Shell shock. *See*: Post Traumatic Stress Disorder

AFVN: Armed Forces Vietnam Network radio station.

Agent orange: A defoliant chemical identifiable by the orange band of the shipping drums, principally used to defoliate dense protective jungle, thus denying the enemy his cover. The defoliant was dumped from C-123 flying boxcar tankers that used the motto "We Prevent Forests." Agent orange was first used during "Operation Ranch Hand" in 1962 and henceforth men working the chemicals referred to themselves as "ranch hands."
Since the war it has been blamed for countless birth deformities, diseases and disorders.

Air America: The airline that was technically civilian-owned, but worked extensively with the CIA. Operated in both Laos and Vietnam

Airborne Ranger: President Kennedy needed soldiers with special skills so he created the Rangers. Though most of the elite fighting men also became airborne qualified which means they could parachute. A common training cadence song went like this: "I wanna be an Airborne Ranger, I wanna go to Vietnam." *See*: Ranger

Air Cav or Air Cavalry: lst Cavalry Division. Instead of using horses, these cavalry units used armored carriers and helicopters. The words *air cavalry* became a generic attached to any number of units using or armored vehicles or helicopters.. The best known unit was the lst Air Cavalry Dividion.

AIT: Advanced Infantry Training

AK-47: A Soviet Union produced assault rifle that was believed by most to be in many ways superior to the American made Colt M-16 assault rifle.
It fired green tracers and had a distinctive "crack/pop" sound when fired.

Allies: Our Allies were Korea, Australia, Philippines, New Zealand

Alpha: Slang for ass. As in, "That is one alpha kicking company."

Alpha Bravo: Radio term for ambush.

Americal Division: 23rd Infantry Division. The only division in Vietnam that could officially be called by its name. The division which often consisted of the least trained soldier in Vietnam, suffering a staggering 17,5000 casualties during the war. The division was originally formed on the island of New Caledonia, which is just west of Australia, during World War II. At division headquarters at Chu Lai, South Vietnam, a sign read, "Under the Southern Cross." *See:* Southern Cross

Ammo dump: An exceptionally secure and/or well fortified location where live ammunition is stored and distributed.

AO: Area of Operation.

***Ao Dai*:** A dress worn by the Vietnamese women, split at the hips, creating a front and back panel that is worn over pants.

AP: *See:* The Associated Press

APC: Armored Personnel Carrier. Also: a capsule used for pain. It was a combination of Aspirin, Phenacetin and Caffeine. Sometimes called the All Purpose Capsule. *See:* Armored Personnel Carrier

Ap Bac: The 2 January 1963 battle was the first real battle of South Vietnam. It was fought with Americans advisors, APCs and helicopters. Considered the first major battlefield loss.

Arc Light: Code name for a B-52 Stratofortress mission. *See*: B-52 bomber

AR-15: The shorter and lighter version of the M-16 assault rifle. *See*: M-16 rifle

Armored Personnel Carrier or APC: The M-113 was a light armored aluminum vehicle equipped with either an M-60 machine gun or .50 caliber Browning heavy machine gun. It could carry eleven infantrymen, one driver and a machine gunner. In the field the soldiers would line the interior with sandbags. When they traveled, the infantrymen usually sat on the roof protected by sandbags because the vehicle could be easily punctured by an AK-47 round , a number of rockets or light anti-vehicle weapons. The foot soldier infantrymen referred to them as taxies.

ARVN: (pronounced: ar-vin) Army of the Republic of Vietnam. Also a single ARVN soldier.

ASAP: As Soon As Possible. e.g. "I want it done ASAP."

Associated Press: (AP) A world wide news wire service network. It, along with *United Press International* (UPI) and the *New York Times*, were said by many to have caused the loss of the Vietnam War through their fervent and unrelenting coverage

AWOL: Absent without leave. Also known to some as "A Way Of Loosening (up)."

B-52 Bomber: The B-52 Bomber, a long-range bomber, first flew in 1954. The Boeing-built bomber called the stratofortress, often called "BUFF" (Big Ugly Fat Fellow). It holds a crew of six and approximately 70,000 pounds of artillery, is capable of flying 10,000 miles at high subsonic speeds at altitudes up to 50,000 feet, and can carry nuclear or conventional ordnance. Often carried 96 five-hundred-pound bombs and dropped them from 30,000 feet. North Vietnam's main defense against these bombers was the SAM Missile.

Bandoleer: A broad shoulder belt of ammunition or something with pockets for ammunition. The M-60 machine gun bandoleers were chains of ammunition. The M-16 bandoleer came inside cloth bandoleers. The ammunition itself would be held together with a steel bar for quick loading. The infantry soldier needed only to take a bandoleer and drape it over his shoulders or pack.

Bandoleer Torpedo: A length of high explosive pipe developed during World War II that was set underneath barbed wire to made a breach for passage.

Bao Chi: Vietnamese language for "journalist".

Baptism of Fire: Another way to say "Welcome to hell." In a religious baptism, water is used. In a war led is used. A person is baptized by fire when they've been targeted for death. . Fire being the combat term for lethal projectile.

BAR: Browning Automatic Rifle.

Baseball Grenade: Slang for a hand grenade that has the shape of a baseball. *See:* M-33 hand grenade

Base Camp: The location of a unit's headquarters and resupply. Also called rear area.

Basket Boat: A round boat that looked like a huge basket. Water easily passed through the reeds but remained buoyant enough to float. They could be fished from or could be used to paddle out to the bigger fishing vessels.

Basic Training: The initial training period that is required for all new military personal.

Battalion: A Marine or Army unit that consists of three or more companies.

Battery: An artillery unit that is equivalent in nature to an infantry company.

BC: Body count. Radio terminology would be bravo charlie. e.g. "What is the bravo charlie? Over."

Beaucoup: (pronounced boo-coo) French language for "much" or "plentiful." Many soldiers mistook it for a Vietnamese word.

Beehive round: An antipersonnel round which delivers thousands of small metal projectiles.

Bell Telephone Hour: To interrogate VC
suspects by using electric shocks generated by a field radio.

Betel nut: A mixture of nut, lime, and tobacco the Vietnamese mixed and chewed, which caused a slight "high." and blacken the teeth.

Bewitching Hour: Midnight or 2400 hrs.

Big Boys: Artillery

Big PX: As in "Land of the big PZ" which means the United States. *See*: World, PX

Big Red One: Name for the First Division. Its insignia was a red numeral I. "If you're going to be One, be a Big Red One."
Bird: Any kind of helicopter.
Bird Dog: Radio name for any light fixed wing observation airplane.
Biscuit bitch: *See*: Donut Dolly , Pastry Pigs
Black magic: Slang for an M-16. *See:* M-16 rifle
Black syphilis or Chinese black syphilis: It was rumored that if you caught this highly contagious venereal disease you would be shipped to a secret island near Da Nang to die and be listed as KIA or MIA.
Bleeding Heart: Derogatory term for a person who opposed the war , or a person participating in the war who didn't agree with the brutality of war. Also one who one who did not fully support their fighting men.
Block: As in "blocking force" . Means a unit of army is placed in a stationary position with the purpose of intercepting enemy personnel that are swept toward them. *See:* Sweep
Blood or Bro's: The word used with pride when referring to/for/about black soldiers.
Blood stripes: Promotions given due directly to a combat assignment. In its purest state, Blood Stripes were those given to a soldier when a vacancy was created by the casualty of an NCO. The sergeant would point to the three stripes on his sleeve and say, "These are blood stripes, mister."
Blooper: *See:* M-79 Grenade Launcher
Blown Away: A slang phrase similar in meaning to "wasted." The essence of the words describe a person high on drugs or killed. "Let's get blown away tonight." "He got blown away."
Body bags: The OD or black bag that KIA's were zipped inside for shipment to the rear. A plastic body bag cost 37 cents.
Body count: (BC) Counting enemy bodies. Sometimes it was an accurate count but most often an exaggerated approximation. The success of an operation was often decided solely on the BC. The more the merrier since the Vietnam War was billed as the War of Attrition. *See*: War of Attrition
Booby trap: A hidden explosive charge, often connected to an everyday and apparently harmless object.
Boo-coo: *See*: *Beaucoup*
Boom boom: GI slang for intercourse. "Wanna boom boom?" Why not? Numba one.
Boonies or boondocks: Other terms are field, bush, jungle, the sticks, Indian country. Any remote or uninhabited place that is away from a military base camp or city. *See*: Indian Country
Boonie hat: Olive drab or camouflage-patterned cloth hat with a full brim and a nylon band with slots for bullets or camouflage materials, and a chin draw string. Used by LRRP's and others when authorized.
Boonie-rat: *See* Grunt
Bought the Farm: Dead or Killed. "Johnnie bought the farm back in Snipers Alley."
Bouncing Betty: An American trip-wire mine that bounces to groin height before exploding.
Brain Bucket: Term used to refer to the steel pot which was designed to protect the soldier from head wounds.

Brass: Slang for officers. *See*: Yahoo

Bravo company: The military term for company "B."
Breaking squelch: Disrupting the natural static of a radio by depressing the transmit bar. *See*: Squelch

Brigade: A tactical and administrative military unit composed of one or more battalions.

Brown Bars: Also Hershey Bars, Butter Bars. Derogatory term for second lieutenants.

Brown-Water Navy: US Navy units operating in the shallow waters of the Mekong Delta.
BUFs: *See:* B-52 bomber

Buffalo Soldier: Slang for a black Vietnam War soldier. Derived from the 1870's when the Indians called the black soldiers, Buffalo Soldiers.

Bug Juice: Slang for mosquito repellant.

Bunker: A roofed structure built with sandbags for the purpose of withstanding an enemy attack. They can be big enough to house equipment or small enough to handle four soldiers. *See*: foxhole

Burn Shit: *See*: Shit burning

Butt pack: *See*: fanny pack

Bush: *See*: Boonies

Bushmaster: Name given to elite units skilled in jungle operations. Possibly derived from the South American venomous snake.

Bust Caps: A slang term for firing small arms ammunition.

C-4: A waterproof high powered white plastic used in claymore mine and other weapons of war. Often times a soldier would break apart a claymore and use the C-4 to heat C-rations.

C-130: The designation for a medium-sized cargo airplane called the Hercules.

C-141: Designation for a large cargo airplane called the Starlifter.

CA: Combat Assault. An assault made on an enemy position using helicopters.

Cache: Term used for hidden supplies.

Cadre: Housing for the key group of permanent residents in charge of an installation.

Candy Man: Derogatory name for an officer who gives out Medals of Valor for his own purpose.

Canh Sat: *See:* White mice

Canine team: Consists of the dog and handler.

Cannon Fodder: A term used since the Civil War to denote throw away troops. "You go out there and you'll be cannon fodder."

Carbine Rifle: A WW II and Korean era American Armed Forces 30 caliber semi-automatic rifle that was replaced by the semi-automatic M-14 and later by the semi or full-automatic M-16 rifle. Because of their reliability and light weight they were issued during the Vietnam War to local Vietnamese forces.

Cav or Cavalry: These infantry units used APC or helicopter to go into battle. *See*: Air Cavalry

CH-47: *See:* Chinook

Charlie: The phonetic alphabet for Viet Cong is Victor Charlie. The GIs shortened the name to Charlie or Mr. Charles. *See*: Dink

Charlie Cong: *See*: VC

Charlie Mike: Radio term for "continue mission."

Cheap Charlie: GI slang for, no good or bad. "This grass no cheap charlie. Me no lie, GI."

Cherry: A derogatory name for a GI who is new to a situation or unit.

Chicken Colonel: Slang for a full bird colonel.

Chicken plate: Term used for fragmentation vests or personal fragmentation equipment used by helicopter pilots or gunners to sit on or draped around their legs.

Chi Com: Chinese Communist. Used in conjunction with any object from Red China, often times used in reference to a Chinese manufactured hand grenade.

Chieu Hoi: Vietnamese for "Open Arms." Name given an amnesty program to encourage enemy soldiers to rally to the South Vietnamese government.

Chinook: A large twin-rotor cargo helicopter, the CH-47. The soldiers nicknamed them shit-hooks because on landing they would send a flurry of stinging rocks and debris across the landing field. Wind velocity at the tip of the rotors reportedly reached 130 mph. A full armed gunship was called a *Go Go*. It could put a round of ammunition every inch of a New York city block in fifteen seconds.

Choke and puke: Slang name for the C-ration meal of Ham and Scrambled Eggs. Even the dogs would walk away from this ration. Also for any food that you choke on when trying to eat it, only to puke it up later. *See:* Ham and Mothers

Choi oi: An expression of surprise or amazement in Vietnamese.

Choo Choo Cherry: *See*: Smoke grenade

Chop-chop: GI slang for "eat" or "food." Also it means to hurry. "Let's move it! Chop chop."

Chopper: Any helicopter, but particularly the Huey. *See*: Huey, Slick

Chopper pad: A specific area designated for the landing of a helicopter.

Chuck: Slang for VC. *See*: dink

Church key: Another name for a beer can opener.

CIA: Central Intelligence Agency.

CIB: Combat Infantry Badge. The badge was established in 1943 and can only be awarded to an infantryman who was in a combat. Considered one of the most prestigious of the U.S. Army combat awards. When the badge is awarded it is customary for the officer to say, "Soldier, you are bound to go to heaven because this CIB shows you've served your time in hell."

Claymore Mine: Anti-personnel mine packed with C-4 behind 700 small steel spheres with a lethal range of fifty-feet wide and 250 feet deep. The claymore was the heart behind a mechanical ambush and was always set around the infantryman's night defense positions.

Cluster f-word: When infantry soldiers, especially those in the field cluster together to talk they make a big and easy target for the enemy. "Let's break this cluster f-word up and spread it out. One round could kill you all."

CO: Commanding Officer

Cobra Gunship: An AH-1G attack helicopter. The only helicopter built with the sole purpose of being a gunship. The gunship's main fuselage was hardly over four feet wide with the co-pilot sitting directly behind the pilot. Capable of carrying an impressive arsenal. *See*: Gunship

Coca-Cola: The only American soft drink in a bottle the Vietnamese sold to Americans. To the Vietnamese the refillable bottle was as important as the liquid inside. A Coca-Cola sold for 50 cents for 12 ounces.

Code of the Bush: What happens in the bush, stays in the bush. Usually refers to discrepancies about certain activities or actions a soldier might have participated in that those not involved could never sympathize with or possible understand. "When you're ass is on the line, you'd be surprised what you'll do." The code later became the all encompassing code of silence. *See*: Code of silence

Code of Conduct: Rules of conduct used by American soldiers while in Vietnam.

Code of Silence: What happened in Vietnam during the war stays with the veterans and will not be shared with those who didn't fight. The Vietnam veteran writer is often accused of breaking the sacred Code of Silence.

Cold LZ: A Helicopter Landing Zone that has no enemy activity.

Combat Assault: To be brought into a battle by a helicopter, in order to engage the enemy.

Combat Infantry Badge: *See*: CIB

Combat Photographer: Though a soldier could be a combat photographer and get published in the *Stars and Stripes* it most often refers to civilian photo-journalist attached or freelancing during the war. Some of the best know were Tim Page, Larry Burrows, Sean Flynn, Dana Stone, Terry Khoo and Horst Faas.

Command Detonate: When the detonation of a mine is performed by a human verses trip wire or pressure sensitive.

Commie: Short for Communist. During the Vietnam War it was believed the North Vietnamese were being supported by the Red Chinese and the Soviet Union.

Company: A military unit consisting of two or more platoons.

Concertina Wire: Coiled barbed wire. Used at every permanent and temporary installation throughout Vietnam.

Condom: Prophylactics were stretched over the muzzle of a rifle to keep out water and dirt.

Cong: Short for Viet Cong or Vietnamese Communist.

Congressional Medal of Honor: The highest U.S. military decoration awarded for conspicuous gallantry at the risk of life, above and beyond the call of duty.

Connex: Steel container used to ship equipment. The empty containers would subsequently be used as storage huts, field communication buildings and infrastructure of a bunker.

Contact: Firing or being fired upon with intent to kill.

CONUS: Continental United States

Cook-off: A hand grenade has an eight second fuse. If a soldier needs it to detonate sooner after leaving his hand he must let it cook-off. Which mean, while still holding the hand grenade he must release the detonation spoon then throw it. *See: Hand Grenade*

Corpsman: Medic

Corps I or I Corps: (pronounced: eye-core) Vietnam was divided into four military tactical zones. I Corps, the most northern zone, bordered the DMZ.

Corps II: The military tactical zone that covered northern central South Vietnam.

Corps III: Military tactical zone that included Saigon.

Corps IV: The most southern tactical zone, which included the Plain of Reeds and the Mekong Delta.

CP: Command Post

CQ: Charge of Quarters e.g. "If you need supplies check with your CQ."

C-rations, C-rats: Individual rations that are ready to eat with an SP pack. Twelve full meals to a case weighing twenty-five pounds. They were: Tuna Fish; Pork Slices Cooked with Juices; Beef Slices & Potatoes W/Gravy; Beans with Meat Balls in Tomato Sauce; Chicken or Turkey, Boned; Turkey Loaf; Beef W/Spiced Sauce; Ham and Eggs, Chopped; Beans W/Frankfurter Chunks in Tomato Sauce; Ham and Lima beans; Spaghetti W/Beef Chunks in Sauce; Beef stew; Ham Sliced, Cooked with Juices. There was an sp-package inside ever ration box which had a P-38 can opener, toilet paper, spoon, napkin, pepper and salt, and a four-pack of cigarettes. Special Note: There were several meals added and subtracted depending on the year packaged. For instance, in 1967 we ate rations dating as far back as 1945 and most ration boxes dated from the time of the Korean War. Not until the latter part of 1968 did they issue fruit and a spaghetti meal and later eliminated the Ham and Lima Beans. *See*: Lurp ration

Crispy critter: A person burned severely or burned to death by either white phosphorous or napalm. If even a spot of napalm touched the skin, it could not be smothered as easily as normal fire. Name derived from the name of a breakfast cereal.

Crocodile: Southeast Asians believe that word could put a curse on a person.

Cronkite, Walter: Working as an anchor for CBS. He was the first high profile media announcer to have doubts about our involvement in the Vietnam War.

CS: As in a CS gas grenade. A lethal form of tear gas.

Cu Chi: The district of Cu Chi was famous for its network of tunnels. In the 1940's the first of the tunnel systems were dug to fight against the Japanese. By the middle 1960's the tunnels were said to extend over 200 miles. The system boasted of underground hospitals, schools, eating areas, meeting rooms and sleeping quarters. Some of the larger complexes on the Cambodian border were said to even have TV'S and air conditioning. The Cu Chi area became the most bombed, gassed, defoliated, and devastated area during the war because of Americans *attempts* to destroy the tunnel system. *See*: Tunnel Rat and Tunnel warfare

Daily-daily: Malaria pills that were to be taken daily. *See*: Horse pill

Daisy cutters: A ten or fifteen thousand pound bomb that would be dropped to clear of landing zones in dense vegetation. The bomb could only be carried by the CH-54 Sky Crane helicopter. *See*: Sky Crane

Dak To: One of the major battles between the Americans and the NVA. It started in November 1967.

Darvon capsules: A high potency pain killer given out by the medics. Outside of its intended purpose if you pulled the capsule apart, and only ingested the red balls you could get high.

Date with Chris: Chris Noel was an aspiring actress from Hollywood when she first came to Vietnam in 1966. Soon after her first tour of the country she landed a job with the Armed Forces Radio that aired her show "Date with Chris" from 1966-71. She was the first female announcer since the Second World War. The show as so popular that the VC put a $10,000 bounty on her head. Besides doing the radio show she toured the country with other entertainers or by herself. Her artifacts are on display at the Vietnam War museum in San Antonio, Texas, across from the Alamo.

Dealer of Death: *See*: Ace of Spades

Dear John: Derived from a 1940's radio program called "Dear John".It became a catch phrase for a letter sent by a girlfriend or wife who had decided to end the relationship.

Death Card or Payback card: An ace of spades card with a skull and cross bones. *See*: Ace of Spades

Delayed Distress Reaction: *See:* Post Traumatic Stress Disorder.

Delta: Refers to the Mekong River Delta area south of Saigon which encompassed the Plain of Reeds.

Dencap: A peaceful operation involving a military dentist plus assistants and guards who went into villages for part of a day to offer their skills. *See*: Medcap

DEROS: Date of Expected Return from Over Seas.
Duration eligible for return from overseas. For the U.S. Army is was 12 months. For the Marines it was 13 months.

Deuce-and-a-half: Military slang for a 2 ½ ton truck, also known as a 6x6. It was the all around transportation work horse.

DI: Drill instructor. Specifically a DI was used to teach basic military skills. "When I say jump, you ask how high!"

Diddy bopping: A very loose shoulder form of walk. In the infantry it was the name for someone not watching what they were doing while on patrol.

Di Di (dee-dee) Vietnamese for run or move quickly. The GI's used the phrase, "Let's di di outta here!"

***Di di dao*:** Vietnamese for crazy

Di di mau: Vietnamese for "run, run fast." GIs used it to mean, "Let's get the hell out of here!"

Diem, Ngo Dinh: The Vietnamese president of South Vietnam. Assassinated within a month of President Kennedy's death. *See*: Thieu, Nguyen Van

Dien Bien Phu: In December 1953 General Giap began to move his soldiers into position around the French forces near the town of Dien Bien Phu. The siege started on March 13, 1954, and the French surrendered on May 7, 1954. The battle was often thrown up as an example during the Vietnam War of what could happen. *Hell in a Very Small Place* was a book about the battle that became required reading for the officers.

Dink: A derogatory term for the Vietnamese people. Perhaps derived from *dinky dao*, Vietnamese for "crazy." Other terms: Gook, slope head, spearchucker, yellow man. Luke the Gook, Chink,Link the Chink, Mr. Charles, Charlie.

Charlie. *See*: Charlie, Luke the Gook

Dink lover: Am American soldier who sympathized the enemy or the Vietnamese people.

Dink squat: To squat with feet flat on the ground and the knees bent sharply so the buttocks rest on one's calves. Most Americans found it a hard position to maintain but the orientals found it a very natural position.

Dinky dao: American slang for *di di dao* which means crazy.

Dispatch: A Vietnam based news agency, co-founded by Michael Morrow. Seymour Hersh, the Pulitzer Prize winner who wrote the My Lai story, let Michael print it for the first time in 1969. *See*: My Lai Massacre

Dispatches: The term used for a magazine articles. Also the name of Michael Herr's best selling book "Dispatches."

DMZ: Demilitarized Zone. At the signing of the Geneva Agreement on July 21, 1954 a line was drawn at the 17th Parallel dividing the country into North and South Vietnam. Also referred to as the McNamara line because the then Secretary of Defense Robert McNamara pointed to the line daring the North Vietnames e to cross it - and they did! GI slang for the line was Z.

Doc: The troops name for their medic. However there were called "Medic!" when someone was hit. Also corpsman. Slang names were "Band Aid" and "Suzie."

Dodge City: Slang for the area east of Da Nang that was never pacified. Derived from Dodge City, Kansas, which came to symbolize gunfighters and the American "Wild West."

Dong Ap Bia, Hill 937: The American forces showed outstanding courage in capturing this mountain situated one mile from the Laotian border in the A Shau Valley. The Montagnards called the mountain, "Mountain of the crouching beast." *See*: Hamburger Hill

Donut dollies: Red Cross girlss who would go into the field with donuts and coffee to give to the troops. A group of women who never received proper respect for their honest efforts. Also called Biscuit bitches, or pastry pigs.

Doo-mommie: Americanization of Vietnamese 'Duma' meaning "F-word your mother."

Doper: A pot smoker

Double veteran: A soldier who has sex with a women then kills her.

Dove: Someone who is against the war. *See*: Hawk

Draft dodger: Someone who doesn't show up to the military when required, but has to be hunted down and forced to serve.

Draft: The draft is when the Congress, Senate, and President approves a law requiring all able-bodied young men to serve in the military

DMZ: Demilitarized Zone. At the signing of the Geneva Agreement on July 21, 1954, a line was drawn along the Ben Hai River, the 17th parallel, dividing the country into North and South Vietnam. Also referred to as the McNamara line because the then Secretary Of Defense, Robert McNamara, pointed to the line daring the North Vietnamese to cross it – they did. GI slang for the DMZ was, the "Z."

Dragon: The dragons of Southeast Asian are considered kings and gods. Often the Asians will find council with a dragon when considering matters of state or matters of religion.

Dragon Lady: Madama Nhu , the wife of President Diem's brother. Fashioning herself as a feminist, she went about trying to run the country by controlling the newspapers and through issuing government decrees. Her biggest mistake was in making light of the Buddhist monks who in protest by burning themselves to death in public. Because of her outlandish ways she became know as Dragon Lady. *See*: Madam Nhu

Dung lai: (pronounced: young-lie) Vietnamese for "stop."

Dustoff: Another name for Medical evacuation by helicopter. The name was derived from an incident where an American colonel with the call sign "dustoff" was killed while on a Medevac. *See*: Medevac

Eagle flights: A large combat assault with helicopters.

E-1: Private E-One. The lowest military pay grade for enlisted men.

E-2: Private E-two. Next to the lowest pay grade for enlisted men.

Echo mike: Radio terminology for enlisted man.

81mm: The American 81mm mortar. Commonly referred to as infantry field artillery.

82mm: The 82mm mortar was used by the communists. The idea was that they could use the American ammunition but the Americans could not use theirs.
Electric Strawberry: Nickname for the 25th Infantry Division because their patch was strawberry shaped with a lightning bolt running its length.
Elephant Grass: An grass possessing razor edges that could grew up to fifteen-feet in height. Dense elephant grass could cut visibility down to a yard.
Eleven Bravo Termed for soldiers with an eleven-b MOS, which was infantry.
ETS: End of Term of Service. The scheduled date for discharge from active duty.
F-4: Phantom jet fighter bomber. The work horse jet of the war. Range: 1,000 miles. Speed: 1,400 mph. Payload: 10,000 lbs.
Fatigues: Refers to olive drab jungle combat clothes.
Fanny pack: A pack only large enough for a few days of supplies. They came with suspenders that attached to the pistol belt.
Field: *See*: Boonies
Field Cross: A structure that represented a cross built with the equipment of the soldier or soldiers who had died. Oftentimes it looked like just a pile of equipment but specifically it would be built with a boot pierced by a rifle-mounted bayonet and with a steel pot placed over the butt of the rifle.
Field of fire: An effective area that a weapon or fixed position is capable of covering. "This will be your field of fire. This section will be mine."
Field strip: Meaning to render something unrecognizable or unusable when discarded. It is considered standard procedure in a combat zone. As in "field strip your cigarette."
51: A communist .51-caliber heavy machine gun used against both personnel and aircraft.
Finger nail: The Vietnamese often let the left hand small finger nail grow as a fashion statement but also to honor an emperor of ancient times. The GIs laughed saying it was long so they could better "wipe their butt."
Fire at will: Artillery terminology to say that the shells are hitting at the right places and they can continue to fire without further communication from the forward observer.
Fire Base: An artillery firing position, usually on high ground, which would be secured by infantry and supplied by helicopter. They could be established very rapidly and were often in existence for only a brief period of time, although many were permanent all-weather bases. *See*: Fire Support Base
Fire Brigade: An extremely mobile infantry unit rushed to the scene of an enemy attack.
Firefight: Exchange of mortar and small arms rifle fire with the enemy.
Fire for Effect: *See*: fire mission
Fire In the Hole!: The warning yelled when a grenade or other explosives are ready to be detonated.
Fire Mission: The term used when calling for artillery support. There were basically two steps to the mission. First you called for spotter rounds which on impact gave the field spotter a chance to move the artillery round a few meters in any direction. After the spotter rounds were located the second call would be "fire for effect." The fire for effect mission could entail any amount of artillery rounds as were deemed necessary by the field spotter.
Fire support: Term for artillery support fire.
Fire support base: An artillery base established to provide security for a given area. e.g. "Get FSB Dolly on the hook. We need some support in here."
Fire team: To divide an infantry squad into four man teams. *e.g.* "Assault in fire team formation."
Firefly: A Huey gunship teamed with a Loach helicopter that flies in the lead position with the purpose of drawing enemy fire. When the Loach is fired upon the Huey gunship swoops in for the attack. *See*: Loach
First Cav: Short for the First Air Cavalry.
Five O' Clock Follies: *See*: JUSPAO
Flak jacket: Fragmentation protective body armor vest. The U.S. Army's version of the vest was filled with multiple layers of ballistic nylon material. The Marines version was filled

with kevlar plates. The vest was designed to stop low velocity missile fragments from mines, grenades, mortar shells, and artillery fire. It could also decrease the severity of wounds from bullets.

Flare: An illumination projectile fired into the air.

Fleshets: Beehive rounds loaded into howitzers and used for direct shooting against a closely packed enemy trying to overrun a position. The dart-shaped projectiles sound like a swarm of bees when fired. Word comes from the French, Flechette meaning small arrows.

Flynn, Sean: Sean was the son of movie star Errol Flynn. He landed in Vietnam in 1965 and was present at the battle of Ia Drang Valley, one of the earliest major battles with the NVA. Though his photographs could rank with some of the best he would continuously be discounted as a serious photo/journalist. He was captured in 1970 along with his friend Dana Stone while working with CBS. Neither returned.

FNG: Means f-wordin' new guy. Probably the most widely used slang for a new replacement. Also cherry, NFG, newbee. *See*: NFG

FO: Forward Observer, a man who helps target artillery in the field.

Fonda, Jane: *See*: Hanoi Jane

Foo-gas: Word is derived from the French Feu Gaz , meaning fire and gasoline. See: Phougas.

4-F: The category a person gets when they receive a permanent deferral from military service.

Foxhole: A one or two soldier hole dug to about waist deep without a roof. Usually built as an overnight two-soldier fortification.

Frag: Short for fragmentation hand grenade.

Fragging: Slang to mean an officer or lifer's own men have killed or are trying to kill them. *e.g.* "I'm gonna frag the mother!"

Fragmentation vest: Also Frag jacket *See*: Flak jacket

Freak: Shortened term for radio frequency.

Freckle face strawberry: *See*:Smoke grenade

Freedom bird: slang for the flight out of Vietnam, or any commercial aircraft see flying over-head.

Free fire zone: An area known as an enemy stronghold that was supposedly free of all civilians. A designated area where the American military could, without specific permission, shoot to kill anything that moved.

Freelance: Usually refers to a journalist or photo journalist. A person who sells their work by the hour, day, or job rather than being on a regular salary basis. *See*: Photo Stringer

Friendlies: Vietnamese that were on the side of the South Vietnamese government. Also any Vietnamese that worked well with the American soldier. *e.g.* "They said there are no friendlies in the area."

Friendly fire: The term used for your own deadly projectiles that hopefully aren't aimed at you. *See*: Killed by friendly fire

Friendship bracelet: See: Montagnard friendship bracelet

F-word: The most used word during the entire war. Sentences and conversations were seldom heard without he spice of the f-word word. The term for kill the enemy was "F-word with 'em."

F-word it: The word used the could create denial. "Don't think about it man. F-word it." Also used as "Just f-word it."

F-word stick: Also ass hole, shitbird, or pecker-head. A man who messed something up.

F-word-you lizard: GI name for the gecko lizard, whose call sounds like the words "f-word you." Asians believed seven calls in a row portend good luck.

F-worded up: To be wounded or killed. Also, to get excessively high on marijuana or alcohol.

Fugazi: Mad or screwed up.

Full bird colonel: The higher of the colonel ranks, one rank above lieutenant colonel; or, as the soldiers called them, "Chicken colonel." The slang was derived from the rank's eagle insignia.

G-2: Division level intelligence. *See*: S-2
General Abrams: *See*: Abrams.
General Harkin: President John F. Kennedy's first commander to South Vietnam. General Harkin likened himself to General Patton of the Second World War. This general made so many miscalculation that his name became a catch phrase for a mistake. e.g. "He pulled a Harkin."
General Henri Navarre: The French commander in chief for Indochina. Built the outpost at Dien Bien Phu in 1953 and ultimately lost it to the Vietminh forces under General Giap.
General Vo Nguyn Giap: The commander of the Vietnamese forces that beat both the French and American fighting forces. To this day considered a military genius in strategy in much the same way as Field Marshal Erwin Rommel, the Desert Fox, had been to the British.
General William Westmoreland: The commander of the American forces during the Vietnam War from 1965-1968. The troops sometimes called him "Westy."
Get some: Kill an enemy.
GI: "Government Issue," slang for an American soldier.
Gold star: As in "Gold Star Mother." A gold pin that is sent to the widow, parents, or other next of kin of a military person killed in action or serving presently in a military conflict.
Go Go: *See:* Chinook
Good training: Term used to make light of anything that was extremely physically or mentally trying. "That was one long hump." "Good training."
Goofy grape: Term used for purple smoke grenade. Other colors were called Freckle Face strawberry, Loud Mouth lime, Choo-choo Cherry, and OJ orange. The colors were named for drinks made by a competitor of Kool-Aid. *See*: Smoke grenade
Gook: *See*: dink
Greased: Killed
Green Berets: Name used for the Special Forces of the U.S. Army. They wore the green beret as a mark of distinction. Based at Nha Trang.
Greenbacking: Employing mercenaries. Vietnamese minority groups such as Khmer, Nung, Hmong, Montagnard.
Greenstar Duster: Means an enemy ground attack.
Grunt: MOS 11b infantry. An infantry soldier whose only means of transportation is to walk. "You'll have to be a grunt for the day." The word derives from the groaning sounds that come from the inner chest of someone carrying a heavy backpack. Other names: boonie-rat, eleven bush, ground pounder, or straight-leg. *See*: Infantryman
Guerrilla: An organized resistance movement, group or member of such a group.
Guerilla warfare: Military resistance carried out by independent indigenous forces which engage in sneak attacks and other harassing tactics verse proper military forces, e.g. NVA.
Gung ho: Adjective describing an officer who is looking to make a name for himself. When used to describe a grunt it means devoted, zealous, or committed more. Derived from the Chinese *keng ho* meaning awe-inspiring or literally "more fiery."
Guns and Butter: President Johnson's idea for a Great Society. The policy would give the military more money and therefore protect the world against Communism, and also give more money to social welfare programs to care for the poor and underprivileged.
Gunship: Armed helicopter. Commonly refers to a Huey with two door gunners manning M-60 flex machine guns mounted on a pod or suspended on a suspension cable. The more deadly version also had mounted under and around the fuselage mini guns, rocket launchers, 30mm cannons, and nose mounted M-5 40mm grenade launchers. *See*: Cobra Gunship
Halberstam, David: David Halberstam of the *New York Times* arrived in Vietnam in 1962. Out of his experiences he wrote his 1965 book *The Making of a Quagmire*. His later book *The Best and the Brightest* was about Secrecary of Defense Robert McNamara. He was considered one of the most influential writers of the war. Other influential and import trend setting writers of the era where Horst Faas and Peter Arnett of AP; Neil Sheehan who wrote *A Bright Shinning Lie* and Malcolm Browne of UPI.
Ham and mothers or Ham and motherf-worders: C-ration can of ham and lima beans. *See*: Choke and puck.

Hamburger Hill: In May, 1969 the 101st Airborne Division fought with conspicuous courage against the North Vietnamese Army. Intensive public debate centered over the decision to capture the hill regardless of the casualties. Because of the intensity of the fighting the men referred to the battle site as "Hamburger Hill." *See*: Dong Ap Bia

Hamlet: A small rural village.

Hand grenade: The M-26 was the standard hand grenade that had smooth sides but shaped like a pineapple. The M-33 hand grenade A hand grenade that was more powerful though less reliable than the M-26. Considered unreliable and sometimes called the baseball grenade because of its round shape. Soldier would often carry a mix of both the M-26 and M-33 in the field. *See*: Pineapple hand grenade

Hanoi Jane: The nickname for Jane Fonda. A movie star who went to Hanoi, North Vietnam during the war to denounce US involvement in Southeast Asia.

Harkin: *See*: General Harkin

Haul Ass: To leave quickly.

Hawk: Someone who supported the war. *See*: Dove

Head: Smoke marijuana to excess. *See*: Pot Head

Hit: A puff on a marijuana cigarette.

HE: High explosive. An HE artillery round.

Hearts and Minds: President Johnson believed the war could be won if the Americans could win the hearts and minds of the Vietnamese people. It became a catch phrase for an American victory. The military personnel would change it to say "grab 'em by the balls and their hearts and minds will follow."

Heat Tab: A flammable purple tablet used to heat C-rations in the field. However, they were always in short supply so the grunts most often had to eat the fat-caked rations cold or break open a claymore mine and use the explosive C-4 inside to heat their meals. *See*: C-4

Heel Stomp: When a soldier smashes their heel into an enemy soldier's head hoping to crush their skull.

Helmet: The generic term for the helmet liner, steel pot, and helmet cover. *See*: Steel Pot, Brain Bucket

Helmet Cover: The helmet cover was a piece of camouflage cloth that would fit snugly over the steel pot. Foliage and additional camouflage could be slid through the holes cut into the cover. The helmet cover often times became a soldiers talisman as well as a soul board. They would attach crosses and other items that would protect them from evil along with the names of their girlfriends, wife, etc. *See*: Steel Pot

Helmet Liner: The helmet liner contained the head webbing. Under the head webbing soldiers would often keep their valuable letter from home and writings material because it was the last place that would get wet. *See*: Steel Pot, Helmet Cover

H & I: Harassing and Interdiction - Term for an artillery fire mission called into an area where the enemy is *thought* to be. *See*: Fire mission

Hit: A puff on a marijuana cigarette.

Ho Chi Minh: The GI's shortened his name to Uncle Ho. The communist leader of North Vietnam. Born in a province of the central highlands on May 19, 1900. He died in 1969, before the war ended in 1975. Ho Chi Minh means "He who enlightens."

Ho Chi Minh's Revenge: GI slang for diarrhea. Medical journals use the term to describe a particularly severe case of diarrhea. *See*: The GIs.

Ho Chi Minh sandals: Sandals ingeniously constructed by the Vietnamese. Soles were made from vehicle tire treads and the foot securing straps were made from inner tubes.

Ho Chi Minh Trail: The main North Vietnamese supply route. From the Laos, Mu Gia Pass and along the Cambodia border the trail ran some 250 linear miles. The trail itself was a tangled mess of camouflaged footpaths, dirt roads, paved surfaces and river crossing which covered approximately 9,600 miles. Some of the heaviest fighting took place on the trail's arteries into South Vietnam. A North Vietnamese could carry 50 pounds of equipment on his back 15 miles a day. A bicycle could carry 150 lbs. *See*: Sihanoukville Port Route

Hoi Chanh: The name for a Vietnamese who has joined the Chieu Hoi program. *See: Chieu Hoi*

Honcho: The boss
Hook or Horn: Terms that referred to the hand-set receiver on a PRC-25 field radio. e.g. "Sarge, they want you on the horn."
Hootch: Any building from a wattle, to straw shack, to a modern structure. A derivative of a Japanese word for "house." Also referred to a temporary make-shift field enclosure built by GIs.
Hootchgirl or Hootchmaid: A Vietnamese maid
Horse pill: Name for the big orange pill taken weekly to prevent malaria. *See*: Daily daily
Hot: An area that is being fired upon or is likely to be fired upon. As in a "Hot LZ."
Hotel Alpha: Phonetic alphabet meaning to "haul ass."
Howitzer: Cannons used at fire support bases. There was commonly the 105, 155, and 175 version of the Howitzer used at the fire support bases.
Huey: The UH-1 helicopter. It had a cruising speed of 127 mph and a range of 318 miles. This particular helicopter played such an important part in the war that it actually came to symbolize the conflict. And the distinctive noises developed by this helicopter became the most thought-provoking sounds of the war.
Hump: To patrol in the field; to walk; to carry a backpack, equipment, or anything else. e.g. "Hump this over to the sarge."
***Ia Drang* Valley:** The first real battle between the American military and the NVA started on November 17th, 1965. In four days of extremely heavy fighting the 7th Cavalry, which had been Custer's regiment at the Little Big Horn, was nearly wiped out. In four days the battle took 230 American lives.
Immersion foot: Condition resulting from feet being wet or damp for a prolonged period of time. Symptoms are cracked skin and bleeding feet.
In-country: In Vietnam - literally
Incoming: Receiving enemy fire. "Incoming!" was also the word a soldier yelled to warn of hostile fire.
Incendiary Grenade: The incendiary grenade is used for cutting through metal or to start a fire. Does not need oxygen when activated and will burn underwater.
Indian Country: A name given to remote and uninhabited areas know to have enemy activity. *See*: Free fire zone, boonies
Infantryman: Soldiers skilled in the use of light weapons. Originally described soldiers or units where walking is the only mode of transportation. *See*: Grunt
Instant Mother (F-worder): An army private who attended a special NCO school and on completion received the rank of sergeant. *See*: Shake 'n' Bake
Iron Triangle: A triangular area of sixty square miles located northeast of Saigon, bordered by Cu Chi, Ben Cat, and Ho Bo Forest. Known to be a VC sanctuary which had some of the most extensive tunnel systems in the country.
I & I: Intercourse and Intoxication, which played on the letters R&R which meant Rest and Relaxation. *See*: R&R
Jacob's Ladder: The rope ladder suspended from helicopters when there was no place to land.
Jack/Jank/Jink: To make evasive maneuvers in a helicopter.
Jamming Jenny: Slang used mostly to refer to the early models of the M-16 that were prone to malfunction. The reasons for the malfunction, which caused the death of many GI's, were the springs in the magazines, the re-coil spring in the stock, and dirty ammunition. Although these causes were remedied the M-16 still continued to jam. I know, mine did, and I almost bought the farm.
Jar Head: The popular nickname for a soldier in the U.S. Marine Corps. *See*: Leather neck
Jesus Nut: The mythical nut that holds the rotors onto a helicopter.
Jody: The name given to a guy who steals a soldier's girlfriend while the soldier's away serving his country. Where are the ethics, man?

John Wayne: A movie star whose movies most soldiers in Vietnam enjoyed watching. Would find they were sadly mistaken in their belief that John Wayne movies depiction of war was even remotely correct when applied to the Vietnam War.
Joint: A marijuana cigarette.
Jolly Green Giant: Sikorsky HH-53 helicopter, a large gunship that's main function was to rescue downed pilots. It's fire power and might was equivalent to a company of infantry soldiers.
Johnson, Lyndon Baines: President of the United States during the build up of forces during the war Vietnam War.
.Jungle Rot: *See*: Immersion foot
JUSPAO: Joint United States Public Affairs Office. The organization that covered information from both US military and civil sources. It was where the media personnel had to go to get accredited. It ran the infamous "Five 0'clock Follies," which was slang for the information session which tried to explain, or justify the daily events of the war. For several years it was held at the Rex in Saigon.
K-9 Team: The term used to refer a canine and its handler. There were three basic uses for the dogs during the war. 1) Law enforcement and customs. The highly trained animals would sniff-out luggage, people, and break up bar fights. 2) Sentry. The dog would attack without command and operate under gunfire. 3) Patrols. Would only attack on command. They could walk near the point position on a patrol and could alert soldiers to probable danger. They could also hold a suspect at bay while the handler conducted a search and would attack at any sign of provocation. The most widely used dogs were German Shepards and Dobermans.
Ka-Bar: The common term used for a Marine combat knife. However, the actual knife came into being during World War II and production ended in 1945. The only authentic Ka-Bars were made by Ka-Bar Knives of Olean, New York, and were fashioned after the Bowie knife of the 1830's. The "Ka-Bar" marking is short for the misspelled words, "Killed a Bear."
Kennedy, John F.: The president of the United States who first put military advisors in South Vietnam.
Khe Sanh: The name of the U.S. Marine Corps base in I Corps which came under siege for 77 days starting on January 21, 1968. During the battle a lot of comparisons were made between Khe Sanh and the French stronghold of Dien Bien Phu which fell to the enemy in 1954. There was a public outcry when General Westmoreland ordered Khe Sanh abandoned just before he was relieved of command.
Khmer Rouge: Cambodian communists. Average age of these extremely vicious young soldiers was twelve.
KIA: Killed in Action. As a noun, a person killed in action or killed while on duty.
Killed by friendly fire: Means that a soldier was mistakenly killed by his own countrymen. An area around an explosive device in which 95 per cent fatalities is predicted. Also the area at the head of a column of soldiers that would be the first to make enemy contact.
Kissenger, Henry: Foreign policy consultant to Presidents Kennedy and Johnson. In 1969 under President Nixon he became special assistant for national security affairs. Served as Secretary of State under President Gerald Ford.
Kit Carson Scout: A VC or NVA defector working with an American infantry unit as an interpreter and scout. The name was taken from a famous American mountain man and Civil War scout.
Klick: A kilometer
KP: Kitchen police. Means you had to work in the kitchen.
***Lai dai*:** (pronounced: lie-day) Vietnamese for, come here.
LAW: 72 Light Antitank Weapon. A shoulder-fired, 66-mm rocket in a collapsible and disposable fiberglass firing tube. Carried by the infantry because of its effectiveness against bunkers.

LBJ: Slang for the Long Binh Jail (stockade), made famous by the coincidence of fitting President Lyndon Baines Johnson's initials. This was the American military's main stockade for errant GI's in South Vietnam.

Leather neck: A soldier in the USMC. *See*: Jarhead

Liberation Day: On April 30, 1975 Vietnam was liberated by communist troops. There is a yearly festival in Vietnam to commemorate that day.

Lifer: Derogatory term for a noncommissioned career soldier.

Light Observation Helicopter, OH-6A: Smallest of the helicopters used in Vietnam.

LMG: Light Machine Gun - the Soviet made RPD. A bi-pod mounted, belt-fed weapon similar to the American M-60 machine gun. The RPD fires the same cartridge as the AK-47.

Link the Chink: *See*: Dink, VC

Loach or LOH: Light observation helicopter, OH-6A. Smallest of the helicopters used in Vietnam. *See*: Firefly

Lock 'n' Load: Means to lock the weapon then load a round into the firing chamber.

Logar or Night Logar: Term used by the infantry to describe their night time defense perimeter. "We're gonna logar here tonight."

Long Binh Jail: *See*: LBJ

Long Tom: Nickname for the 175mm Howitzer which could fire a 147 pound shell twenty miles. *See*: Howitzer

Loud Mouth Lime: *See*: Goofy grape, Smoke grenade

LP: Listening post. A small group of soldiers, usually two or three who are sent beyond a perimeter to hide and listen for the enemy. Extremely hazardous since these are the soldiers who are the first target before a full scale attack *See*: OP

LRRP: (Pronounced lurp) Long Range Reconnaissance Patrol. An elite team usually consisting of five to seven men. Their primary mission was to observe enemy activity without initiating contact. Sometimes referred to as Night Crawlers.

Luke the Gook: *See*: Dink, VC

Lurp rations: Phonetic pronunciation of LRRP. Dehydrated light-weight meals (one third the weight of C-ration) named after the LRRP soldier to whom they were most often issued. Note: The U.S. military has gone exclusively to the dehydrated meals.

LZ: Landing Zone. Usually a small clearing secured temporarily for landing troops, resupply or medevac helicopters. Some became more permanent, and then were given proper names (e.g.LZ Baldy) so it was also a common term for any place a helicopter could land.

M-1 Rifle: A vintage carbine rifle used extensively during World War II that was issued to the Vietnamese army. *See*: Carbine rifle

M-14 Rifle: This rifle, used early during the Vietnam War, was believed by many to be vastly superior to the M-16. It didn't have to be cleaned so meticulously and didn't have a problem with jamming. The M-14, accurate at 1,000 yards, became the preferred rifle by American snipers. *See*: Sniper

M-16 Rifle: The American gas-operated assault rifle which weighed 7.6 pounds unloaded and 8.3 pounds with a 20-round magazine (thirty round magazines showed up late in the war). Could be fired on automatic or semi-automatic. It was designed for close jungle warfare and therefore had an effective range of only 400 yards. Nicknamed the Widow Maker and Jamming Jenny. It fired red tracer rounds. *See*: Jamming Jenny, Tonka Toy and Mattel Toy *Also*: AR-15

M-60 Machine gun: The standard belt-fed American light infantry machine gun.

M-79 Grenade Launcher: An American single shot 40 mm grenade launcher. GI term for the weapon was either Thumper or Blooper. Looked like a giant shotgun which could lob a round 400 yards with fair accuracy. The rounds available were illumination, rubber, PD round (detonate at any distance), gas canisters, fleshettes comprised of 500 little steel darts, white phosphorous, HE high explosive round which was made of wire wrapped around an explosive core, and armor piercing. Note: For safety purposes the HE round had to rotate a certain amount of times before it would arm itself.

M-113: *See*: Armored Personnel Carrier

MACV: Military Assistance Command, Vietnam

Madam Nhu: Madam Hgo Dinh Nhu. South Vietnam's President Diem never married so his brother's wife Madam Nhu became the unofficial First Lady of South Vietnam. She was out of the country when in 1963, both Diem and his brother were assasinated.
Mad Minute: A weapons "free-fire." A concentration of all weapons at maximum output for the duration of one minute. Used to: scare away any impending attacker; to clear the area so an ambush could get out; a way to check to be sure all the weapons are functional. Also referred to as the Magic Minute, Miracle Minute or Mike-mike.
***Mia Noi*:** Vietnamese for girlfriend or more literally minor wife.
Magazine: A steel sleeve filled with ammunition that is inserted into a rifle or other weapon.
Mamma-san: The name GIs gave a mature Vietnamese woman derived from the Korean War.
Marble Mountain: An amazing rock formation with sheer cliffs outside of Da Nang. The Marines had an LZ at the top of the rock and the VC had a hospital inside its many catacombs.
Marijuana: Cannabis (hemp), a narcotic. Rolled in paper like a cigarette and often times as large as a cigarette. Most commonly referred to as a joint, reefer, pot, weed or grass. The final quarter inch was referred to as the roach. Area terms were, Khmer Rouge, Delta Dust, Laotian Red, Buddha grass. "I've got a bag of Delta Dust, so let's party."
Marker round: The first round fired by artillery used for the purpose of adjusting the following rounds onto the target. Sometimes, but not always, it was a white phosphorous round that could easily be seen for miles. For instance if the soldiers couldn't figure out their corordinates in the field they would call for a marker round with know location.
MARS: Military Affiliate Radio Station. Used by soldiers to call home, via Signal Corps and ham radio equipment.
MASH: Mobile Army Surgical Hospital
McNamara, Robert S. : US Secretary of Defense from 1961-68. Increased the military presence in Vietnam and in so doing created a quagmire of deception and a water shed for self serving special interest groups. McNamara, the power-hungry, cocky, can-do Cabinet chief, along with President Johnson were two of three most hated political figures of the war era. It was recommended that they both be put on trial for war crimes. Later wrote in his book *In Retrospect* how he regretted all his mistakes. All the soul searching in the world won't bring back all the dead or help the homeless veterans living in cardboard boxes.
McNamara Line: *See*: DMZ
Meat Wagon: *See*: Medevac
Medcap: Medical Civil Action Program. When a field medic or doctor goes to a village to give medical care. *See*: Dencap
Medevac: Medical Evacuation. Usually associated with the helicopter. Because of the efficiency of the helicopter, the medevac survival rate of wounded soldiers on reaching a treatment center was 97%. Critically wounded were sent ASAP to Japan, making their death no part of the statistics. Note: Approximately 800 thousand American soldiers were subjected to any form of enemy activity. Of those 361,000 were wounded, 75,000 were disabled and over 58,000 died while still in-country. Often referred to also as "Meat wagon." *See*: Dustoff
MIA: Missing in Action. Also represents a person whose body was never retrieved, even if they are known for certain to have died.
Mighty Mite: A large blower used to force tear gas through tunnel systems. Also the name of a very small jeep used in airborne operations.
Mike-mike: Radio terminology for Mad Minute. *See*: Mad Minute
MIKE force: Special Forces Mobile Strike Force Command. Mercenary troops consisting mainly of Cambodian, Montagnard, and Nung tribesmen and some South Vietnamese who were trained and commanded by twelve-man Special Forces teams. They were among the best-trained and most reliable troops in South Vietnam and because of this they were often referred to as "The Best of the Best." However, they also had a reputation for being the most brutal troops in the country.

Million-dollar wound: A non-crippling wound serious enough to warrant leaving the field or returning to the United States.
Mine Sweep: Roads outside of the American installation were constantly checked for mines by a "sweep team." The infantry provided security for the sweep team, therefore were required to walk over the still undetected, live mines.
Miracle Minute: *See*: Mad Minute
Monsoon: The rainy season of South East Asia.
Montagnard Friendship bracelet: A piece of solid brass welding rod formed into a bracelet by the Montagnard people. The bracelet was commonly considered by the GIs as a good luck bracelet. There were as many versions of this bracelet as there were hill tribes, but a popular version had sets of three vertical lines and groups of slashes that represented some unknown legend. In the book "Mountains in the Mist" by Gerald Hickey, it is explained that in 1891 a fabled shaman named the King of Fire and Water gave an Englishman by the name Cupet a brass bracelet explaining that it would symbolize their friendship.
Montagnards: French for "hill tribes." The mountain or hill people were primitive tribes who occupied the Highlands of Vietnam. The docile but fiercely loyal Montagnards hated the Vietnamese and refused to fight on their behalf but were willing to fight and die for the Americans. Various Montagnard groups fought on both the North and South Vietnamese sides.
Mortars: A muzzle-loaded high angle firing field artillery. Their maximum range was just over one mile. The infantry used the 61mm and 81mm mortar. The NVA and VC carried with them the 62mm and 82mm that was capable of using the American ammunition. Commonly used rounds were the high explosive, white phosphorus, and illumination. In modern times mortars have become exclusively an infantrymen's field artillery.
MOS: Military Occupational Specialty. A soldier's job title-code.
MP: Military Police
MPC: Military Payment Certificates. Special money to be used on American military bases in a war zone to discourage black marketeering.
Mustang: An officer who has proven himself by coming up through the ranks.
My Lai Massacre: On the morning of March 16, 1968, Americal Division troops headed by Army Lt. William Calley swept through My Lai, a hamlet that is part of the village of Son My located 95 miles south of Da Nang, hunting for Viet Cong guerrillas. In the aftermath over two-hundred civilians lay dead. The scandal rocked America's conscience and Lt. Calley along with some 25 of his command were implicated with murder. Lt. Calley alone was charged for the death of 122 and sentenced on March 29, 1971. His conviction of murder was later overturned in 1974. My Lai may be the most known atrocity, but atrocities on all sides were quite common occurrences, often times much worse than My Lai. According to "Dictionary of the Vietnam War" the Vietcong Security Service alone were responsible for nearly 37,000 assassinations. Even conservative estimates put the civilian deaths during the Vietnam War at more than 250,000. An inquiring mind might ask themselves why was the My Lai incident picked to have world wide exposure.
Name Stone: Individual houses set-up their own shrines during holiday to worship their deceased relative. The shrine consisted of candles, pictures, a sacred cross of Buddha, and name stones. The name stones were used in the absence of a picture. On the stone they would write the person's name and draw a picture of some memorable trait of the deceased.
Nam: Shortened form of Vietnam. *See*: The 'Nam
Napalm: A jellied gasoline. Although developed and used during World War II, napalm didn't receive wide use until the Vietnam War. On impact napalm will explode into flames that could engulf large areas, sucking up the oxygen and emitting intense heat, thick black smoke, and give off a stench reminiscent of burning flesh. Napalm was adopted for three uses. One: released from a slow moving aircraft in large canisters that dropped lazily and inaccurately to the ground, or dropped from a jet aircraft in the form of a bomb. Two: used to fuel flame thrower. It could burn out enemy bunkers or entire villages. Three: used as a booby-traps within the base camp perimeter defense. It was claimed that if napalm even landed near a person it could collapse their lungs. Napalm's properties are such that it clings to whatever it touches and it cannot be wiped off. *See*: Crispy Critter

NATO: North Atlantic Treaty Organization

Navarre, Henri: *See*: General Henri Navarre

NCO: Noncommissioned Officer. Sergeants are NCOs.

NFG: New F-wordin' Guy. *See*: FGN

Nguyen Thi Binh: Became the head of the National Liberation Front (NFL; *see* Viet Cong) at the 1968 Paris peace talks. After the Fall of Saigon in 1975 and the end of the war she became a minister of education.

Night Crawler: *See*: LRRP

Night Logar: The term sometimes used by the infantry to describe the night's defensive position. e.g. "Let's set up the logar around the opening." *See*: Logar

Night soil: The term that refers to feces that would be used as a fertilizer in the Vietnamese gardens.

Nixon, Richard M.: The president of the United States that withdrew troops from South Vietnam.

No Cheap Charlie: *See*: Cheap Charlie

Noel, Chris: *See*: Date With Chris

No Name: The name Vietnamese children would used when addressing a soldier.

No sweat: Slang for no problem, easy to do, or little effort needed.

November alpha: Radio terminology for night ambush.

Nui Lon Mountain: It was on that mountain that in 1969 a unit from the Americal Division refused a direct order to engage the enemy.

Number One: The best or prime

Number Ten: The worst

Nuoc mam: Vietnamese fermented fish sauce, famous for its strong smell, literally "fish water." Some claimed that Sa Dec province, south of Saigon in the Delta, produced the best known sauce.

NVA: North Vietnamese Army or North Vietnamese soldier

OD: Olive Drab. The color of ordinary military equipment during the Vietnam War.

OJ Orange: *See*: Goofy grape, smoke grenade

OP: Observation Post. A small group of soldiers, usually seven, positioned at a likely route of attack outside a base to give advanced warning of an enemy advance. Not something you'd want to volunteer for. *See*: LP

Opinions: "They're like assholes—everyone has one."

Out Post: A perimeter manned by a platoon or larger for the purpose of observation.

P-38: A tiny two-part collapsible can opener that comes with the C-rations. They look so flimsy that you'd expect it to break on the first can. Mine lasted for months at a time.

Paddies: Flooded rice fields in which rice is growing under the water.

Papa-san: A mature Vietnamese man but more specifically a father.

Pardon Crucifix: With Ecclesiastical Sanction January 15, 1907. The Pardon Crucifix, the aim of which is to obtain pardon of God and to pardon one's neighbor.

Paris Peace Talks: An effort of America to negotiate for a peace settlement of the Vietnam War. The accord was signed on January 25, 1973. The Accord didn't hold up and North Vietnam went on to unconditionally win the war.

Parrot's Beak: Name of a region of Cambodia that juts into South Vietnam west of Saigon and north of the Mekong Delta. The region became a safe haven for the VC and NVA who made it a base for their operations into South Vietnam.

Pastry Pigs: *See: Donut Dollies, Biscuit Bitches*

Pathfinders: They were airborne qualified soldiers that were the equivalent of on sight air traffic controllers. They would be dropped into an area to direct combat assaults, establishment of bases, etc.

Payback: Revenge

Payload: The amount of weight an aircraft is capable of carrying or is hauling at the moment.

Peacenik: An anti-war demonstrator.

Pee: American pronunciation of piaster. *See*: Piaster

Perforated Steel Planking: Used as a temporary landing surface for helicopters.
Perimeter: Outer limits of a defensive position. The area beyond belonged to the enemy.
Pentagon Papers: On June 13, 1971 the Pentagon Papers became public. They outlines how the Johnson administration had told out right lies about U.S. involvement in the Vietnam War.
PFC: Private First Class. There were two lower ranks, Private E-1 and Private E-2.
PF: *See*: Puff and RF
Photo stringer: The news agencies had people that were not on their regular payroll, but on minimum payroll vs freelance which they could call and ask to do special assignments. *See*: freelance
Phougas: A homemade type of napalm bomb that was a 55 gallon drum filled with gasoline and soap flakes. It was either dropped from helicopters or placed inside a mine field.
Piaster: Unit of Vietnamese currency. One piaster was nearly equal to one cent U.S. A piaster was a French Indo-Chinese colonial denomination of money.
Pig: Slang for the M-60 machine gun and the soldier who lugged the heavy, though reliable, machine gun in the field. Also the name adopted by the hippies to refer to police officers.
Pineapple Hand grenade: The hand grenade used by American forces during WWII that had a shape and sides of a pineapple. The Chinese adopted it's shape and the North Vietnamese used it extensively during the Vietnam War. *See*: M-26 hand grenade
Piss tube: Length of drainage pipe set in the ground at an angle for the soldiers to urinate into.
Platoon: Three squads equals a platoon. A platoon consisted of about forty soldiers.
Platoon Leader: A first or second lieutenant who is in charge of a platoon of soldiers.
Platoon Sergeant: A sergeant in charge of a platoon of soldiers.
Point or Pointman: The lead soldier of a moving combat patrol. Considered the most dangerous position during the Vietnam War. The position carried with it the shortest life expectancy, less than a split-second at the moment of contact with enemy.
Police the Area: To clean up the area, or rather put your gear away and pick of the garbage. e.g. "Police this area up. It looks like a pig's pen."
Poncho liner: A camouflage nylon liner that could be tied into the water proof poncho as a blanket.
Popular Force: Local militia forces organized within the village.
Pop Smoke: To mark your position with a smoke grenade.
Post-traumatic Stress Disorder (PTSD): Sometimes referred to as the "Bloodless Wound." During the American Civil War the disorder was known as "nostalgia" or "soldier's heart." During WW I it was known as "shell shock." During WW II it was known as "battle fatigue." During the Korean War it was known as "operational exhaustion" or "nerves." A psychologically traumatic shock outside the range of normal human experiences could evoke this disorder. A reaction to the extreme stress people were placed under during and after a war. Persons with the disorder sometimes create illusions that become very vivid and real. The Vietnam War version of PTSD was far more defined than in previous wars.
Pot: Marijuana or hashish. *See*: Marijuana
Pot Head: *See*: Head
POW: Prisoner of War
PRC-25: The standard infantry radio carried by the RTO (radio telephone operator). Nicknamed the "prick."
Prep: Preparation or pre-strike of an area by artillery, air strike, or helicopter just before landing or assault by troops.
Profile: A prohibition from certain types of duty due to injury or disability.
PSP: Perforated steel planking. Used as a temporary landing surface for helicopters. *See*: Tarmac
PT: Physical Training
PTSD: *See*: Post traumatic stress disorder

Pucker Factor: When the cheeks of your butt tighten from fear or stress. If you have a pucker factor of number-10 you're in the middle of or on the verge of some serious life threatening situation.
Puff: Vietnamese Popular Forces or PF. Local paramilitary forces organized for village or hamlet defense. Nickname is derogatory to mean threatening as a "cream puff" or a puff of wind. *See*: RF
Puff the Magic Dragon: Spooky: AC-47 helicopter gunship that could put a bullet in every square inch of a football field-sized area in sixty-seconds. Name came from "Puff the Magic Dragon," a song popularized by the group of Peter, Paul and Mary.
Punji Pit: A Vietnamese booby trap intended to maim GIs feet. A hole dug out, filled with punji sticks and then camouflaged. *See*: Punji stakes
Punji Stake or Punji Stick: Length of bamboo or wood with one end sharpened into a hook and often fire-hardened. Originally used by Vietnamese villagers in place of fences, to confine livestock and keep undesirable animals out. Later used in booby traps. Sometimes placed in hidden pits, sometimes on a swinging poles or swinging boards. Tip could puncture a GI boot, and, if coated with animal feces, cause a deadly infection.
Puppet Troops: The NVA's derogative term for the Army of the Republic of South Vietnam, meaning they were the puppets of American policy.
Purple Heart: The oldest U.S. honor, dating from the Revolutionary War, when it was awarded for conspicuous military service. Since World War II, awarded for wounds or blood drawn while under hostile fire.
PX: Post exchange. Retail store for military and associated personal, usually with relatively low prices and no tax. *See*: The Big PX
PZ: Military term for pickup zone.
Quad 50: A four barreled .50 caliber machine guns originally designed as an anti-aircraft gun. Portioned on perimeter throughout Vietnam to be used against enemy forces. Often times mounted with a motorized turret.
Quick loader: Refers to a molded piece of steel that when attached to an ammunition magazine can facilitate rapid loading.
RA: Regular Army. Designation for someone who enlists voluntarily in the services. Most often used as slang for a person who enlisted, e.g., "You're RA? That's crazy."
Radio code: Coordinates of location translated into letters for radio transmission. The code could change daily.
Rack: Slang for military bed.
Ranch Hands: The name given to the special unit that flew defoliation missions. *See*: Agent Orange
Ranger: A soldier specially trained for reconnaissance and specialized combat missions. Created by President John F. Kennedy who needed these specialized soldiers. *See*: Airborne Ranger
Rear: Means to be out of the field and in a secure place. e.g. "Safe in the rear with the gear."
Recon-by-fire: (reconnaissance) Refers to searching an area with the use of firing weapons or artillery.
Red Catchers: Nickname for the 199th Light Infantry Brigade.
Redleg: Term for artilleryman, but also for the projectile they fire. e.g. "Let's get some red leg in here."
Regional forces: Semi-professional local troops. *See*: RF
REMF: Slang: "Rear Echelon Motherf-worder." Non-combat troops at basecamps that dealt with supplies and administration. e.g. "One of those useless order generating bastards who try to get us grunts killed."
Re-up: A generic term to reenlist in the service. On signing a soldier usually receives bonus money and a thirty-day leave. It also meant they would probably get another tour of duty in Vietnam.
RF: The Vietnamese regional fighting forces. Sometimes referred to as "Ruff and Puff." *See*: PF

Rice field: Overall designation for a planted field area.
Rice paddies: Term for muddy, water-logged fields; 'paddy' refers to the rice plants from which rice grains are later threshed.
Rifle Poncho Stretcher: Two rifles folded inside poncho to form the poles for a stretcher.
Roach: The last quarter inch of a marijuana cigarette.
Road Sweep: To clear a road of mines and booby traps. *See*: Sweep Team
Rock 'n' roll: Slang for firing a weapon on full automatic or going into battle ready to fight. e.g. "What are we waitin' for? Let's rock 'n' roll."
Rockpile: A mountain near the DMZ, so named by the occupying Marines because it resembled a pile of rocks in the middle of nowhere.
ROKs: (pronounced 'rocks') Republic of Korea soldier
Rough Puffs: *See*: Puff
Round Eyes: Slang name for American women. Derived from the fact that oriental women's eyes appear slanted.
ROTC: Reserve Officer's Training Corps that was usually connected to college or university. Often called "rot-see," from the initials.
RPG: Rocket Propelled Grenade
R & R: Military term for Rest & Recreation, Rest & Recuperation, or Rest & Relaxation. GI's commonly called it Rape & Rampage. In-country R&Rs were at China Beach for the Marines near Da Nang and Vung Tau for the Army near Saigon. Out of country R&Rs were Bangkok, Manila, Tokyo, Hawaii, Sydney Australia, Taipei, Tokyo, Penang, and Kuala Lumpur. The VC had their R&Rs at Ca Mau Peninsula and, rumors had it, Vung Tau.
RTO: The designation given to the field radio telephone operator. The infantry RTO was the favorite target of snipers because they could target the whip antenna.
Rubber lady: Slang for an issue rubber air mattress.
Rucksack: Consisted of a nylon pack which was strapped to a metal frame. Commonly referred to as ruck, pack or simply gear."
Rules of Engagement: Specific regulations for the conduct of U.S. and allied forces during the Vietnam War.
RVN: Republic of Vietnam (South Vietnam)
S-2: The section of military command, at battalion level, that dealt with the gathering intelligence information on the enemy. *See*: G-2
Saddle: A low slope between two hills.
Saddle up: A common command for grunts to hoist their rucksack onto their backs and prepare to march. e.g. "Saddle up! We're movin' out."
Saigon: The capital of South Vietnam during the Vietnam War. Because of its beauty the French called it the Pearl of the Orient and believe it reminiscent of Paris, France. After the Fall of Saigon in 1975 it was renamed Ho Chi Minh City. *See*: Ho Chi Minh
Saigon tea: A non-alcoholic tea mixture served to bar girls in Vietnamese bars.
Saigon Warriors: Slang for all the non-combat American personal station in the capital city of South Vietnam.
SAM Missile: The Soviet-supplied surface-to-air missile the North Vietnamese considered their most effective anti-aircraft defense.
Sampan: A small boat used by the Vietnamese peasants.
***Sao*:** Vietnamese for a stupid person.
Sapper: A VC or NVA who infiltrates a camp for sabotage. An enemy soldier or demolition squad who carried a satchel charge, sometimes strapped to their bodies, capable of blowing up a bunker. Seldom did they ever carry a weapon to defend themselves. Though often times a sapper would be killed by their own bombs, they would never go on a mission with the intentions of committing suicide *See*: Satchel Charge
Satchel charge: A bag of high explosives carried by VC sappers, which could be detonated at will. A sapper would carry a charge in his hand ready to hurl, and carry extra ones strapped around their waist. The concussion alone from the charge could blow out a person's brain.
Sat cong: Vietnamese for "kill communists."

Scale: To kill a person but also to "scale a beer."
Screaming Eagles: Nickname for U.S. Army's 101st Airborne Division.
Seabee: Highly skilled construction naval personal. They would erect bridges, built landing zones, buildings, bunkers, etc.
SEAL: Navy special-warfare force members.
Search and Clear: In the middle of 1968, command decided they needed a nicer word than "destroy." So they changed "search and destroy" to "search and clear."
Search and destroy: An operation strategy of attrition used from 1965 to 1968, designed to destroy and apprehend enemy supplies in a village area. Most of the soldiers interpreted it to mean "destroy then search."
See the Elephant: A term that simply meant the soldier had experienced the weight of death and the reality of war.
1) Derived from a proverb about three blind men who gave their individual view of an entire elephant but was misleading because one only touched the foot, the second only the tail and the third only the trunk. If the blind men were given sight, or a soldier given the reality of true war, they would "see the elephant." 2) During the California gold rush of the 1800's the term "see the elephant" was also used. It was a colloquialism that referred to seeking adventure.
Seminole Indian Wars: The Vietnam War has often been compared to the Seminole Indian Wars because the Indians were never defeated by the United States, nor were the Vietnamese. It cost the US government one million dollars for every Seminole killed, approximately the same as it cost for every Vietnamese killed.
Service Flag: Sometimes called the Blue Star Flag. A small blue flag bearing one star. The blue stands for the country and the star representing a person in the service. Displayed by the family of a member serving in the Armed Forces of America. Usually placed in the front window. Although not an official United States government flag, it is still officially recognized. Part of the flag's proceeds go to the American Red Cross.
Shake 'n' Bake: The term came from a popular chicken coating, and referred an officer who received their rank by getting rushed through training. More generally, anyone who received rank without seniority. *See*: Instant mother
Shit burning: The process of incineration of feces. Most of the outhouses in South Vietnam used by American soldiers had half- fifty-five gallon drums under them to catch the feces. When the bucket was full they doused it with diesel fuel and set it aflame.
Shit Detail: When a soldier is assigned to shit burn.
Shit hook: Slang for the CH-47 Chinook helicopter which had such high velocity on its blades that the rocks and debris stung and hurt it they hit a soldier. *See*: Chinook
Short: Universal term to mean one does not have much time left in Vietnam or in the service. "I'm short, man. I ain't gotta do nothin'. Leave me alone!"
Short timer: Someone who has less than 30 days left in country.
Short timer's calendar: A calendar that usually showed a women divided into 100 parts. Men would use them to mark off the last hundred days they were in Vietnam.
Short-timer's stick: A stick a grunt would notch to count down his last days in Vietnam.
Shotgun or Back-blast: Blowing marijuana down the barrel of a shotgun or when one man puts the burning end of a joint into his mouth and blows it directly into another man's mouth.
Shrapnel: Small pieces of metal; also, shells with an explosive charge that would shower an area with metal. Named for H. Shrapnel, the British Army officer who invented this type of projectile.
Sihanoukville Port Route: North Vietnamese sea vessels would sail along the Vietnam coast to Cambodia where they would dock and unload at the Sihanoukville Port. From there they would infiltrate by land. The land route from the port was called the Sihanoukville Port Route. *See*: Ho Chi Minh Trail
Sink hole: The hole an artillery round leaves in a rice field, which subsequently fills with sludge.
Sin Loi: (Actually spelling, *in lot*) Vietnamese meaning, "tough luck" or "too bad."
Silver Star: U.S. military decoration awarded for gallantry while under fire.

Sit rep: Military term for "situation report."
Skate: A task or situation that requires very little effort to complete.
S.S.: Soviet semi-automatic rifle.
Sky Crane: This helicopter was used as a workhorse, airlifting heavy equipment into and out of battle zones, retrieving damaged planes, helicopters and vehicles. It had the distinction of being the aircraft capable of carrying a Daisy Cutter. *See*: Daisy Cutter
Slick: A resupply or troop carrying Huey that sometimes had two door gunners.
Slope head: *See*: dink
Slow Poke: Nickname for an infantry radio telephone operator. Because of the extra twenty-five pound radio they were often the slowest moving.
Smoke grenade: A smoke grenade which came in yellow, green, red or purple. *See*: Goofy grape
Snakes: In Vietnam of the 133 species of snakes 131 were said to be poisonous. The most common and poisonous were the krait, cobra, and bamboo viper. The bamboo viper was known as the "three step snake" because if bitten you would drop dead after only three steps.
SNAFU: Situation normal (all funked up).
Sniper: To shoot a select enemy from a concealed position. Also the termed used for the soldier equipped with a rifle and scope can has the ability to be accurate from long distances. The American sniper's ability with a rifle was legendary. They often used a special "accurized" version of the M-14 rifle.
SOP: Military term for "Standard Operating Procedure."
Southern Cross: The Americal Division, 23rd Infantry, used The Southern Cross as their insignia. The insignia was derived from the a four-star constellation in the southern hemisphere that, when connected, represents the cross Jesus was nailed onto. In ancient times when men saw the constellation they swore they saw Jesus. *See*: Americal Division
SP pack: One of these cellophane packages was found in every meal of C-rations. They contained toiletries and cigarettes.
Spearchucker: *See*: dink
Spider hole: A small VC foxhole that is concealed from view.
Spook: Slang for CIA agent
Spooky: An AC-47 aircraft with Gatling guns protruding from the port windows. *See*: Puff the Magic Dragon.
Spotter: Forward observer; common name whether the person's in aircraft or on foot.
Squelch: The sound the handset makes on a field radio when the transmission button is pressed and released. Usually used when, for security reasons, one can't talk but wants to communicate a predetermined condition. We referred to the action as "Breaking Squelch."
Stand down: An infantry unit's return from the field to base camp for refitting and rest.
Starlight scope: A night vision scope. It was a cumbersome scope that can be handheld or rifle mounted, that intensifies image by amplifying the light of the moon and stars. The image appears in shades of green. Nicknamed "Twinkle."
Stars and Strips: A weekly military newspaper publication
Stash: One's personal supply of drugs.
Steam and Cream: Steam houses in the towns that also would supply sexual favors.
Steel pot: The combat helmet consisted of a helmet liner, a steel pot and a helmet cover. The steel pot would protect the soldier from head wounds from bullets as well as shrapnel. It could be detached and used for various purposes. For example you could use it to dig a hole or as a boil water and make a stew. You could attach a rope to the straps and turn it into a bucket ready to lower into a water well. It could carry water or serve as a sink to wash or a shower if poured over the head. You could also use it as a stool or chair. The imagination was the only limit to its use by the soldiers. Flower pot? *See*: Brain bucket, Helmet, Helmet cover
Sticks: *See*: Boondocks

Stone, Dana: Dana was counted among the best and bravest of Combat Photographers during the Vietnam War. He and his friend Sean Flynn were captured in 1970 and presumed killed. *See*: Combat Photographer and Sean Flynn
Strac: Strickly adhere to regulations.
Straight-leg: *See*: Grunt
Street Without Joy: Highway 1 is Vietnam's main north-south highway. It stretched from Saigon to Hanoi. The French sardonically named it *la rue sans jolie*, the street without joy. American soldiers adopted the name for the I Corps section of the road .
Sucking Chest Wound: A wound that punctures the lungs, causing air to flow into the chest, deflating the lung. Usually fatal.
Sundry pack: Given to the troops every week. It included ten cartons of cigarettes, a razor and razor blades, candy, soap, toothpaste, chewing tobacco, shaving cream, chewing gum, a needle and thread, envelopes, paper, pens, foul-tasting chocolate bars, and a five-pack of Havatampa cigars.
Survivor's Smile: In most cases a soldier would have a sense of exhilaration in the aftermath of battle. All the dead and wounded were around and yet they survived. It is just the opposite of feeling guilty about surviving.
S.W.A.K: The initials for "Sealed With A Kiss." Normally the initials were placed across the envelope flap. *See*: XOXO
Sweep: As in "sweeping a village." A group of men moves through an area to clear it of any enemy personnel or war related materials. Sometimes used in conjunction with a blocking force. *See*: Block
Sweep Team: Soldier who specialized in clearing roads of mine and booby traps. There main tool was a metal detector. On finding a mine they would put a charge of C-4 next to it and blow up the suspected mine.
Talk-the-talk: The entire phrase is "You can talk-the-talk but can you walk-the-walk?" Standard exclusionary term used by veterans to mean if you haven't been in Vietnam you couldn't possibly understand it so why waste a conversation. Therefore, they will not talk to you.
Tagged and bagged: American soldier killed in Vietnam would have a 'tag' attached to their bodies with their name, rank, serial number (usually attached to the big toe). Then they were placed in a body 'bag.' "You don't wanna be tagged and bagged, man." Sometimes called "tagged, booked and bagged."
Tango sierra: Radio call sign for "tough shit." From the phonetic alphabet terms for T and S.
Tan Son Nhut: Name of the huge military airbase in Saigon, South Vietnam.
Tarmac: A permanent landing field for aircraft that can not be lifted or carried away. *See*: PSP
TDY: Military term for "temporary duty." TDY to the infantry usually became "permanent duty."
Tet: The Vietnamese Lunar New Year, which is the same as Chinese Lunar New Year, is calculated similar to our Easter but always starts in January. Traditionally all Vietnamese celebrate their birthday on these days and also become one year older. Militarily it commonly refers to the January 29 thu 31, 1968 **Tet Offensive** at which time the VC with NVA made a surprise attack on major cities, towns and military bases in the country. After twenty days of fierce fighting the enemy forces retreated. The 1968 Tet Offensive is considered by most to have been the turning point in the Vietnam War effort giving the public a clear idea US was losing, not winning the war. In fact it was a military victory for Saigon and allies, for the VC were seriously decimated. The aftermath gave NVA a greater hand in future fighting.
The Big One: A common reference to the Second World War.
The GIs: The American soldiers term for diarrhea. Also called the GI Shits. *See*: Ho Chi Minh's Revenge
The Green Machine: The name so aptly given American Armed Forces assigned to the Vietnam War.
The 'Nam: Refers to being in the country of Vietnam. e.g. "I'm in d'Nam, man."

The Wall: The common name for the Vietnam Veterans Memorial in Washington, D.C. *See*: Vietnam Veterans Memorial
Thieu, Nguyen Van: Became the president of South Vietnam in 1967 with Nguyen Cao Ky as vice president.
Thousand-yard stare: Refers to the look in a soldier's eyes when he has experienced a certain amount of death or has been in war too long. In WW II they called it the two thousand-yard stare
Three-quarter: A three-quarter ton truck
Thumper: Nickname for the M-79 grenade launcher. *See*: M-79 Grenade Launcher
Titi: Small or little. From the French *petite*.
Time against Americans: This is the way Vietnamese make reference to the American "Vietnam war."
Tonka Toy: The name of a toy maker. Sometimes the M-16 was referred to as a Tonka Toy because of it's light-weight plastic parts. *See*: M-16
Top: First Sergeant of a company, who was also called First Shirt.
Tracer round: A round chemically treated to glow so that its flight could be followed.
Track: Slang for an Armored personnel carrier, which moved on treads like a tank. *See*: APC
Trench Foot: *See:* Immersion foot
Trip Flare: A flare triggered by a wire used to signal and illuminate the approach of an enemy.
Triple canopy jungle: Botanical term for a tropical forest consisting of three main heights of primary vegetation.
Tropic Lightning: Nickname for the 25th Infantry Division.
Truth: The first casualty of war.
Tunnel rat: Special tunnel teams dubbed "tunnel rats." They were all volunteers who could withstand the physical and mental terror of crawling into underground tunnels in search of the enemy. The Vietnamese developed a duck waddle in which they could actually walk inside a one meter tunnel. *See*: Cu Chi
Tunnel warfare: The first tunnels were dug by the Viet Minh for communication access routes in fighting the French during the 1940's. The tunnel network proved so efficient that the 45 miles of tunnels were excavated during the French fighting reached nearly well over 200 miles during the fighting with the Americans. *See*: Cu Chi
Ty, Nguyen Cao: Became the vice president of South Vietnam in 1967.
Uncle Ho: *See*: Ho Chi Minh
Uncle Sugar: Slang used by civilians who worked under contact for the US Government. It referred to the exorbitant amount of money and benefits the job offered. The term is a wry word-play on the usual personification of the government or the country, Uncle Sam.
University of South Vietnam: There may have been a university with such a name but when an American soldier used the term he meant simply, he completed his tour of duty in Vietnam. Example: "I'm a graduate from the University of South Vietnam."
UPI: United Press International, an American news wire-service.
US: The beginning designation on their identification for a person drafted into the armed forces. Often used in slang, "A bunch of US guys." A disproportionate amount of US men ended up in the infantry.
USO: United Service Organizations
Valorous Unit Emblem (Award): Equivalent to the individual award of a Silver Star for gallantry.
Vann, John Paul: Colonel John Paul Vann who resigned his commission from the U.S. Army. His understanding and experience learned during the Vietnam War are legendary. If any single man could embody the era it would have been John Paul Vann. Though he resigned his commission, he later became known as the Civilian General. His life is chronicled in Neil Sheehan's award winning book *A Bright Shinning Lie*. He was killed in a helicopter crash in South Vietnam on June 9, 1972.
Veteran or Vet: A former member of the military.

VC: Vietcong, Vietnamese Communist or Victor Charlie. Formal name was "National Liberation Front." Organized by 16 Vietnamese at a secret meeting in Cu Chi in 1960. One of their known bases during the war was Tay Ninh. *See*: Dink

Vietcong: The name is short for Vietnamese Communists. Formally known as the National Liberation Front. *See*: Vietminh, VC

Vietminh: During the French occupation of Vietnam the resistance was known as the Vietminh. Vietminh stood for League for the Independence of Vietnam.

Vietnamization: President Nixon began to pull American troops out of Vietnam in 1969 and slowly had the Vietnamese take over the fighting duties.

Vietnam Veteran's Memorial: Conceived by Jan C. Scruggs, a combat infantryman. Designed by Maya Lin, a Yale architecture student. It is a monument in Washington, D.C., made out of granite and it has engraved on its surface the names of the men killed in Vietnam. Nicknames The Wall. *See*: The Wall

Vietnam Veteran's Memorial Moving Wall: Conceived by John Devitt. A half scale replica of the Vietnam Veteran's Memorial in Washington, D.C., which is taken to other cities for display. *See*: The Wall

Wake-up: It was how many days before departure from Vietnam. "I got 14 days and a wake-up. I'm so short I can't tie my boots."

Walk in the Sun: This was the phrase adopted by the grunts to denote a movement that was free of risk of combat.

Walk the Walk: The point of this phrase, used by veteran, is that everyone can describe concepts and ideas with words but did they actual perform the deed. Only a true veteran can say they have "Walk the Walk." *See*: Talk the talk

War of Attrition: It was the primary U.S. strategy adopted from the American Indian War. The concept was to wear away enemy forces until they were unable or unwilling to continue fighting. To kill as many as possible, then the rest will give up. This led to "body count" since they had to verify the number of kills.

Waste: Used 'all' word to mean kill or destroy. "Waste the gook" "Waste the village!" "I got really wasted last night." "Oh yeah, I remember him. He got wasted on some hill a month ago." "This is all a waste." "That hump wasted me." *See*: Scale and Blow Away

Water Buffalo: Slang used by GIs for a water tanker. Also the name of the animal. The water buffalo was the most important domesticated animal in Vietnam because they were used as draft animals by the Vietnamese farmers.

Web gear: A small backpack held by suspenders and a pistol belt.

Weed: Slang for marijuana. *See*: Marijuana

Westmoreland: *See*: General William Westmoreland

White Lie Ward: The Da Nang hospital ward for hopeless cases.

White mice: In Vietnamese, *canh sat*. South Vietnamese civilian police, who wore white helmets and white gloves.

White Phosphorous: When united with oxygen it produces intense flames, heat and smoke. Since it needed no oxygen to burn it could not be extinguished. *See*: Willy Peter

WIA: Wounded In Action

Widow maker: *See*: M-16

Wilco: Radio language for "will comply."

Willy Peter: White Phosphorous. WP rounds were used as spotter rounds for artillery. White phosphorous doesn't need oxygen, so if it landed on a person, it could not be extinguished. *See*: Crispy critter

Winchester: Radio term for "out of ammunition".

Womb to Tomb: Another one of President Johnson's policies that was based on socialism. It meant he would take care of all Americans from the womb to tomb literally.

World: The USA or anyplace other than Vietnam, also: Real World. *See*: Big PX

Xin Loi: A Vietnamese idiom meaning, "Sorry about that."

XOXO: Means hugs and kisses. Letter from and from the troops in Vietnam sealed the letter and put the XOXO across the seam. *See*: S.W.A.K.

Yards: Short for a Montagnard soldier. *See*: Montagnard

Year Of The Monkey: Bases on the Chinese astrology 1968 was the Year Of The Monkey.
Yellow Man: The yellowish tint of the east Asian people is thought to be a side effect of their diet. *See*: Dink
Z: *See*: DMZ
ZAP: Slang for killing an enemy. Also: deep six, grease, waste, or snuff.
Zippo Mission: The nickname for a flame thrower which was named after the popular cigarette lighter. Also, when the mission was to burn a village, the troops would take out their Zippo lighters to burn the hootches.
Zoo: The jungle
Zonked: Drugged up

ABOUT THE AUTHOR

Fred Leo Brown was severely wounded October 26, 1968 after serving as a Vietnam combat infantryman for eleven months. He spent the next seven months at the Fort Bliss Army Hospital in El Paso, Texas. Though permanently disabled, he returned to active duty to serve out his three year enlistment.

He married Barbara Ann Connolly in 1973 and they have two children, Cara Dorothy and Kathryn Christine, both of whom are in college.

During the bicentennial year of our nation, 1976, he rode his bicycle across America in dedication to his friends who died in Vietnam. In so doing he became the first person to ever complete the Bikecentennial Trans American Trail from Jamestown, Virginia to Reedsport, Oregon, a total of 4250 miles. Averaging 115 miles per day he arrived just days before the Fourth of July Celebration in Reedsport, Oregon. His feat was broadcast and carried in newspapers across the nation.

In 1993, he restored a 1953 M-37 Korean War-Vietnam Era 3/4 ton truck. Driving the truck to California, he start his second Trans American bike ride which he named "Journey To The Wall". First stop was in Oakland, the home and burial site of his war friend, Benji Yamane, who had died in his arms on March 16,1968. The journey logged a total of 10,000 miles in fifty-five days. He arrived in Washington, D.C. on Father's Day, June 23, 1993.

Fred Leo Brown now writes full time. He also travels to schools around the nation performing and story telling using his program entitled "Lessons of War".

a traveling play that teaches

Types of Appearances:

Theater Production: Using 17 of your volunteer students (to role play, assist) the author will create-a-setting in the school theater, gym or large band room.

Story Telling: Author will Story Tell throughout the day in an assigned classroom

for further information:
Story Teller Fred Leo Brown
P.O. Box 39
Palos Heights, IL 60463

Phone: 708-361-1488 Fax: 708-361-9584

www.lessonsofwar.com
e-mail fredleo22@aol.com

suppose V.C. or N.V. suppose to
ryone
s either loyalist with the
Vietnamese kill some one otherwise there
you can. we are
he about that. It looks like a shade
place there are a couple
sort of a lean to.

up on an open area. Bomb
fairly large. There is a
T to it. It was made by
Bomb B. The market place
nded by Rice patties. The
lled A little stem off the
s in this letter. This Rice is
Ready to pick.

Taking it easy today. The reason
lent as soon as you read B.C. Company
sentences. We left to about
the temperature rose fragment proof,
flak jackets, for B men
shirts. We went had had
Our platoon first platoon
fatigue. passed out. water
man sweat so bad that at times
shirts. I felt just streamed
shower. The water also we
messed up. Those

CO D 4th Brown
10 8 12 APO 96217

atch has been
have been
it say how I needed
can I guess Bear in my
the Teddy Bear

icated your cool A
fruit. I have 2 of
Tey left today. The we just
re Be. 7:45. We and
is exactly artillery
led firing

Mad Minute. see we have
nipped at 3 days in a raw one
last night at dusk they popped some
in. So we had to push our ambushes
rather Rat Patrol out. So every one
the perimeter firers 18 round of M-16.
rounds of machine gun ammunition and
M-79 rounds. The whole perimeter
wild.

in a company
it has taken
bunker. It is
at night now.
Stack. It
good music

We are set up
perimeter or base camp
3 days to build
strong real ha
well I found a
band
30 NA

Lot 8
But I have
entry chance 2 get
are up

To get this letter
Everything is a has
well, every thing is
now. So I will contin
I am going to
this letter.
bye for

Dear Ma and Dad
Well it is night. I
can not see hardly
at all.
I recived your
package of fruit,
chili, Spanish rice,
and beef stew. And
the writing paper.
I recieved it
this [illegible]. I hung[illegible]
[illegible]

But it is
[illegible] has people
we have

...try
...to know
...tomarrow.
...and have
...a frog thick...
...was ... so nice for th...
...ill try to write
Well I will finish
...way I had a direct...
...ea. At the time we had...
...s and I was sleeping on...
...eping gear was turned...
The colonel said this was
one layer of sand bags
the fin to the mortar we...
...ttom of our bunker...
of us was hurt. I hope...
...d have. Since we have...

Oh well, I am still in...
I will continue to march. By for...
Well, today is the 13th...
It is now 2:00 AM. I had...
Well, it looks like we are goin...
put another layer of sand bags...
one of the Co. found rockets,...
also Russian machine guns. They...
The NVA out there have a lot...
The thing is we have them on...
Because we have air strikes...
pounding the whole area.
Well, it looks like we w...

...men
...tod m...
...pul...
...s...ngs.
...lear...
RTO and
...o Be Treaded
...ch. And I woul...
...ked last to
...xtra jo...

...your...
Try and
...because I try to
...to both of you
...to get

Dear Ma & Dad

Is our line...
Bunker I wonder what
are going to do 2...
Fred [illegible]

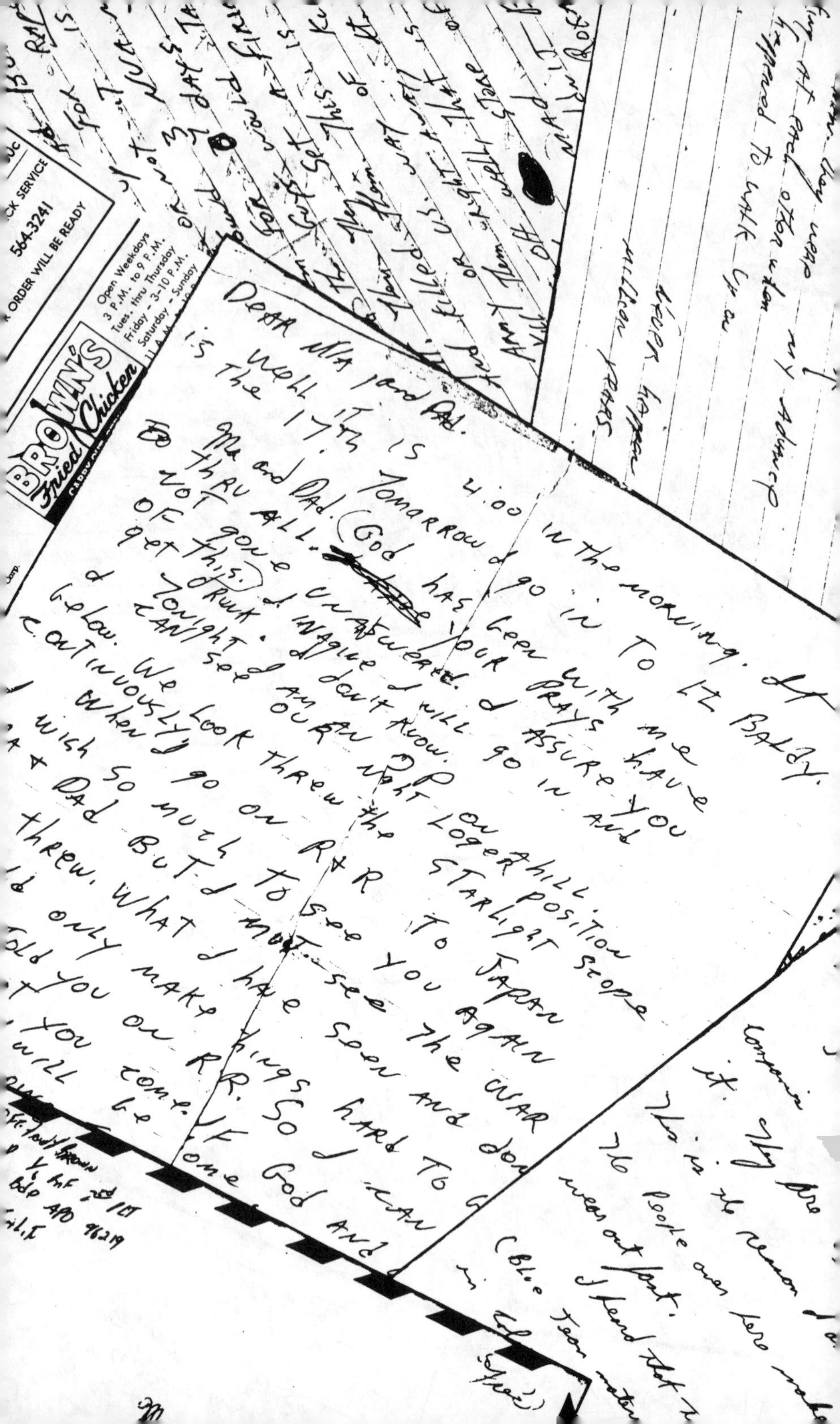

DEAR Ma and Dad.
Well it is 4:00 in the morning. It
is the 17th. Tomarrow I go in to LZ Baldy.
Ma and Dad. God has been with me
thru all. your prays have
not gone unanswered. I assure you
of this. I imagine I will go in and
get drunk. I don't know.
Tonight I am on OP on a hill.
I can't see our night loger position
Glow. We look threw the starlight scope
continuously. When I go on R&R to Japan
I wish so much to see you again
Ma & Dad but I must see the war
threw. What I have seen and done
would only make things hard to
told you on R.R. So I can
that you come. If God and
will be come

men on
And lost
men because
going to the Re
That is about
I have seen get
killed and leave.
is just my platoon
about 30 men
You sta
when all of
are the oldes
your platoon

and ran
I shot the other
It was time to pull
So we backed off
bullets. every inch of
Finally reached thick shru
we held up for the night.
Wow! That was hairy. I ma
killed. We had a couple
rockets
By the way 1 man
2 AK-47

2 NOV 1968
APO 9637

V.C. The other 2
or innocent civilians.
talion is getting tough.
prisoners. We learned
were real real close
have no mercy left
have something

Jan 68

Dear Ma,
Remember the last letter. I talked about
Joan Tocket.
days ago one man
life saved

75 mm
R.L.
DEAD SPACE
500 m
BUN

Today 23

The fi... in an other place th...
up all day ... at night and
last few days I have had a col...
My mind is a little ... know h...
slow to write.

I have found out. Blood ...
Keep men like me in the field
Blood - Our buddies are killed. Our
Or rather kill and get killed
Tears - Our Homes ...
Our agonies and the thin...
Guts - What keeps us going. Ha...
To die. Takes point But
consiquences.

Brief descriptions. You kn...
I will go to Australia on ...
I get 6 days there only
Hawaii.

By the way R&R did not ...
Been better off without it. My
beyond repair in a few days. It
...east a year now.
Nothing is happening. I am
feel it is about the safest
... but I am coming home. It doesn't ma...
Bye for now. I am alright just am a
sick and am a little frustrated
Bye until later,
Fred Lee

Got all your packages
I used the ...

Dear Roxanna
what a da...

US Postal Service
2 NOV 1968
96374
APO

Mr & Mrs John R. Brown
8027 S...

Freddy Brown
APO 96219

Well lately I have been getting
lots of Bees. Bla! It doesn't
taste good. I like to take letters.
Beautiful knife!
Really needed. B...
...oil stone
Small...

...is the 11th
...I am on guard of
for 2 hours. But
...look at the watch
...of guard. How
Bunker in good
way. Let me
...I am in the
...every man carr...
...wall up. It
...big enough
...the...

... thicker
... you want me
OK
... the one ...
OK. Maybe two. OK
also a Pck.
... pen is running out of
I will not be able
... foot locker

About you
Write...
Fred Lee

...one
...ck
physical
a little
a while but
to 2 power H...
don't carr...
my 2...